# Fair Isle Ghosts

# Fair Isle Ghosts

## Carol Tweedie

The Shetland Times Ltd.
Lerwick
2015

# *Fair Isle Ghosts*

First published by The Shetland Times Ltd., 2015.

A catalogue record for this book is available from the British Library.

ISBN 978-1-910997-01-7

Printed and published by
The Shetland Times Ltd.,
Gremista, Lerwick,
Shetland ZE1 0PX.

For Andrew

# Contents

# Preface

When I retired from my lecturing job in Edinburgh, I finally found time to examine the family's dusty collection of old photographs, carelessly stored in albums and boxes.

Those from Fair Isle were particularly intriguing to someone with a background in history, but sadly, not all were identified. Research began into Fair Isle, involving wider aspects of Scottish history and contact with many living descendents of those who had once called the island their home.

Gradually the ordinary people and their exceptional story emerged. Fair Isle's fishing and crofting society had been pushed to the brink of extinction, as it struggled to survive during the momentous change that occurred throughout Scotland during the second half of the 19th century.

The project is not complete. There are still unnamed photographs and stories to be told. Perhaps this book will encourage more people to respond.

I am humbled by the support I have received from my family, my new, extended family and all the unexpected friends I have unearthed in the course of this project.

I encourage anyone lucky enough to possess a cache of old photographs, to name them, discover the stories and thus preserve the history of ordinary people.

*Carol Tweedie*

# Taft Wilson / *Quoy Irvine* Family Tree

**Laurence Wilson (1770-1856) m Agnes Irvine**

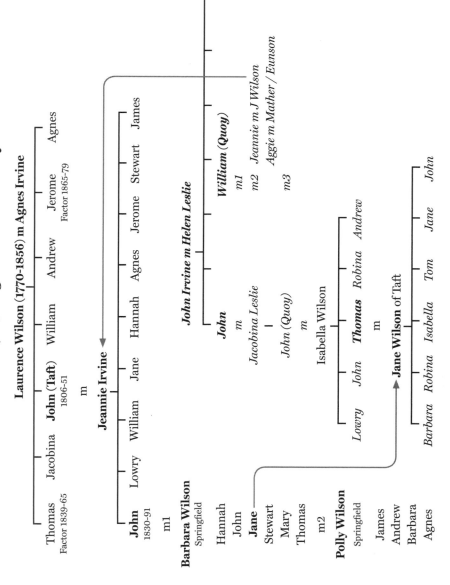

Thomas
Factor 1839-65

Jacobina

**John (Taft)**
1806-51

William

Andrew

Jerome
Factor 1865-79

Agnes

m

**Jeannie Irvine**

John
1830-91

Lowry

William

Jane

Hannah

Agnes

Jerome

Stewart

James

m1

**Barbara Wilson**
Springfield

Hannah

John

**Jane**

Stewart

Mary

Thomas

m2

**Polly Wilson**
Springfield

James

Andrew

Barbara

Agnes

*John Irvine m Helen Leslie*

**John**

m

*Jacobina Leslie*

—

*John (Quoy)*

m

Isabella Wilson

**William (Quoy)**

m1

m2 *Jeannie m J Wilson*

*Aggie m Mather / Eunson*

m3

*Lowry*  *John*  **Thomas**  *Robina*  *Andrew*

m

**Jane Wilson** of Taft

*Barbara*  *Robina*  *Isabella*  *Tom*  *Jane*  *John*

Detailed OS maps of Fair Isle can be downloaded from the National Library of Scotland database:

*Publication date 1881:*
**http://maps.nls.uk/view/74430969**

*Publication date 1903:*
**http://maps.nls.uk/view/76411855**

The later map includes detail of the lighthouses.

Both maps can be purchased as jpegs from NLS.

Shetland

Fair Isle

Orkney

Scotland

B. Wilson

# *Introduction*

Very close to the north-east tip of Scotland lie the Northern Isles: two distinct archipelagos that straggle from South Ronaldsay up to Unst, 164 miles away. Orkney boasts rich arable land and the men here were farmers who fished, while the more northerly Shetland Isles boasted fishermen who farmed, since their land was less fertile. Thanks to incessant and often salt-laden winds, even today there are few trees in the Northern Isles, revealing extraordinary, harsh, bare, often stunning landscapes. Large swathes of rough grass and moor are interspersed by areas of cultivated croft land, where man seeks to tame his surroundings. Differences in seasons, weather and light reveal a wide range of panoramas, while sudden squalls, gales and hurricane-force winds mean that the surrounding seas can be magnificently turbulent. Strong tidal streams and eddies defy even the local fishermen. There is a long history of shipwrecks.

Fifty empty miles separate Orkney and Shetland, empty that is except for Fair Isle, a tiny island that rears up halfway between the two: an unexpected, isolated outcrop of rock, defiantly challenging humanity to land here and survive. And yet, from prehistoric times people have chosen to make their homes on the island, at the mercy of the elements which could cut them off from the rest of the world for weeks on end.

Fair Isle is about three and a quarter miles long and one and a half miles wide, with precipitous cliffs that can soar to 400 feet above the waves. A fertile area lies to the south and this is where people built their croft houses and kept their boats, using a small, rock-strewn indentation as their 'harbour'. A second landing area lies to the north.

The name and the knitting are synonymous. The origins of the colourful, intricate patterns are uncertain, although some say they were brought to the isle by Spaniards when the *El Gran Grifon* (part of the Spanish Armada) was shipwrecked there in 1588. Other theories exist, but whatever its origins the knitting was invaluable to island families who bartered or sold it to ensure that they survived when times were hard. Times were usually hard.

By the middle of the 19th century the majority of Scotland's population still lived in the countryside, many involved in subsistence farming, although this way of life was gradually changing as improved communication, industrialisation and new employment opportunities in towns encouraged the growing rural population to emigrate. But Fair Isle's population had always been on the move, simply because there was such a limited area of land available for the people to live and grow crops. Orkney and Shetland were the first ports of call for many, but fishing communities on the east coast of Scotland and England were also common destinations.

Parents understood that not all their offspring would stay. John Irvine (1740-1815) was the schoolteacher for many years. He had seven children, three of whom left the island. His eldest daughter Jane had eight youngsters, five of whom moved, while the three who stayed had an additional twenty-four children, most of whom married. Without pestilence, famine, or war, such a fertile population could not survive in such a small place. Of course there was illness; measles and tuberculosis took considerable numbers to an early grave. Famine too was a regular threat and reliance on imported meal during difficult times was a recurrent theme, for a bad harvest could threaten catastrophe. Furthermore, after the end of the Napoleonic wars when the press gangs stopped their work, few local men thought of joining the Royal Navy. Thus, the population's ability to reproduce and survive meant that a regular stream of people must leave. Usually it was the young who felt the strongest need and the old who were left to mourn their loss.

In 1851, according to the census, Fair Isle was supporting 280 people who lived in small, one or two-roomed, rough stone buildings, with turf roofs, earthen floors and of course, no plumbing. With only small windows set into thick walls and a peat fire lying in the centre of the floor of the main room, these were dark, damp, cramped, crowded, smoke-filled homes. Visitors commented that the inhabitants were thin, ill-fed and poorly dressed, but in truth, life in Fair Isle was not dramatically different from that of the rural poor across much of the rest of Scotland.

The fishermen used tried and tested methods that had had been handed down from father to son over many hundreds of years, but the sea was a hard master. The roosts (fierce, conflicting currents of water) that surrounded the island were a constant challenge to those who fished in their vicinity, while uncertain weather regularly tested the men's experience and intuition. A jagged, difficult coastline further threatened the unwary sailor. Despite almost unparalleled levels of skill, men could lose both their craft and their lives in a careless instant.

Isolation and a challenging lifestyle did not disconcert most islanders. The comfortable rhythm of the seasons, familiar customs, and extended family relationships provided a strong sense of collective security. When times were good there was meal, kail, fish, milk, cheese and even a bit of lamb. Birds, both migrating and breeding, offered a range of meat and eggs in the late spring and summer. For those who had clear rights to both land and a boat there was little reason to consider exchanging this close-knit lifestyle for a similar one in a strange environment where you lacked family support. For households with a more tenuous claim to land, emigration might offer more, although often it was the laird who provided this opportunity and thus your destination. The long summer twilight (the simmer dim) rewarded those who had endured the long winter darkness with its occasional, magical and colourful aurora borealis (northern lights). Fair Isle was a special place, challenging to be sure, but uniquely rewarding when times were good.

When the devastating Irish potato blight spread to northern Scotland in 1846 it brought the threat of famine to the Northern Isles, only prevented by limited charity sent from the south of Scotland. This philanthropy had, however, dissipated by February 1851, so that a bartering trip from Fair Isle to Dunrossness in Shetland was essential for families who needed grain.

# Chapter 1

# A Sea Crossing

In murky darkness the men launched the two boats into frigidly cold water, taking care to stay as dry as possible. Their goal was Shetland, a 25-mile trip that could take up to seven hours, depending on conditions. The sea anywhere in this part of the world can be extremely challenging, as local weather is famed for the ease with which it can quickly deteriorate. In the depths of winter all knew that even a fair day had the potential to develop into cold sheets of rain and terrifying, hulking waves, potentially destructive forces. Reading weather patterns is an essential skill for all fishermen, but it is one that lacks certainty. Since their route would take them round 'the headland of the roaring tideway' at the south of Dunrossness, where the Atlantic Ocean collides vigorously with the North Sea, stamina was essential. On a good February day in the 21st century you can get an easy sea passage from Fair Isle to Shetland, but seldom does anyone attempt the journey in a Fair Isle yoal. And even today, with all the technology and buoyancy of a modern craft, that winter passage can be 'difficult'.

Yoals are slight, flexible, open-decked boats, with a shallow draft. They are about sixteen feet in length, with three planks (tafts) as seats, three sets of oars and a single sail. From any distance they are their forebears' miniature Viking craft. Yoals were designed to allow fishermen to navigate close to the rocky northern coastlines, their flexible manoeuvrability ideal for such conditions, although only in the hands of experts. They were easily managed by three men (or two men and two boys) for a day's fishing some distance from land and yet were light enough to be drawn well up the beach to safety when the work was over, lest the sea decide to claim them in the night. Seamanship was drilled into every boy from an early age and strangers marvelled at the sight of this small craft's ability to flit through singularly turbulent seas. Oars were short and thus the seamen's stroke swift, exhibiting a dexterity and skill that defied replication by anyone who had not experienced a long apprenticeship. Extended journeys to either Orkney or

Shetland were undertaken, but were always treated with respect since men and boats were vital island assets.

Thus when this small trading expedition to Shetland was considered, it was well planned and much discussed over the Christmas period. The day started fair and all were confident as they made their way down to South Harbour where the yoals were safely beached in their noosts, the curved, stone-lined nests dug into the ground behind the beach that kept the boats safe from the sea until their next trip. The heavy stones that weighed the craft down were quickly removed and the crews carried the boats to the water's edge. Everyone knew their task, so apart from the odd grunt there was no conversation.

Dressed as warmly as possible, swathed in woollens topped by sheepskin and with heads cocooned in the local knitted keps, two stalwart crews set off in darkness, five men to each yoal. A good, clear morning eventually emerged and they all settled down to their task, telling each other that it would be a fine day surely. There was only a little chat at this early hour, each man working mechanically, pulling steadily and building to a rhythm that continued seamlessly throughout the day, for although they had the sail raised there was for once not a lot of wind.

There were no boys today, only men who had endured the hard apprenticeship that gave them the right to take part in such a journey. Mere boys would never be included on a long winter trip. Yoals and the men who sailed in them were too precious to take a chance with youngsters who might not have built up the necessary levels of endurance. The journey would take a good part of the day, depending on luck and weather, either of which could add or subtract time at will. Difficult conditions might decide exactly where they made landfall, but today their focus was on the small trading centre of Grutness, at the southern edge of Shetland. In this weather they foresaw no problem.

Those who began this journey in near darkness would end it similarly, for there are quite limited hours of daylight at this latitude in February. In summer it barely gets dark, and on bad days in winter there can be almost no light at all. That is how people live this far north of the equator. They endure long, cold, dark months so that they can enjoy long, bright (and when they are lucky) warm summer months.

Thick winter darkness always adds a note of tension for those who sail in open boats far from home, but the men were warmly dressed and carried some food for the journey, stored in flat straw bags that they sat on, to keep them dry. Additionally, there were small casks of bland (a fermented whey) which was their substitute for ale.

They aimed to barter some of the women's knitted goods in exchange for grain and any other food that would add to their meagre winter diet. Sometimes they could barter with passing ships, with knitting their main currency at this time of the year, but few ships had passed Fair Isle recently and when there had been sails on the horizon bad weather had prevented the launching of yoals. Today the men hoped for a fairer rate of exchange on Shetland than that offered by their only other option in Fair Isle, the laird's factor. The master's representative was never over-generous with his valuation of the women's knitting, particularly in mid-winter when he knew his tenants had no other option. It is, however, always in the nature of a free man to seek an alternative to a grasping superior and this fact fuelled the men's exertions. Two wooden kists of knitting held their hopes for the day and were carefully wedged in, so that they would be safe even if the Sumburgh roost gave their craft a hard time. That particular current was famed for its ability to destroy small boats, but with their skill and Robert Stevenson's lighthouse on Sumburgh Head acting as a guide, the passage was well within their ability.

The day wore on slowly and, although the weather stayed fair, over time damp winter cold bit into their souls. Still they pulled away relentlessly as the hours piled sluggishly by. All were utterly weary and chilled by the time they approached Shetland, but now minds were heartened by the knowledge that the marathon was almost over, the noise of the waves thundering on Sumburgh's cliffs a welcome sound of terra firma. None could see their companion boat in the gloom, but each crew knew that their fellows were out there somewhere, steadily duplicating their own efforts.

When the Taft yoal felt the first terrifying lurch of power strike it broadsides, its crew knew almost at once that there was nothing to be done. In the grey cold and with such heavy clothes, none had any real doubt about the outcome. Despite their combined years of skill, experience, strength and intuitive ability, they could not deal with an aberration such as this, one that came suddenly out of the darkness to overwhelm them in a moment. It was simply the stuff of nightmares.

Freak waves were once thought to be the poor excuse of a mediocre sailor, but we now have scientific proof of their reality. A freak wave is one that will occasionally and idiosyncratically suck power from its neighbours and build up until it is a force that can casually toss aside anything unlucky enough to be in its path. This particular surge was no leviathan, no titanic monster of the kind that has been known to overwhelm an ocean-going liner. This wave was simply of sufficient force and power to tip five strong men from a fragile craft into the deep, dark, chasmal trench of water that it bore in front of it, before burying them under its weight. The sudden shocking lurch, together with sharp numbing cold, quickly sucked air from the men's lungs. Each of the five deaths was quite unspectacular: a few initial grunts, some desperate lashing to catch hold of a plank, an oar or a companion, then fast-numbing cold and death. Already chilled to the bone, they had little energy left to fight.

There were of course a few appeals to God, as you would expect from a Christian community, while some moaned long-loved names – Jeannie, Aggie, Midder – and then silence, the silence of asphyxiation and passing. There was no one to hear or make any attempt to save them, so these were quick and lonely deaths. In 1851 the lives of the poor were not held in high esteem anywhere, so there would be no widespread interest in their loss. Although for their families it would mean a personal catastrophe, seafaring catastrophes were not in the least exceptional at this time.

The yoal broke its back in the tumble and its boards would continue to splinter into smaller and smaller fragments over the coming days and weeks. Tides would move the flotsam back and forth, out towards the Atlantic then back again towards the land until some of the most militant pieces beat themselves into shreds against Shetland's unkind rocks. Finally there would be nothing left to say that any of these bits of wood had been a boat at all, nothing left of the careful workmanship that was a yoal. Tides carried the men's bodies away from the islands, fish ate their rotting flesh and finally, with the pressure of time and tides, their skeletons fragmented. No one would ever find any trace of the boat, or the men who had so very nearly achieved their goal.

There was, however, one irrational survivor. The sturdy kist of knitting, the purpose of the trip, obstinately refused to break up or sink. Solidly made by one of those who perished and tightly bound by ropes created by another, this perverse box survived its tumble and bobbed forward on its solitary, watertight journey towards Shetland's shore. Perhaps it became caught up in a current? Perhaps a higher being took an interest in its fate? Against all odds it was finally stranded well up into a crack in the rocks, to be left by an ebbing tide not all that far from its destination. There it rested in the darkness, waiting to rot, to be destroyed by waves or to be found by man, as fate directed. The kist of knitting would be the men's only memorial.

## Chapter 2

# Home Comforts

"Is there no one here but me with the sense to see how much there is to do? Just because your father's away there's no excuse to lie about the place idling. Your father didn't raise his family to be lazy. Believe me, the devil's just waiting to catch folk that are idling. You'll all go to the burning fire if that one catches you! Lounging about, that's what it is you're all doing, just lounging about!"

Immediately everyone moved their limbs in a variety of ways to show that it was not they who were at fault. Someone else should be the focus, both for their mother's wrath and the devil's attention. After all, it was a big family. The older ones had already developed the knack of speedily moving into a position that suggested positive activity, so that it was not they who caught their mother's eye when she was in a mood like this. Even picking something off the floor could be viewed as constructive and it gave you time to plan your next move. The younger ones were still learning, however, and were more likely either to be clumsy, or simply to sit in open-mouthed astonishment at the outburst. The big ones hoped that such poor reactions would focus their mother's wrath in their small siblings' direction.

To be fair, lounging was not a regular Fair Isle habit, even if there had been the space for such an activity in the crowded kitchen/living/sleeping area of any island house. The but-end of the croft where they were all currently gathered had little enough space, what with the family, the pig, the chickens, a fire in the centre of the floor, buckets, a spinning wheel, a kist, a meal girnal and the few odd sticks of furniture that the Wilsons had amassed over the years.

John, the eldest boy, found himself wondering where his mother had heard of such a decadent activity. Lounging wasn't Jeannie's usual choice of vocabulary at all, but as he considered it more, he decided that he liked the word. It suggested taking your ease somewhere soft, spacious and warm, somewhere you could stretch out and relax. Mr

Cheyne had a book about the Romans, with a drawing of people lying on long benches, eating what he had told them were grapes. Now that was what you might consider lounging. John looked about him at the wee ones crushed close together on the room's only wooden settle and at the rest squeezed up on boxes and a couple of chairs that were fitted into odd spaces, just outwith the perimeter of the smoky fire in the centre of the floor. It was hard to imagine anyone ever finding anywhere to lounge in Taft. Even at night, since you shared your small bed with at least one and perhaps two or more relatives, you had to be careful where you put your limbs. No. Lounging was not a Fair Isle activity.

But now his mother's voice pushed him back into the here and now, focusing all their minds on the day and its needs.

"We need water, peat for the fire, peat from the hill, more feed for the cows from the barn and I've got a washing to do as well as meal to grind when the dishes are done. Then there's a couple of messages to be run."

When they were not engaged in other activities, children in Fair Isle were always running between the different croft houses, carrying messages for their elders. They wondered (though never aloud) why it was that adults needed to spend so much of their lives sending missives, both physical and verbal, from one house to the next. Keeping busy was never a problem for Fair Isle children. Finding a minute to yourself was much more of an issue. This morning had been a short break from the norm that all were enjoying, at least they had been until Jeannie swept into the room like a huge wave on the beach, scattering them all like pebbles in her path. Suddenly, everyone was up and looking for something to do.

The morning had begun like all the rest. All had taken porridge from the communal wooden trencher, set out on the small table that served the family for a multitude of purposes. They did not sit round it, for it was hardly big enough to accommodate a Fair Isle family and, anyway, there were not enough chairs, not to mention a lack of eating utensils. This table's meagre surface was the only raised area for food preparation, laying out meals, writing letters, doing homework, spreading out the big Bible, or cutting material when you made clothes. Of necessity, the act of sitting round a table to eat was not part of life in many Scottish homes at this time. Big families and small tables do not make for fine dining.

All had taken water, tea or milk, depending on age and preference, not that there was much milk at this time of the year to set out for the young ones. Although the cows were not quite dry, they were not producing a great deal. This was how they started all the days, sharing the porridge that filled empty bellies. Morning porridge was a habit mirrored in each and every croft house on the island, as it was in the majority of

Scottish homes, as long as there was meal in the house. Porridge filled you up and no one thought if they liked it, for that was not relevant. Meals were there to fill the void in empty stomachs and you were just grateful when there was something. The idea of liking specific foods was arcane, almost as much as that of fancy individual bowls and cups. There was in fact, seldom a sufficient quantity of anything in a large family and you learned never to complain, for you knew your mother did her best to give you what she could.

Having all taken a share of the solid grey mass that was breakfast, the youngsters had been sitting quietly, listening to their grandfather talking about the olden times and enjoying a calm moment before the day took over. It was another dark, cold mid-winter morning, so no one was over-anxious to move on to their next allotted task. There were no boats going out either, which was why the older boys were relaxed, though they might try fishing off the rocks with a rod if Jeannie said she needed some fresh fish to augment the dried food she had stored in the rafters.

It had been just fine to sit and listen (with both good manners and interest) to their grandfather, Laurence Wilson. Although they had lived with him when they were younger, when the new crofts were built he had stayed at Gaila with his eldest son, Thomas, who was factor to the laird. Last night the old man had decided to visit Taft and stay. Laurence had some standing in the community, his good name having been hard earned over many years. Some said that luck had played a part in his success, luck and his family's good relationship with the laird. Jeannie had married his second son and, although John lacked the security of his older brother, he too was a successful and respected man by local standards, someone who tried to have a tiny surplus when the annual day of reckoning with the laird came around. Success was measured in small degrees in Fair Isle, particularly after the potato blight. Any surplus at all was regarded as success. Even a small loss was not thought shameful.

In addition to his other virtues their father was a good carpenter, responsible for their wooden settle, fashioned from timber recovered from the wreck of some poor ship. Their grandfather was seated in another of his creations, Jeannie's high, straw-backed chair, with small drawers at the bottom for her knitting. With the added help of one sheepskin laid over its back and another on the seat, draughts were kept from the old man and padding provided for his scrawny posterior. John and Lowry, the eldest boys, were perched on two low kitchen chairs, while the family dog lay on the floor scratching lazily and the two remaining chickens pecked at their feet on the hard packed, dirt floor.

To a wealthy man this was a scene of desperate poverty, but to fellow islanders this croft spoke of a level of prosperity to which not everyone could aspire. There was some dried meat and fish hanging from the rafters. The family had fuel for the fire and everyone was clothed, not well, but relatively respectably. Here, as in all poor homes, clothes were a necessity rather than an indulgence and it was always hard for Jeannie to cast an item into the rag-basket when finally it was deemed useless for anything else. Even then it would be used to concoct a rug, stuff a hole, or as a cleaning cloth. Jeannie was hard pushed to see that everyone had a half-decent outfit when they attended the weekend worship meetings that the Methodists held in each other's houses, decent sometimes meaning that no one had an obvious tear anywhere that showed. Her own wardrobe was reduced to the ragged clothes she stood up in, with a couple of blouses and a slightly less worn skirt kept for religious meetings and celebrations. Her undergarments were usually threadbare. There were always hap shawls of course. All the women swathed themselves in these thick, dark wraps throughout the winter, but they, too, quickly developed holes and pulls, as house and farm work picked, tugged and tore at them. When it was cold, people didn't really give a hoot about how they looked, although the young girls possibly cared a bit more than the boys, particularly when they were courting.

Currently at Taft it was 11-year-old Jane who needed new clothes. At least as first girl she might have something new, if Jeannie couldn't scrounge a cast-off from a relative. Poor Aggie, her younger sister, would be more likely to survive on hand-me-downs. Keeping a family decently covered was just one of a long list of nightmares that mothers faced in Fair Isle. There was never enough of anything and always some unexpected surprise waiting round the corner to catch you out, just as you thought you had things in some sort of order.

So when Jeannie came into the room that morning, struggling with two heavy buckets of water, the tranquil family scene had filled her not with satisfaction but with ire. There was so much to do. There was always so much to do and it would never be done if the family sat about on their hands. The girls weren't even knitting for goodness sakes! Girls sitting without their knitting! What next? Mayhem surely followed on the heels of such indolence. No wonder there was an edge to her voice. Jeannie herself truly feared fiery retribution from the Lord as a punishment for indolence. That was how she had been raised.

She was also tired and cold. She hadn't slept after John left last night and not much before either. It wasn't that she was unduly worried about this trip, but she hated anything that was different from her usual routine. Above all, she hated it when John was away, not least because this happened so seldom. Illogical though it might seem, different was dangerous. Normally she knew where everyone was at any given time and that knowledge made her feel comfortable, despite the fact that the men were usually at sea. Local men were so competent with their yoals that seldom was there a problem, although they regularly had to make an effort to save strangers who wrecked their ships on Fair Isle's shores. However, John was not fishing round the island today, and tonight he would not be home. Jeannie had never left this small outpost of humanity and knew that she never would, so Shetland seemed strange and otherworldly. Who knew what might happen to a person in Shetland? It would have been the same had it been London or Paris, for in Jeannie's mind anything that was not Fair Isle was exotic and therefore worrying.

And she was hungry, for she had eaten nothing even though she had been first to rise, since the small table that held the food was always hers at the end of a meal. It was her job to ensure that the men took priority. If a croft let its men lose their powers then no one would eat. Then the children had to be fed to ensure that they kept their health, for sick children took up your time, as well as causing you worry. A mother had what was left at the end of a meal, or a cup of sweet tea if there was nothing to spare, though you never heard mothers complaining of hunger. Necessity ensured that women always thought of themselves last, so that you would be hard put to find anywhere on the island a wife that was not scrawny. Scrawny women were the norm, because in addition to lacking sufficient nourishment they worked hard, both in the house and on the land. Once married there was generally a new child to be born and suckled every second year, farm work to be done in season, help given at the peat digging, food to be prepared, knitting to be worked at, animals to be cared for and families to be raised. Husband and family were the altars on which mothers sacrificed their health and for which they renounced all. That was what girls learned at their mother's knee and took with them when they married and left home. Although the men and the fishing were the mainstay of the family, without their women's sacrifices the community would not survive.

Jeannie was a hard-working and intelligent wife who was proud of what she had achieved. Her marriage to John had been a good one, better than some she might have found. Now they had seven children to find a living for on a five-acre croft, a real challenge even if you were supposed to be amongst the island's more fortunate. It was all a matter of degree. Of course, some said that they had been allocated Taft because Thomas was the factor, but John had been amongst the most successful of those working the old run rig system, when they had all lived in one of the four hamlets. Taft was only five acres after all, not eight like Gaila or Springfield, although the land was good and John was a hard worker and a good manager. Jeannie toiled as hard as she could to support him, so that the Taft Wilsons might keep their heads above water. Their home did not differ all that much from the rest. It was just that some families were slightly closer to the edge.

Like most Fair Isle mothers, Jeannie had lost some pregnancies and then Hannah had died when she was just a toddler. She never forgot Hannah. Childbirth was dangerous both for mothers and babies and not all children were expected to survive the long trek through to adulthood. Other people sometimes forgot the children who died along the way, but never the mothers. Still, despite the fact that she loved them all, Jeannie liked to keep her remaining family in check, having been immersed in the dangers of the seven deadly sins from childhood. When John was away they must be kept on their toes, for Jeannie truly believed that the devil was real and that he was always looking out for idle hands to lead into mischief. Without John, she was the devil's only adversary at Taft and she would keep him at bay with elbow grease, sweat and her tongue. Her children would not go to the burning fire if she could help it. Storms and crop failures were beyond her powers, but mischief and laziness could be battled. A caring body if you were in need, if you were slacking Jeannie Wilson was not a comfortable person to be around.

So now even her old father-in-law felt obliged to defend himself. At eighty years of age, Laurence felt entitled to choose for himself when to budge and when to rest his arthritic limbs and did not take kindly to a young body suggesting otherwise. He made a point of grunting painfully as he struggled to rise, pulling a blanket closer round his shoulders as if to suggest he was about to go out to face the elements. It was an old-age act of bravado, but one he felt entitled to make.

"I'll be away mistress. I don't want to be in your way. I don't want to hold you all back." The edge to his voice warned her that he was offended.

Jeannie was irritable, but not with the old man. He had come to show young John and Lowry an old bit of carving he had found in his barn, but really he had decided to visit knowing that John would be away and Jeannie might need some company. His daughter-in-law also knew that Laurence enjoyed a change of scene over the winter months. It was hard to feel useful at his age, trapped inside day after monotonous winter day, with arthritic pain in his back, knees and increasingly useless fingers. Walking alone outside was more of a bother than ever in strong winds and quite impossible on some days, even with help. Getting up in the night to pee had become more of a task for the old man too.

Sometimes Laurence felt he would be glad when it was all over and he could take his peace in the graveyard, alongside his wife. He longed for the summer more than any of them, when his chair could sit outside the door of the croft for much of the day and he could see what was going on, not to mention having a bit of a chat with anyone who passed. There was usually someone passing the door in the summer months and there were more small chores about the place that he could do to feel useful. Time went faster if you were doing something. On good days he sometimes made it down to the landing place at South Harbour, where he could watch them all working away, offering advice and even helping with the odd, easy task.

Life inside a croft house in winter was claustrophobic, when both people and animals were forced to shelter away from the elements and big families in small cluttered rooms often squabbled. Then there was the irritation of everlastingly wet clothes strung about all over the place, adding to the congestion. Women were forever washing small children's bits and pieces, as well as trying to dry off outer clothing that had been soaked by the weather, in an effort to ensure that the family could start the following day in some comfort. It was a lost cause really, but another of those battles that the mothers had to fight.

John's older boys had been happy see their grandfather, John giving up his place in their box bed and both happy to walk slowly back to Gaila when the old man was so minded. For Laurence, the grandchildren were a constant pleasure, mainly because now he had the time to listen. Seven of his own children had lived and they had seemed like a terrible responsibility when he was younger, as he struggled to feed and clothe them and set them all off on the right path. Now he had fifty grandchildren and marvelled at the idea, enjoying those who had chosen to remain on the island. As to the rest, well you lost them when they left to try for a better life. Despite the occasional letter that you read till it fell to bits, sometimes it was as if they had never been, although their loss deepened your connection with those you could still touch and see. Some families had never learned to write well at all and for them the boat that took their children away was a final farewell, almost as if they had died. Children leaving was a constant fear in island life, yet leave they must, for if they all stayed, Fair Isle would quickly become untenable. That was the one absolute about Fair Isle, its size.

"For goodness sake, Faither, I didn't mean you. Sit down and take your ease. You know perfectly well that it's these young ones I need to get going. They'd lie around all day if you left them. Sit there and talk to John and Lowry as long as you wish. Your John will be glad enough to see you here when he gets home. He likes to bring you the news from the mainland first. Be at peace. I suppose the jobs for the older boys won't go away. John, get your grandfather another cup of tea. Don't just sit there like a big useless lump of peat. Move yourself!"

For a few seconds the atmosphere in the crowded room lightened, as John leapt up to do his mother's bidding. The younger ones had been the first focus for her ire but now her beloved John was in trouble. Such joy!

It didn't take long, however, before she had the wee ones in her sights. "You lot, get moving! You all have tasks to do, as you know well enough. As for two girls of mine just sitting there with no knitting! Well, I never thought I'd see the day when my girls thought they could sit around without wires in their hands!"

Thus Jeannie moved around the room, as irritating as the winter wind itself, reaching into every corner, picking, poking and prodding, animals and family alike. Although battered by hard work, lack of food and endless childbearing, she retained the essence of the forceful personality that had attracted John when she was a fresh-faced, young thing. And however old they were, the children all knew that their father would ask how it had gone when he was away and no one wanted a bad report. John's presence was deferred to, even when absent. Their father pushed himself to the limit and expected no less from each of his children, for his family were brought up to honour God, parents and work in equal measure. As far as John Wilson was concerned, work was ordained by God just as much as formal worship on the Sabbath. Disappointment would not be met with a raised hand either, as it was in some of the other crofts. At Taft it was met with a vexed, bushy, raised eyebrow, which for all his children was enough. Only the wee ones got the occasional skelp on the bum and that was a warning as much as a punishment.

So as the younger children jumped up to resume their usual morning pattern, Jeannie relaxed a bit. Change disrupts routines and Jeannie liked her routines. It was being in charge that unsettled her, not that she would have stated this out loud. Her actions spoke volumes, however, even if the younger ones didn't understand the message. John was away, so the croft was destabilised. The woman just wanted her husband back home again, to take his place and put everything back on track.

There had been no option but to try to sell the knitting. Certainly they still had some stock up on the hill, but sheep were for selling, or wool, so that only a few could be killed for eating. Cattle were for selling too and most folk didn't have all that many to begin with. So many people were selling their cattle since the potato blight hit Scotland that the price on the mainland had dropped dramatically, although a new milk cow still cost between £2 and £3, a big sum for most crofters to find after they had paid their rent for the year. A sheep cost just 30 or 40 pence, so they were sometimes eaten, even if the wiry Fair Isle beasts were not all that meaty. Fish was their mainstay, but a family couldn't live on fish alone. Since there was still a scarcity of good potatoes, more grain was needed than before. But there was not enough land to grow sufficient at the best of times, so that in the five years since the blight had raised its head the lack of grain had become even more problematic.

Knitting was Taft's saving grace, as it was in every other croft. The women and girls knitted whenever they were not doing something else, and if they were in a rush to finish a garment they would knit even while working. In summer it was not unusual to see women walking and knitting at the same time. And since it was mandatory, Jane and Aggie knew quite well that they should not have let their wires lie unattended. They had, of course, jumped to pick them up as soon as Jeannie spoke, but this morning nothing they did was right.

"For goodness sake, girls, put your wires down. You get ready for school, Aggie, and Jane, you keep Stewart away from the fire and get the place tidied a bit. We don't need the wee one in the fire again. That'll be a nice thing for your father to come home to, the peerie one burned."

The girls sighed slightly. First it was pick up your knitting and get on with it, then it was put it down again and do something else. There was no pleasing her today. And they couldn't be responsible for Stewart. He was a wee devil that one.

Two-year-old Stewart had a fascination with the fire that none of the others had shown. Of course, most toddlers were attracted by the colour, movement and occasional sparks that came from the pile of smoking peat in the centre of the floor. Occasionally they all got too close by accident, even with the ring of stones to act as a small barrier, but unlike his siblings this child had walked up and even into the edge of the fire more than once, reaching out to touch the flames even when they singed his fingers. Jeannie wondered what ailed the child. You would think that with bare feet he would have learned the lesson the first time he went too far. But no. Recently he had been slightly burned when he tried to poke a cinder from the glowing pile of ash, but still he was fascinated.

Some of the other island ladies had suggested (in a less than kindly way) that he was simple. But he wasn't. Jeannie was sure of that. He just needed a lot of attention to keep him safe, more than the others had done. Perhaps that's why he did it. Perhaps when you were the smallest in a crowded room you had to do something to draw attention to yourself, something that would bring your mother running, even if it hurt. Whatever the reason, Jeannie had little sympathy for her toddler for it meant that she always had to have an eye on him, or he was hobbled to the ground like a beast while she got on with her tasks. Well, today he would be hobbled. That would sort him out. There was too much for her to do to pander to a toddler, and he was too big now to carry around on her hip all day.

"Bring him over here, Jeannie." The old man spoke quietly, as if he had heard her thoughts. Jeannie was taken aback. "Tie him in this chair and I'll play with him while you get on. Give us a bit of string and a couple of pieces of bones or sticks and we'll get along together just fine. Here's a bit of wool he can use to wind things up. Come on peerie boy, now make me a kishie that I can use for the peats."

As she gathered a few bits for her father-in-law, Jeannie was indeed surprised, though she had the sense not to show it. Childcare was not a grown man's job, so that from cradle to the grave they studiously found lots of other things to occupy their time. The old man must feel sorry for her. Or perhaps he too was slightly anxious, though this he was unlikely to say and certainly never to her. Perhaps he was looking for distraction from the same demons that had her out of bed earlier than usual this morning. Whatever his reason, she was grateful. Anything that made her day easier was appreciated. She had been dead tired from the moment she pushed herself out of bed and everything she did now would seem more difficult because of that. For the moment, she was simply grateful that the wee one had a minder.

Entranced by unusual attention, and even though tied into a chair, Stewart was quite at peace. He played happily, requiring little from his grandfather except the odd encouraging word and the occasional untangling of knots in the wool that he rolled endlessly round some sticks. As with most youngsters in a large family, just a little undivided attention kept him happy. His two eldest siblings continued to talk to his grandfather and ignore him, as was the norm. Older boys had little to do with young children if they could help it. It was their way of showing they were no longer boys themselves, but fledging adults who were ready to spread their wings.

Stewart out of the way, there was the real work of the morning to be organised. John insisted that all his children went to school to learn what they could. At the moment that meant Aggie was attending. The three older boys were finished, and Jane (who was eleven) had also stopped so that she was able to help full-time at home, and when Jerry started Aggie might leave, provided Jeannie could persuade John that she needed the girl in the house.

It didn't cost much to send a child to school but there was a small charge and you had to balance your wish for education with your budget. Of course, you let the boys go on a bit longer than the girls. After all, apart from a bit of reading, what did a girl need with the school? Some people had neither the budget nor the hankering to educate their children much at all, even though the teacher never chased anyone to pay. Mr Cheyne did a bit of farming like the rest of them and knew their problems intimately, accepting fish if people had nothing else. He was also happy to negotiate for a pile of peat, or lamp oil, for in winter both his house and the school room needed to be heated and lit. Since there was no law that said you had to educate your children, the Fair Isle teacher had to be pragmatic about who chose to use his services and for how long. Although it was expected that everyone should attend school for some time and learn to read a bit, not everyone learned to write their name. There was pressure from the Church of Scotland to ensure that everyone could read the Bible and know the catechism, but school attendance remained random.

Jeannie's three older boys could all read, write and count as well as anyone in Fair Isle. John in particular had learned everything old Cheyne could teach him, her husband paying a few pence extra for classes in bookkeeping and English grammar. My, what a boy he was for the books, more than his father even. At 20 years of age he knew great swathes of the Bible by heart, and poetry too. But what difference such a lot of learning would make to him was not quite clear to Jeannie, unless he hoped to become the factor at some time in the future. Most likely the factor would suggest one of his own sons would follow him, so that John would be a fisherman, a farmer and possibly a joiner, since he had skilled fingers with wood.

Jeannie hadn't really minded the boys learning so much, but the girls were needed at home to help her, as well as learning how to run a home smoothly, for that was where their future lay, as mothers, knitters, cooks, farmers, housewives and beasts of burden. Jane already knew more bookwork than was necessary, and to Jeannie it was much more important that she helped her at home. Aggie was useful too, since even a small pair of hands could carry peat or water, knit, run errands, or mind a baby. But John was adamant that she stayed on for the moment, so Jeannie must manage as best she could with just one girl at home. Women with more girls in their family had an easier time at home, but with more boys you had men who could fish. What you needed was a balance.

"Aggie, where are you? Get yourself ready for school. Where's the silly child gone now? She needs to be off."

The girl had absented herself to the byre which adjoined the but-end of the croft; an area the womenfolk, in particular, used as a toilet. Aggie had long ago learned that the best and easiest way to avoid her mother's attention was to slip into the byre, where the cows' gentle presence was usually much more soothing than anything to be found in the main room. The animals chewed on regardless, whatever the weather through the house, glancing sideways at her and perhaps swinging a tail in recognition, but offering no trouble. Aggie gave the youngest a hug, her reliable solidity and warmth providing comfort. However, just a few minutes grace was allowed in the byre and the girl could hear her mother ordering everyone around even from here, so she slunk back into the main room quietly, trying to evade attention.

"Willie! If you've finished your porridge, we need peat. The stack outside is down a fair bit now, so I need as much as you can bring down while the weather holds. Take a run up to the hill and start to collect what's on that small stack we left up there. You know where it is. We need to take advantage of any good weather while it's about. Who knows what we'll be facing in a week or two. The peat all has to come down sometime and today's as good a day as any."

"Jane helps me get the peat from the hill! And it's not as if we've run out yet. The stack's only half down. It'll last for ages," Willie moaned quietly.

The great pile of peat at the side of the house, which had in the autumn been as tall as a man, was now diminishing. Willie mumbled his complaint half to himself, so that his mother could not really make out the words, for in this house, outright defiance was never allowed. And although the boy pretended outrage at his onerous task he knew it was a lost cause. He was just making a point. When you were third boy you had to make the point that you were growing up too. Bringing down the peat from the hill was a job for younger members of a family at this time of the year and Willie was trying to raise himself above the rank of Peat Boy. The trouble was that with only a little fishing being done at the moment, his new role as Beach Boy was largely redundant. Until the better weather came, he was Errand Boy, Peat Boy and any other kind of Boy his mother chose to make him. Even though he knew that Jane could only do so much and Aggie had to go to school, Willie envied John and Lowry, who in his opinion were excused far too much drudgery around the house because they were now 'men'. Of course, if it had been a big task they would have been drawn into it, but Willie knew it was not, so bringing down peat today would be his lot.

"Get yourself together, my lad. You catch a pony and tie on a couple of kishies as soon as you can and take yourself up to the hill. Be sure and fill them to the top mind, or it's even more trips you'll be making. I want to see the stack back up to where it was before Yule, in case we have a bit of bad weather. You just remember that nobody likes to walk up to the peat beds in a winter storm."

The peat beds were a good walk to the north even in warm weather, but on bad days, with inadequate clothing and a strong wind battering your limbs, it would seem much longer. Today it was not too cold and Willie would not be alone, for by now the big stacks of peat were all well down and everyone would take advantage of this break in the weather. You never knew at this time of the year how long a good patch of weather would last, so you took a chance when you could.

There were hundreds of people clustered at the southern part of the island and you were hard put to do anything at all without bumping into someone, as like as not a relative, for in this close-knit environment almost everyone seemed to marry a cousin of sorts. Since crofts were too small to contain families comfortably throughout the day, unless it was pouring down with rain or desperately windy the women tried to find useful outdoor tasks for all their children.

Willie knew his mother was right about the weather. During a storm the strongest men could be blown off their feet, and anything that was not safely tethered might become a dangerous missile that would injure anyone daft enough to get in its way. Children were kept safely inside on such days, when the family could only listen to the power of nature's destruction, praying that the ropes that held the heavy stones on their straw and turf roof would hold. Everyone knew that on the very worst days some damage to buildings, yoals or dykes was inevitable. So today, sighing as much as he dared, Willie took down a couple of rope kishies from a hook on the wall in the barn and went out to see if he could catch one of their ponies to help him retrieve the remaining precious peat.

"That reminds me, you older boys need to think of making me a new kishie, not to mention a couple of budies and a peerie hovie as well, now that I think on it. I noticed yesterday that quite a few of the baskets in the barn were a bit worn. Straw baskets with holes in them are no use to me in the spring and your father likes a good stock set by for the start of the fishing. There's still plenty of simmens there for you to be using."

Simmens were the straw ropes that the men twisted to use when they were making chair backs, anchors for thatch, or straw baskets. Hovies were the smaller straw baskets, often used for carrying limpet bait. Budies were designed to carry fish, with the larger mill budie for carrying corn on a man's back, while the big round kishie was more often used to carry peat. Each basket had many additional uses of course and all it took to make them was straw, skill, effort and time. There was a particular need to have a big stock ready for springtime, when there was not a moment spare for any additional work. With only the small ponies and people's backs to transport fish, corn and peat around the island, a large range of different sizes and shapes was vital.

"Tomorrow, Mither. We'll start them tomorrow." John made an effort to sound confident, knowing full well that if his mother insisted, they would stay. Even at 20, he knew his limits with Jeannie. But he smiled hopefully as he pushed his own agenda for the day. "Today's bright enough to look for wood and the boys at the beach said there was quite a bit on the tide yesterday when we were down working with faither to get everything ready for this morning. I said we'd go up the cliffs with the Springfield boys to have a look, if Ald Daa doesn't mind us moving out for a bit and you don't need us to fish from the rocks. There might even be some grand, big stuff."

The boy turned to his grandfather. "You'll surely still be here when we get back, for us to show you what we get?"

The old man nodded. He would stay. In all honesty he could do little else, given the state of his legs. When he did go home he would need someone to walk with him to Gaila.

The boys hesitated, needing an acknowledgement from Jeannie that they might go. After her outburst they wanted to be sure she was fine with their plan, for with their father away she must be obeyed. Despite their advancing years, in this home Jeannie was absolutely in charge of their time when their father was absent.

"Och, away you go the pair of you, if you have to, though if Willie doesn't get all the peat down today I'll have you at that job tomorrow. Look, there's a couple of brunnies left from what we made for your faither. Take that to keep you from starving. Aggie, you get off to school right now. You know Mr Cheyne doesn't like you to be late. And take care not to dawdle on the way."

The girl left in a flurry, more than anxious to escape, leaving Jeannie to clear the table and eat the few remaining scraps of porridge. Then she slipped out of the door to check that Willie was on his way. Sometimes he needed the encouragement of her tongue, but not today. She could see him running to join a couple of lads who were also on their way northwards.

Laurence had a word with the older boys just before they left. "There was a good east wind last night, so there may be even more of worth further up the coast than yesterday. You know, I wouldn't mind a nice solid wee piece for the leg of a stool I'm mending at the moment, over at Gaila. Just a peerie bit would do, but something that will last. Seems a shame to use any of the bigger bits that your uncle has in his barn, but all the small lengths he has lying around are not up to the job. A bit about this long would be perfect, but solid mind."

Now the trip was justified. Laurence needed a bit of wood, so John and Lowry could leave with an easy heart. There was in all probability something that would do the job already in their own barn, but they were hardly going to bring that up. Everyone knew perfectly well that they were off for a bit of a jaunt and could find more mundane work around the croft quite easily, but searching for salvage along the line of the tide was what island men did to get out and about at this time of the year, when there was neither fishing nor farming that really needed them. In the spring there would be birds' eggs as an excuse, but in February it was just the flotsam and jetsam of the ocean that gave you a reason to look.

There were always ditches to be cleaned and turf roofs to check and mend, but all that sort of thing could wait when there was the rumour of bounty from the sea. Just occasionally there would be a special prize. On Fair Isle's coastline anything could arrive, and even if casks of gin and brandy were unusual such gifts were not completely unknown. In truth, anything could turn up at this remote place in the midst of international shipping lanes. Once, the Taft boys had rescued an entire sail that some poor wrecked vessel had forfeited, one that was more than big enough to use on a yoal, and saved the family money it could then use for something else. Another time there had been several big tea chests where the contents were, in the main, still quite usable and several families enjoyed this unexpected bounty. Sometimes it was the gift of huge timbers that had to be hauled up on land to safety, until a boat could get round to float them to a more accessible area.

The sea was a vast lottery and all the men on the island were fully-fledged gamblers. It cost nothing to play, just the energy it took to get yourself to the right spot at the right time. Sometimes lives were risked as they climbed down the towering cliffs, with huge waves threatening to wash them into the maelstrom far below, but they never told the women. Like the fishing, all the men undertook a long apprenticeship on the cliffs and understood their dangers, even if they couldn't always avoid them. It helped no one if the women thought of beachcombing as a dangerous pursuit.

So old Laurence nodded and smiled at the boys as he watched them make a rather quick get-away, in case their mother changed her mind and asked them to do something more useful. He remembered the excitement of anticipation on a day like this.

"Me too, me too!" Finally young Jerry thought to join in, but he was too late and far too ambitious. They were hardly going to volunteer to take a four-year-old, and to be fair, their mother was never going to suggest they took Jerry on a walk that involved high cliffs and the sea. Every few years or so a young lad would take a fall and suffer serious injury, or worse. Jerry was not old enough to be allowed anywhere near cliffs without someone responsible being with him. Jeannie knew that with the distraction of their friends and the excitement of the search, the older ones would not pay enough attention. No, Jerry was old enough to run the odd errand, but otherwise he was betwixt and between at this time of the year, getting in the way as much as anything else since he was not yet needed for bait gathering and the farm work was dormant. Not that he contributed a great deal to either of these activities, but he was learning.

It was important that children started early to learn all the skills, so that by the time they were big enough they could do their share of an adult's work. You never knew when you would be called to adulthood, for parental illness or accident regularly promoted children before their time. Next year Jerry would be at school, after which time hardly an hour of the day would pass when his time was his own. In the meantime, all he could do was sit on his frustration as best he could.

"Come away over here, Jerry. See if you can help me with this." Again the old man stepped in to smooth things over. Jeannie began to wonder if he might like to live with them permanently again if he was going to be such a good childminder. Mind you, when she lifted her head, "this" turned out to be old Laurence's knife for working at wood, the one he always had with him in case he found something to whittle. Jeannie raised her eyebrows at the alarming size of the menacing thing that was now clutched in her wee boy's hand. The boy himself was thrilled.

Laurence noted Jeannie's face. "Ach, he'll be fine, won't you laddie."

Jerry nodded enthusiastically, eyes wide in anticipation. Working with his grandfather's knife was a real treat. People usually kept their sharper knives away from him. And there was a grand bit of wood to work at. For the moment, Jerry was in heaven.

"You'll not hurt yourself and get your old granddad into trouble, will you?"

The boy shook his head vehemently.

His mother shrugged her shoulders and sighed. "Well, my lad, you're never too young to learn I suppose, but don't come crying to me if you lose a finger. I won't be sewing it back on for you."

Jeannie knew when to give in. The boy would be fine, or he would learn a lesson, hopefully one short of amputation.

Old Laurence smiled at her as he guided the boy's hand. "None of my boys has lost a finger yet. Right, laddie, you hold it like that, carefully mind, and move the blade away from you all the time. Aye. That's right. Away from you," he stressed. "No. Just wee bits to make a shape in the wood. You're not making kindling boy. And keep your eyes on the knife. That way, you'll stay safe."

Once Jeannie was convinced that it was likely Jerry would keep his fingers a while longer, she turned her attention to 'getting on'. Getting on meant working at several things at once, cleaning the house, removing the remains of the last meal, sweeping the floor, clearing the fire of ashes, grinding meal, preparing food for the next onslaught of hungry mouths and making sure that there was enough feed for the byre and fuel for the fire. Then there was a washing that must be done and since the day was fair she should even get it dry. You had to make the most of dry, windy days in winter, for some of the younger children's things always had to be washed, since they would rot if you left them too long. During long wet periods it sometimes seemed as if the youngsters' washing might lie around till the spring.

So Jeannie got on, moving in and out the two rooms like a dervish, with Jane in her wake, taking orders quietly and doing what she could to please. Jane, as the fourth child and the first girl in the family, had become accustomed to accepting that orders would be her lot until she had a house of her own. Luckily she was an even-minded soul, not one to kick against the traces. For the moment she just got on with it all, realising that this was her place until she married and there were worse places to be the eldest girl than Taft.

For half an hour or so the two youngest were content, Stewart as interested in his brother's antics with the knife as he was in his own playthings, accepting that he would not be given the knife, but watching carefully, just in case. He was already getting more attention than the norm and you never knew where that might lead.

Laurence let his mind wander outside with the older boys as he kept an eye on Jerry. If only he could be there to see what the tide had brought into the deep geos and caves, or scramble down to the rocky beaches to search amongst the rock pools, but that sort of thing was no longer within his grasp. Slippery, worn paths, dark, hidden caves and dangerous, sheer-sided cliff faces were not the habitat of old men whose knees hurt and gave way even on flat ground. Just getting out of a chair was painful enough now and when he'd been sitting for an hour or two it took quite a few minutes to straighten his stiffened legs to get them moving at all. The pain and ignominy of old age and the slow wearing away of powers was depressing, but Laurence reminded himself that he was well beyond his allocated three score years and ten and should perhaps appreciate what he had, rather than dwelling on the past. Some old folk in poorer crofts knew they were now a burden on their families. At least at Gaila, Tom made it clear that he was not that, at least not yet. And perhaps God had some purpose for his old bones. The old man was a great believer in God's will.

As the morning wore on, Jeannie busied herself outside with two washing tubs while Jane laboured to bring her enough warmed water, for it was far too cold to put your hands straight into icy well water on a morning like this. Both made an effort to keep their clothes as dry as possible, for any damp would stay with them for the rest of the day and it was hardly the climate for wet sleeves and hems.

In winter people made do with their clothing as long as they could, some folk waiting longer than others to change into something clean (if they had it), although it was debatable if a few of the older men ever changed anything. Cleanliness, at that time and in these houses, was hardly a priority during the long dark months of the year. Poor people who lived in damp, dirty, cramped, smoky houses, with dried fish and mutton hanging from the rafters, beasts in close proximity and no hint of running water, would never smell sweet. When light was needed in the evening, to supplement the firelight, you lit a creeshy lamp – a flat bowl-shaped holder with a wick that lay on a small spout on the side. Creeshy lamps burned fish oil, which is both smelly and smoky, although they saved people the money that it cost to buy a candle, since fish oil was prepared on the beach.

So, even if your standards were not all that high, on a good day in winter you made an effort to get as much laundry scrubbed and rinsed as possible, greying shirts and blouses having been rubbed hard at cuffs and necks with a big bar of soap and then soaked for a bit to lift some of the dirt from them before you scrubbed. Underclothes had often been turned over to get more wear out of them, but eventually these too had to be washed, although Jeannie felt her boys would wear their underwear forever if they had a chance. Boys didn't seem to care how badly they smelt. At least in Fair Isle you never had trouble finding a windy day when you needed to hang wet clothes on a rope outside. Your only problem was attaching the clothes firmly enough to the line so that you kept your bits and pieces from blowing all the way to Shetland, or Norway even. However hard you tried, everyone lost something sometime, even if they never admitted to it. Nothing was more frustrating than to wash and rinse clothes just to lose them, even if it was only a bit of underwear on its last legs that decided to set off for a new home.

As the morning wore on, the rank pile of dirty clothes was cleaned, rinsed and hung on a rope. There was plenty of wind so it would all be fairly dry by late afternoon, and it was a great joy to see the pile diminish and the clothes-line lengthen until it bent under the strain and needed to be propped up with poles. An empty wash basket gave great pleasure to all the women. Finally, all that had to be done was to clear up, hang up the tubs and dry themselves off, for despite their care, there were always corners of cuffs and trailing shawls that had accidentally been dipped in the water. The pair could see similar lines dancing and waving from their neighbours' crofts, showing that they were not the only ones who appreciated the weather.

"Now then, wee man, I'll be having my knife back to myself now. I think you've done enough damage for the moment." Laurence could see that Jerry was becoming overconfident and wanted to head off the inevitable cut that always followed any lack of respect for a knife. The boy took his wee bit of decorated stick off to show his mother and almost immediately his grandfather heard Jeannie sending him on an errand to Springfield. Young children were like parcels, he thought, passed from croft to croft till they found the sense to amuse themselves.

Stewart, meanwhile, was dropping off to sleep, still safely tied in his chair. His grandfather felt like following him, but shook himself awake. No. An afternoon nap might be fine, but when you started to nap in the morning as well that was a step too far, even if you were in your eightieth year. Perhaps he would take a turn around the crubs and have a look at the kail. The wee one would let them know when he woke up again and the walk would do Laurence good, for not only would he appreciate the meagre warmth of the fire much more when he had been outside for a bit, it was always good to keep the legs working, so that they kept their strength.

"I'm away to take a look at the crubs, Jeannie," he said, when she next stuck her head round the door. "Stewart should be fine for a bit. He's sleeping now."

"Do you want a hand out, Faither?"

"When I can't make it out the door by myself anymore, you can just shoot me," he snapped brusquely. He would be all right when he got going. You had to keep trying, or you would just seize up. He wasn't quite an invalid yet. The very idea that he couldn't make it to the door by himself!

Slowly, the old man drew himself up to his full height, stifling groans at creaking knees and forcing them to work. He let them take his weight for a moment or two, before hobbling round the scant furniture and aiming for his stick that was leaning by the door. At least today there were no stormy gusts to blow him over, and after his outburst to Jeannie he hoped he wouldn't now trip and make a fool of himself. As usual it got a bit easier once his knees were used to the motion, until finally he limped less obviously.

Jeannie dutifully held back, ignoring the old man's painful passage to the outside but watching to see he wrapped the extra blanket round his shoulders before he lifted the door latch to face the elements. Although the croft house was hardly the epitome of comfort, strong walls and a peat fire at least worked up some semblance of a cosy atmosphere, one that contrasted sharply with the breezy, biting cold that skulked outside the door. The shock took the old man's breath away for a second, particularly when he left the shelter of the building. It was, after all, still February.

But with the responsibility for Stewart handed over rather like a relay stick in a race, Laurence felt the reward of freedom, for now it was someone else's job to keep him safe. And he felt legitimised now that he had a genuine purpose out here. Kail was vital to a family's health. A tough, green vegetable akin to cabbage, it was one of the few things that could survive the winter in a place where the spume from the sea on one side of the island was more than capable of sweeping up and all the way over to the other side, casting a salty residue on anything in its wake. This salty precipitation, together with the cold, the dark, and regular, incessant rain, discouraged many plants in such an exposed location. Looking to see if the young kail were coming along was something the younger ones did not always have time to do, so it was a useful task for an older man with time on his hands.

The tall, circular, dry-stone enclosures known as crubs protected the young vegetables from animals and weather until the spring, when the plants would be strong enough to survive in the field without protection. The old man was looking out for dislodged stones in the walls and any evidence of an unwelcome invader like a rabbit, or even a sheep. If he found a flaw he would feel particularly useful, but if not, at least he'd made the effort and saved someone else the bother.

Away in the distance he could see the group over at Leogh working at a blocked field drain that he had heard was causing real problems, a hard and dirty job, but necessary. No doubt their industry had made some of the young beachcombers feel a little guilty as they set off on their jaunt, but perhaps not. The young had still to learn about the burden of guilt that grew with the passage of the years.

The Taft brood were doing well. At twenty, John was a man already and Lowry, although just eighteen, was taller and just as strong as his brother. Lowry was his favourite, not that his grandfather would admit that fact to anyone. Grandparents were not supposed to have favourites but this sensible lad with his light-hearted sense of humour was a hard worker and sensitive to his grandfather's feelings. He always asked for your opinion, as if he needed it to complete a job successfully. John, though you couldn't fault the boy really, was just a little bit too sure of himself and terribly serious much of the time.

From the school to the fishing, young John Wilson was good at it all. What's more, he knew it and was not shy of voicing his opinions, even if he did it in a perfectly civilised manner. As his great-grandfather had been a teacher, Laurence wondered if that was where John got his brains, for you even heard him questioning the preacher at meetings, showing off an encyclopaedic memory of the Bible. Sometimes Laurence felt the boy needed to learn that he did not know it all. Perhaps he needed to remember that old John Irvine had taken to drink in his later years and was forced out of his teaching job, showing that brains did not guarantee that folk remembered you well when you were gone. Sometimes Laurence felt he should remind the boy that pride goeth before a fall. To add to his confidence, John was proving to be good at the woodwork too, already a far better joiner than any of the rest of the family. It seemed as if the boy could do no wrong and, as the eldest of John's boys, he got first choice at everything and that would include Taft when his father was too old to work.

That was how things worked. Young Lowry seemed to accept all of this now, but whether he would feel the same in a few years' time was yet to be seen. Second sons had to accept their position and find their place as they could. John had been lucky to get Taft when they divided up the land into individual crofts, but that was a once-in-a-lifetime event. Given the size of the island and the growing number of families, younger sons who wanted to marry would always face a problem. Mind you, John could live a long time yet, so that even his eldest son could find himself under pressure if he decided to wed sometime soon, for there surely wasn't much room to spare at Taft for another big family.

Whatever they did, the island just kept getting more and more crowded and the rough marginal land to the north couldn't provide much new acreage for planting. Anyway, you needed grazing land for the animals. There were almost two hundred black cattle eating their heads off as it was, not to mention all the sheep and almost as many ponies as cows. Pigs did not roam free, but they needed to be fed all the same. Really, the island was just too small for so many people and their beasts. Laurence hoped that Lowry would not be tempted to follow in the footsteps of the other young lads who left. As long as there was the hope of inheriting Taft, John would surely stay, but Lowry? Who knew what would happen to Lowry?

Laurence's eldest son, Thomas, had been lucky to become his Uncle Andrew's choice as the laird's factor when the older man became ill. Thomas was strong, forthright and confident, as well as having a good track record in bookkeeping and letter writing. With Aggie being the schoolmaster's daughter, she had valued education more than many of the other women, so that all of Laurence's children had been encouraged to learn as much as they could, but only one of them could benefit from the position of factor.

Daily life in Fair Isle had been managed in a range of ways over the years, depending on who owned it and how well these men had organised their estates. By the mid-1700s, the Sinclairs of Quendale in Shetland (who included the island as part of their estate) were coming to the end of their long period of ownership. They had largely managed Fair Isle through factors, some of whom had been based on the mainland. Laurence could remember his father saying that one of these factors was the first Wilson to come to Fair Isle, a David Wilson who came, married a local girl and settled, becoming the ancestor of all the future Wilsons on the island. But although Laurence had a large numbers of Wilson cousins when he was growing up, since he also had four aunts, there were Williamson, Brown, and Eunson cousins as well. When Laurence was a boy, the Wilsons had just been part of the general social mix.

Robert Sinclair was finally forced to sell his estate, in part because the value of his Quendale property on mainland Shetland had diminished. One reason for this sad state of affairs was that blowing sand had breached coastal dunes that had protected the fertile inland areas. No one knew if this was due to a series of huge storms, or damage from sheep or rabbits, but it destroyed both settlements and the fertility of any soil that surrounded them so that tenants had to move on. Robert Sinclair was also rumoured to have gambling debts that contributed to his bankruptcy. When his lands were sold in 1758, Fair Isle was not seen as a valuable asset and was therefore not purchased with the rest of the estate. Instead, in 1770 it went for well under its upset price to James Stewart of Westray, a rich Orkney landowner.

The island was then managed by factors and tacksmen, the latter group paying the laird for the right to set the price for any goods that were bought or sold. Memorably, James Strong was appointed tacksman between 1812 and 1829 and he chose to settle on the island, extracting every possible bit of profit from his neighbours. He also lived a highly colourful lifestyle involving several wives, which may be why this role was not continued after his death.

Andrew Wilson was appointed spokesman for the islanders by 1831, becoming the Stewarts' formal representative on the island and eventually handing the baton on to his nephew Thomas. It was nepotism of course, but Thomas's good fortune was due in no small part to his education. By 1845 he was officially designated factor, which was a double-edged sword, whatever your qualifications for the job. Jealousy was the issue. You aligned yourself with the laird and thus you were accused of privilege, even though you were really not that much better off than your fellow islanders. The Wilson factors never attained wealth as James Strong had done in the past, although their cash earnings did place them on a higher rung of the ladder. Both Andrew and Thomas remained fishermen and farmers to a large extent, but gained an additional payment for the work they undertook for the laird.

Thomas just kept telling folk that someone had to do the job, and it was better that it was one of them rather than an outsider who did not know their ways, or indeed a tyrant like old Strong. Someone had to keep records of all the fish caught and oil processed, not to mention ensuring that the store room was kept stocked with essentials like salt, for without salt a catch could not be preserved. Then there were letters to write and books to be kept. All an island factor could do was implement the laird's orders and try to be fair, and those who thought differently had no option other than to moan, or move. Anyway, no doubt James Stewart in Orkney would dump his factor the moment it suited him and people had to remember that the current Stewart heir was not married. Who knew who might inherit the title next and what he might want? Better the devil you knew, Thomas told his neighbours.

Aye, you never knew what lay ahead of you, Laurence mused. When you had children you had no idea which ones would live through childhood and which of these would then stay on the island. Two of his sons went to work in English ports: sea captains they were, who married women he had never seen and had grandchildren who were just names in letters. He had thought his family blessed when the land was divided into separate crofts in 1845, but that had left some people with no land and others with very little, which had added to the sense of grievance against his family.

Then the potato blight arrived in 1846, demonstrating that even with a reasonable holding you could not necessarily feed yourself. The blight had increased the stream of emigrants, with more young men taking regular work away with the whaling boats, a job from which they did not always return. Often they were tempted by their new shipmates who told tales of an easier life elsewhere. When the blight was at its worst the laird arranged for some grain to be sent to the island and offered to move people to his Orkney estate, to reduce pressure on Fair Isle's resources. Some had taken advantage of this opportunity and more would leave if things didn't improve soon. Perhaps his beloved Lowry would go, for at sixteen and with no dependents he could take a chance. Laurence shook himself. At his age, what was he bothering about the future for? He wouldn't be here to see it.

A cold draught of air caught his chest, sharply reminding him that he had been long enough at his task. The kail was fine and the crubs secure. It was time to rediscover the solace of the fire and warm up his old bones. Choosing his route carefully to avoid rabbit holes, tufts of grass and loose stones, he made his way back, staring fixedly at the ground. Old people might miss what went on round about them, but that was the price you paid for staying upright. Yet when he heard the flock of greylag geese wheel above his head he had to stop and steady himself on his stick, before raising his head to enjoy the sight. Aye, well, if they could make it through the winter and have the enthusiasm to enjoy the day, he supposed that he too could get through to the spring, when all the other birds would return to enrich his life. Laurence loved to watch the procession of feathered visitors that came with the returning sun. Fair Isle's spring was blessed by a seemingly endless range of birds that came either to breed or just to rest for a day or so, before continuing their journey to who knew where. It was a spectacle that all appreciated, although for many it was that the birds provided a change of diet, rather than an ornithological education.

"Jeannie, lass," Laurence called gently, as he put his hand to the heavy wooden door and lifted the latch.

The welcoming, fetid warmth of the croft house enveloped him as soon as he pushed the door open. It wasn't really warm in here, but after the biting wind this gloomy, smoky interior drew him into its gratifying, cheerful grasp. As he briskly pushed the door shut, the smoke from the peat fire winnowed thickly round the room, and through the haze he made out Jane, crouched over the fire and cooking.

"Mither's away to see Aunty Aggie at Quoy, grandad. The baby's not well and Aunt Aggie's all flixed, what with Uncle Willie being away with faither. Mither's gone to tell Aunt Aggie what to do with the child."

Jane was in no doubt that her mother would soon sort out any problem with a recalcitrant baby at Quoy. Meanwhile, she was thrilled that Jeannie had left her in charge. "I've to give us all our dinner and make sure you're fine."

Jane was in fact quite relieved that her mother had taken both herself and her demons somewhere else, for she would have gotten the worst of it over the day, as her mother's spare right hand. It was one thing to work to Jeannie's orders on a good day, but she was the very devil to please when she was not on form.

Stewart was back playing with the bits and pieces of the morning, tied up in the chair and reaching out towards the trencher in the centre of the table, which was about to be piled with potatoes and fish. The boy feared he might be forgotten when the moment came to eat, for he already felt ignored as Jerry and Aggie resumed their morning conversations with their grandfather. He got his fair share, however, and all too soon

Aggie found herself pushed outside again and back to school, while Jane began to clear up. She then sent Jerry out to play with Stewart for a while.

"Make him run around so he tires himself out," she ordered, "and don't go far. Don't let him get too muddy and pick him up and carry him home if he tries to run away. If you lose him, mither will kill you, mind."

Laurence sat contentedly in his high-backed chair, smiling quietly to himself. In truth the children were sufficiently well trained to run the place without their parents. Jane sounded just like Jeannie there, though he felt sure she didn't want to hear that now. Seeing the young ones cope was a reminder that none of us is indispensable the old man thought, as he allowed himself to doze off. Finally he deserved his nap.

Later, with all of the day's tasks done and Stewart cleaned up from a muddy tumble, Jerry was again given the knife to whittle wood, while the toddler was told just to watch and keep out of the fire. For once the youngster seemed happy enough to keep out of trouble and the afternoon passed pleasantly, particularly when the exhausted toddler dozed quietly at their feet. Dry washing was brought in and folded before Jane set about mixing and cooking some brunnies on the girdle. This flat, iron cooking pan was hung from the rafters by its curved handle and could be swung directly over the fire when it was needed. The scones would be eaten with left-over fish and potatoes this evening, but Jane managed to eke out a few extra for an afternoon treat. Willie came back from the hill just as Aggie came in from school and Jane sent the pair out to stack the peat. They complained a bit, but she took no nonsense and truly there were a lot more difficult tasks than stacking peat, particularly with half a warm brunnie to see you on your way.

"I'll be out to check on you all in a minute, so make sure it's all piled evenly," Jane shouted after them as the door closed. "Stack it as high as you can reach."

"My, you remind me of your grandmother," Laurence told her, as he watched the girl bake her next batch of scones.

Jane flushed with pleasure. It was not often that she felt so grown up, so much in charge. She hoped her mother would stay away a while longer.

Over at Quoy, Jeannie had experienced a less calm environment. Her father William was busy in the barn with his nephew, leaving her sisters Bina and Aggie in the house, both preoccupied with a restless baby and chores. Young Ann Wilson of Busta, who had recently moved in to live with them, was grinding meal in the corner. No doubt William found the barn more attractive than the house, for young Joan was quite grizzly and clearly still had a smelly dose of the skitters. She had her mother quite worn down with the worry, not to mention the extra work caused by all the additional washing. Jeannie was happy to take over the child for a bit and suggested a little of the home-made herbal remedy she had brought with her, swearing that it would calm the child down. By now, with nerves worn to a frazzle by the noise and worry, Aggie was pleased to give the child anything that might help. The young mother was overwrought, so that her unsettled child had picked up the vibes and reacted as all small babies do when their mothers are upset. There was nothing nervous about Jeannie, however, so that before long the child was miraculously dozing in her arms, allowing sleep and time to sort out her ailment.

Babies were a terrible worry to young mothers at the time, likely as they were to become gravely ill for no apparent reason. Apart from what one of the older women could devise, you just had to sit any illness out and pray. It might only be a bit of wind that caused an upset, but it might just as easily be the harbinger of a fever, one that could carry your baby away by morning. The graveyard was full of wee scraps that had not made it to their first birthday. It was unfortunate that Joan's illness had coincided with her father's voyage to Shetland, the first long journey Willie had made since Aggie married him, so that she was nervous. The fact that Jeannie seemed not in the least worried about the trip was a great help.

The girls' father, William Irvine of Quoy, had married three times, each wife dying from childbirth-related complications. When his first wife died after their first child, he married Jeannie's mother to help him raise the baby. This second wife bore him four more live children before following her predecessor to the grave as she tried to produce a fifth. Given the by now pressing need to find someone to help him with his growing family, it was perhaps not surprising that the man repeated the exercise. By 1845 he had buried three wives, with eight live children and a lot of heartache to show for the process.

Jeannie was eighteen when her own mother died, so she had taken on the role of mother to Aggie and the two boys when her half-sister moved to Dunrossness. Aggie was still very young and had taken it hard when Jeannie left home to live with John, spending so much time with them that John remarked that this marriage came with a child, one that felt she had as much right to his wife's time as he. He was patient, however, and since most Fair Isle families needed to be fluid in their relationships, he did not complain when the child slept over on the occasional night and regularly popped in for meals and reassurance. Eventually Aggie settled down back with her father's third wife and grew up happily enough. New brothers and sisters changed her status and gave her confidence, but she would always see Jeannie as her mother surrogate and certainly her first child had reinstated this dependence on her sister. It was her good fortune that their two crofts were close enough for her to visit whenever the need arose.

Jeannie had all the confidence of a woman long married, with a large brood successfully raised, but she was always careful of her place in her father's household. Not only had he yet another family after she left home, but her cousin John now lived with them and had indeed helped to build Quoy. He was a quiet, only child, who needed to live with another family when his parents died. Now in his forties, he was simply part of the furniture. When you were single and in need of a home on the island you just had to go where you could, and Quoy was happy to have the support of another fisherman. Ann Wilson from Busta also joined them, because Quoy could afford her some space and food and she was pleased to work there as a servant. Over time most of William's own family left, so that by 1851 only three children remained, two girls and a son. Since he was by now seventy, their father was quite pleased when Aggie added her new husband, Willie Mather from Stackhoull, to the household, particularly when a child followed soon after.

With new youngsters in the making it looked as if Quoy would stay in the family for a while longer and, despite the croft's complicated make-up, it all seemed to work. At this time, before personal space existed as a concept, no one minded extra people coming to stay, just as long as they pulled their weight. It was simply a matter of someone moving over in a bed, finding a place for a box of belongings and making a place round the fire. The kist of possessions was seldom large and sometimes there was no kist at all.

Today Jeannie was more than welcome at Quoy, as she reassured Aggie both about the baby and Willie's safety, so that her sister soon felt more confident about maternal matters and trips to Dunrossness. Before too long Jeannie had them all laughing at her tales of old Laurence caring for young Stewart, as well as a few tasty titbits of gossip that she had picked up last Sunday at the Methodist meeting. Jeannie had joined the Methodist church when she married John, because a woman always followed her husband's religion. Since her own family was Church of Scotland, however, she enjoyed a good giggle at her brothers and sisters in faith when she got the chance. As long as no one else heard her, particularly John, Jeannie felt no guilt. There was never anything scandalous in her tales, just day-to-day island gossip, and anything that distracted Aggie just at the moment had to be a good thing. Anyway, some of the Methodists seemed to Jeannie to be rather more fervent than was entirely necessary, but perhaps that was because Quoy had been a less devout home.

By the time the men came inside, dragging with them half the barn, Jeannie was ready to leave and pleased that she had found a way of getting Aggie through the day. It was quite dark now and cousin John offered to see her home, but she laughed as she wrapped her shawl firmly round her shoulders. The slight moon was sufficient to see the outline of her route, so she didn't need to carry a glowing peat in tongs this evening, to see her way. Women never had to worry about strangers here, since they did not exist.

You had nothing to fear from anyone, night or day, except for the trows, and as she said to John they wouldn't dare try to take her good self away. Jeannie had no doubt that she would scare off any peerie fairy folk that tried to meddle with her.

Opening the door back home she was met by a warm current of air, the aroma of the food and an onslaught of noise, as everyone tried to be heard at once. Immediately, Jeannie changed back to her role as mother.

"Is that brunnies you've made, girls?"

"Yes, Mither. We thought grandad would like a treat. There's still a bit of meal left yet."

"And the cows. Are they milked?"

"Yes, Mither."

"Did you remember the washing?"

"Yes, Mither."

"And you didn't lose Stewart?"

The girls started to laugh. She wasn't severe at all. She was playing with them. They had all worked hard, cleaning and clearing and cooking and knitting and their mother had noticed it all. There was a good pile of peat both outside and in, so Willie had done his work, while John and Lowry were back too, with tales about all the worthwhile debris they had brought home and stowed in the barn for future use. There were two good bits of wood for their grandfather for his stool leg. Best of all, each had already begun to work on making a new kishie. Aye. They were good children, all out to please her this day at least. She saw the meal served and cleared and then John gave the evening Bible reading. Later, they sat around listening to the older boys' tall tales for a bit, while Jeannie and the girls knitted, until it was time to get the wee ones off before they fell asleep where they sat.

Knitting resumed, the girls so accomplished at their work that they barely needed to glance down at their hands, which was just as well given the paucity of light in the darkening room, even when Jeannie lit the lamp. It was second nature to fix on the padded leather belt that kept the wires in place and get on with their garments. Once the wee ones were in bed, they could really concentrate and build up speed, for knitting drove the women as if they had a master with a whip at their backs. It could make the difference between a family surviving, or not.

All the women of Shetland knitted, but Fair Isle women had a special series of patterns that were individual to the island. Some of the work they did was plain of course, for you were not going to waste extra time on everyday wear, but there was also special work that was colourful, soft and prettily complex. Whatever else was problematic on the island, the local sheep were said to have both the softest and longest-lasting wool in the world. There were more than a hundred different patterns, which made the work both distinctive and valued. Over the years the women's work had become currency, so they knitted from the time they were toddlers, almost to the day they died. Even a young child could make basic stitches, although they only worked at first with items the family would wear, people who would not complain about the odd mistake that had been missed by the gimlet eyes of a mentor. Mistakes were not common, however, since young girls spent hours reworking garments when errors were spotted, as usually they were. This fact encouraged them to concentrate so that, surprisingly quickly, little sisters could produce perfect items. Women knitted socks, hats, gloves, sweaters and shawls of various sizes, to wear, sell or barter. The patterned work came from wool that they dyed using island plants, except for indigo, the dark colour they had to buy from the laird.

Knitting was a skill that the young girls worked at with pride, one where growing speed and talent at first brought praise and esteem. Eventually, however, it became a tyrant, one from which you could never escape. No girl could be seen wiling her time away with some other pastime. Even when it was bright enough to read, a girl would be thought mad to waste time at such an activity. Old hands gnarled with arthritis or covered in painful chilblains still had to produce the goods. In summer they took the work outside, where they sat and chatted in the sun. In winter they huddled in the dingy gloom. Only the Sabbath day was exempt and even then, behind closed doors, it was rumoured that some secretly kept to their drudgery.

Merchandising depended on the men. Sometimes they could exchange knitting for goods brought to the island by the laird, or the men took a kist of knitting to the mainland. Regularly, they set out to barter with any passing ship, to see if dry socks, hats, or sweaters could attract a worthwhile exchange. For those who had been at sea for some weeks, fresh clothes could be a godsend. Dried bully beef, salt pork, Dutch cheese or hard sea biscuits could all enliven the boring island menu. Sometimes the sailors had a bit of bread or flour. Clogs or sea boots were also welcome and occasionally someone would offer a book.

A more exotic exchange could also be arranged, as tobacco, brandy or gin were often available. European sailors used such products in a relaxed way that was quite alien to their Scottish neighbours. The women were never pleased to hear that spirits had been taken in part payment, but it was said that most island men had a small, hidden cache of alcohol, for celebrations, or 'emergencies'. Here there were no public houses to tempt men into regular imbibing, but the odd 'medicinal' treatment was not unknown. In earlier times smuggling had been a more common pastime, but the Royal Navy had largely put a stop to that in recent years, so that untaxed alcohol was now more difficult to access. Of course, difficult did not mean impossible, for the Royal Navy had a wide sea to police and few boats to spare for this particular purpose.

There was seldom enough alcohol to cause any great trouble, for no one would wish to endanger either themselves or their boats. Yoals were more than just the means by which the men earned a living. They were a way of contacting the outside world, a manner by which they could display their skill and, for many, a status symbol. Being in charge of a yoal was not just a job, it was a crucial part of being a man. Although they would casually brush off praise, all felt a surge of pride when they survived a severe squall or successfully manoeuvred boats into harbour on a particularly rough day. The boats were put together carefully by those with the gift of carpentry, but the name and feel of every board, every joint, every mast, rudder, helm, compartment, rope and nail, not to mention each foot of fishing line, was familiar to all the men by the time they were qualified to take a yoal out to sea.

Boys started their fishing lives on the shore when they were no more than toddlers, helping mothers and sisters to search for bait, or standing on a rock with a rod and line. When sufficient quantities of limpets had been prepared, the men baited hooks and set them round and round the rims of special bait tubs that were particular to the island. These long, baited lines were gradually released into the sea once the men reached their chosen fishing ground and sometimes the older men would chew a mouthful of limpets till they were finely ground down, before spraying them over the side of the boat to attract fish. Many such tricks had to be learned if you were to be a successful fisherman.

Over time, the boys learned how to set out lines and draw them in carefully, so that they retrieved all of their catch. They became proficient in mastering the simple square sail and the ability to row for hours on end. Once at sea they learned to obey every instruction from the older men as if their life depended on it, for there would be times when it most certainly did. Finally they learned to manipulate the slender, supple craft in and out of one of the world's most difficult harbours, a place littered with rocks of all sizes, above and below the surface of the sea. It was a long apprenticeship, one where danger was a constant companion.

As well as their physical skills, the boys worked at recognising every type of tide, every land-based marker and every nuance of weather. Once you knew how to sail, you had to learn where to fish and how to take the bearings that fixed the right spot at sea from two or more points on land, a skill that helped you find the best fishing grounds.

Then you had to learn the location of each of the 'baas', the treacherous half-submerged rocks that would rip the bottom from your boat as soon as you let your guard down. If no one else had hit that rock before, it gained your name for eternity, an aspect of fame that no one wanted to attain. Finally you had to develop the instinct of the 'moder die', an inner knowledge of the sea that you felt somehow through your feet and that helped you to recognise the direction of the water underneath your craft. During almost all your life at sea you never stopped learning.

Only the weather was impossible to understand entirely, however long you studied it and however long you listened to the older men. Weather was eternally capricious. Perhaps this was why God had such a following on the island. Prayer at least gave you something to do when the day turned more difficult than you had hoped.

Men and women on the island had the pattern of their lives set out from the moment they were born. For a short time they were children and then there was some schooling, but by the time they were ten they could pull their weight: on the land, in the house and at sea. They would need time to grow stronger and refine their knowledge, but the essential skills were there. Much of the time, life was simply sheer hard graft but there was also joy. It was what men and women did and few questioned that there might be an alternative. Those who left might find a better life elsewhere, but possibly not. Many thought it wiser to stick with what they knew and hoped that next year they would see some improvement. There was a great sense of security in knowing intimately the island, its people, and its ways.

# Chapter 3

# The Aftermath

At Grutness, the Eunson boat did not have the slightest suspicion that there might be something amiss and their yoal made land only moments after the tragedy, having missed the wave by dint of being very slightly ahead of their fellows. They made their tired bodies pull the boat well up on to the shingle beach, aided by local men and boys, for despite the hour and the darkness they had been both seen and heard. In a remote seafaring community there was always someone who would catch a glimpse of something unusual, or note a strange sound through the gloom. Soon, out of the darkness, more men and boys materialised to help unload the kist of knitting, fully aware of its importance. Finally the boat was high above the tide, with ropes, sail and oars safely stowed away and a few boulders placed inside to keep it safe. Then empty food baskets were brought hopefully up to the small settlement, a group of houses much the same as those the men lived in back home.

"Have you seen another boat?" The question was aimed at everyone they met.

"No. But it will be close by, surely."

One of the older men nodded down the coast a bit. "The way the tide is running they'll be down there, if they're not behind you a bit. Come up meanwhile and take your ease. They'll be here soon enough. You'll be tired. We'll send some of the boys out to look for them."

Suddenly they were very tired indeed, for tension, their unacknowledged companion, was now allowed to recede. Their journey was over and no one was worried in the least about their companions. Joking and exchanging gossip, Grutness men helped their Fair Isle friends to haul the kist of knitting over to the merchant's house, leaving some of the younger boys to keep a lookout at the shore for the arrival of the next boat. In the middle of a humdrum winter, guests of any kind were a distraction, although the merchant grumbled about the hour and said he would negotiate in the morning when the other boat could bring its load too. By now they were all glad to take a rest. Tomorrow, when they were less fatigued, would be a better day for negotiation.

Jerry Leslie took people back to his croft, neighbours and visitors both. "Come away in. Find a seat if you can, or squat down in front. Push the bairns out of the way. It's time for the wee ones to get to bed anyway. Put them through, Annie."

Young Jerry's wife bustled around, arguing with the children about who should be banished and who should get to stay, all the while trying to find some food, a hot drink and sufficient space for her unexpected guests. Annie's older daughters busied themselves at her command, shy in front of strangers at this time of the day, but excited by the novelty. Eventually everyone was squeezed around the fire, pleased to be in from the cold dark night, with some old boxes brought in for extra seating. Those who had spent the day on the ocean were chilled to the bone and waited for the comfort of heat to seep slowly into their limbs.

Although the people had little, hospitality was an unwritten rule, so the men relished tea and hot potatoes from a pot that had been put on to cook as soon as Annie had realised there would be visitors. Good potatoes were thin on the ground here too, but hospitality demanded they be shared and there was neither the room nor time to bake fresh bannocks, although the meagre remains of an earlier meal was also divided among the group. If the merchant was generous, the visitors would find a way of rewarding their hosts for their kindness before they left.

As the women and girls scuttled around to organise food and drink, the noise level rose and bursts of male laughter rang out as people checked on relatives and friends, for this was a first port of call for many islanders and a variety of bonds had built up over the years. Local people occasionally married Fair Islanders who had moved here, while others had married into the island. The air was full of talk about who had died, married or moved, who had done well and who had lost out. They spoke of last year's poor harvest, the need for more help from the government, the condition of the beasts over the winter and what the laird would expect from them next. There was in truth little difference between the lives of people on the Shetland mainland and other islanders, except for the degree of isolation. Poverty was universal.

Finally, conversation veered towards the other yoal. It would turn up, surely. Jokes were made about how crestfallen they would be if they had fallen behind. Everyone kept an ear open for the local boys' calls, but time passed and the Fair Isle men felt exhaustion taking over as the warmth of the crowded room took its toll. Heads nodded and shoulders were shaken, so that their owners would stay awake.

Meanwhile, the boys on the beach walked further and further in their search for the second boat, hands stuck firmly into trouser pockets and necks hunched well down into jackets, blankets and scarves in an effort to escape the cold. Increasingly they used higher ground to search the dark horizon with their young eyes, even though the wind was sharper up there. The sooner the bliddy thing appeared, they muttered to each other, the better. Intermittent cloud enabled enough moon to reveal the horizon, which remained empty. Time passed slowly until total darkness and the freezing wind-chill drove them back into the huddle of crofts. These men must have been wrong. The other boat must have come ashore much further along the coast. Eventually, their elders agreed that they could call it a night.

The young did not voice any criticism of the older men as they forced their way into the already crowded room, but old Jerry Leslie recognised their tone. He watched them try to get some warmth from the peat fire, without forcing visitors from their privileged positions. The boys knew their place, but their body language spoke for them, eyes and shoulders complaining, inferring that if the older men had had better instincts the young could have been saved from a very uncomfortable evening.

Old Jerry was worried, but not about the opinions of a few immature whelps. No, he was disturbed by his own bad feelings. The man was sure the boat had been close to shore, but now where was it? His proclivity for bad feelings was not one he welcomed, so he stared into the fire uneasily. It was better to stare fixedly into the red embers than to inadvertently catch his son's eye, for wherever these men were, he was by now increasingly sure they were not going to chap on anyone's door, not tonight or any other night.

Young Jerry was all too aware of his father's reputation for second sight, not a reputation he applauded. He didn't believe in all that malarkey himself, for he was a thoroughly modern young man who disdained all the old folk's nonsense. That 'caper', as he deemed it, was playing with the devil, even when you didn't believe in it. The minister had left them in no doubt of his opinion, having heard a local rumour of the ancient superstitions' connection to this house. God's representative had visited, to warn them both of the old man's folly and the dangers that came from encouraging the devil. From that day his father had tried to keep his thoughts to himself, saying very little but still unable to control the strange, unbidden feelings. Tonight, his unusual silence was enough to warn his son that there might be something wrong. As the night drew on, the old man's unease grew and his son could feel him thinking.

The younger boys had enlivened the company for a bit so that the conversation moved on to that amazing story of the Quendale whales. It was a tale all liked to retell, because all hoped it would repeat itself. Just a few years ago a monstrous pod of pilot whales had beached themselves, driving high up onto the gentle sand at Quendale not so very far away, until finally the beasts lay all on top of one another as each struggled to find a place to die. It took the local fishermen hours to dispatch them all, and when it was done they counted the corpses. In disbelief they counted again. One thousand five hundred and forty beasts had died that day, for whatever reason it took them to come ashore. It was a tragedy for the whales but a gift from God to the crofters, for whales meant blubber and whale oil, which meant money for the men who worked at them. Sad to say, the meat was not valued in this area, but Hay & Company alone took one hundred tons of blubber and seven hundred heads, from which the very best oil could be extracted. Local men worked for weeks to dispatch the haul, a hundred of them earning twenty pounds or more each, a fortune in this virtually cashless society, even though others would make much more out of their backbreaking, bloody work when all was processed.

Of course old Grierson, as laird, had the automatic right to a third of anything caught on his land. Since most of the men were well in arrears to him in rent, at the end of the day much of the money went his way. But there had been some cash left over for necessities or treats and all the single men had been rich for a while. Just five years ago that was. You could still dream on the strength of such a tale. People need dreams to sustain them when they are dirt poor.

Eventually the conversation became desultory and the visitors began to nod off. It was agreed that the five men would be housed in two different crofts, sharing beds with one another, as young children were stuffed more closely in with their siblings. The Fair Isle men soon fell into a deep torpor. There was no reason to worry, they told each other as they prepared for bed. Not really. Each one buried their disquiet, too tired to do anything to assuage it. Time would take care of it, they said. Time and sleep.

When young Jerry Leslie had seen his visitors to bed, he went to relieve himself alongside his father in the byre.

He caught the old man's eye. "What is it, Faither?"

"Did I say there was something?"

"You don't have to. Och, I wish you'd stop your capers. The older you get, the worse you are. Sitting there, sweeing over the fire like that, making bad thoughts. I saw you. Don't think I didn't!"

"Laddie, if I feel something bad, I feel it. I don't go looking for it and I certainly don't make it. Do you think it feels good to see what I see? Don't you go disrespecting your faither. I can't help it. It's not my fault. It's in my blood and you should just be grateful it's not in yours. Your granny had it and she gave it to me and it's hardly a blessing, I can tell you. Anyway, maybe I'm wrong. Maybe they're safe. It's just that I see things."

For a moment there was a silence, but then Jerry could not hold himself back. "The black sight you have, may be the devil upon you!" he burst out in a whisper, lest any of their guests might hear. "Have you thought of that, old man? You just keep your mouth shut, for all our sakes. Who knows what sort of trouble we'll find ourselves in if you don't. You should leave the devil's work to himself."

And with that he went to look for his own bed.

Such disrespect was unusual for Jerry, but his father understood that it reflected his depth of discomfort. Now it was out in the open, the bad idea, and there was no putting it back where it came from, so the pair of them would have no sleep. So often his visions were true, at least in part, and this time he had no doubt they were looking at a disaster. He'd seen it in the fire. And his son also knew that in all probability the second boat was lost.

But still the peats were banked up higher than normal in case there was any late knocking at the door. The older man volunteered to spend the night in the high-backed, straw chair, watching the fire and keeping a light at the tiny window, lest it might attract lost sailors. It was a long night.

By morning, with no message from neighbours to the contrary, the Fair Isle men and their hosts took out their boats to search up and down the coast for something that might indicate that their friends had landed. No one said anything negative, although people increasingly began to have dark thoughts. As time passed, the 'what ifs' mounted to a certainty that something had gone wrong.

Finally the men in boats were travelling further and further away, looking into all the deep geos that might shelter (or trap) a yoal, for this coast too was ragged with rocky indentation. Boys roamed the shoreline and even young children joined in a search they did not understand, picking up anxiety and understanding that this was not a joyful day. All wanted to be busy. The women prepared fresh food for later, worrying and trying to quell their fears with activity. Anything was better than the fear that their children might discover something bad, but there was no way they could stop them. The boys were transfixed by the thought of a wreck.

The men rowed, keeping close to the shore (dangerously so at times), searching. Finally it was Strong Eunson, skipper of the Fair Isle yoal, who glimpsed the group of youngsters on the edge of the promontory, waving. His stomach turned and he prayed that it would not be bad news. He steered his craft to the boys, hoping that they had found something after all this time, and that it would be something positive!

At the entrance to the small geo was a kist bound with sturdy rope which had been wedged amongst the jagged rocks as the tide receded. All kists look very similar of course, but such boxes are too precious to lose. You might find bits of broken kists along the seashore and most definitely you will find lengths of rope, but you will only see fully strapped kists bobbing in the water if something has gone terribly wrong.

Strong spoke quietly to his men who turned as one, took in both the sight and its meaning, and then returned to their oars to edge carefully inland, for there was of course the possibility that where there was flotsam there might also be men. They manoeuvred fearfully, in the knowledge that if they found anything it would more likely be a dead body than a live one. Tension etched itself on their deeply lined faces. The youngest were the most afraid of what they might find.

They had, of course, all seen dead bodies before. You paid your respects to relatives and friends when they died. But family normally died at home in their beds, or somewhere close to home, where they stayed until they were buried, viewed by all who knew them in life. On a small island you were part of many deaths and the men regularly hacked a place for yet another body down in the rocky graveyard by the church. You always felt badly, but it was one of life's rituals. The church folk and the old practices organised these events in such a way that you knew your role. Here, they were not at home, and if there was a body it would not be an old person, or a sick person, or even a young child. It would be someone who left Fair Isle yesterday, someone as recently alive and healthy as they were today.

The men worked carefully, synchronising their oars, keeping them away from a collision with rocks and leaning over to gauge the depth and danger of the water, so that Strong was finally able to touch the box's ropes. It was too heavy to pull on board from this angle, so they pushed it up further on the rock until Willie jumped out to heave it up to a point where it would be quite safe. Surrounded by silent boys and using his knife where it was needed, he carefully undid the ropes that bound it and there it was... the dry, safely-wrapped knitting from Fair Isle; all the socks, sweaters, shawls and hats carefully rolled up into neat bundles. The great pile of delicate work looked incongruous in his rough, stained hands.

Willie organised the boys to look further up and down the coast to see if there was anything else, failing to mention that this probably meant either a body, or wreckage, since by this time they all knew. Then he set about retying the ropes and dragging the kist to a place he could load it onto the yoal. The boys shivered in anticipation as they set about their work and the men in the yoal were not much better when they again began to search the sea, methodically moving up and down as close to land as they dared. As word spread, other men joined them, both at sea and on land, and gradually the search spread out for miles. But there was nothing.

Then another short northern day came to an end. All returned to the settlement and the kist came with them. For the hosts it was difficult to say anything that helped. For the visitors it was a nightmare, one that they knew was not yet over, for they must return home with some sort of explanation.

There were the four options. If they had been in difficulty the crew might have been picked up by a ship and taken to its home port, for although ships did pick up sailors in distress they would not always alter their route for them. Or they might have been blown well off course when they lost the kist for some reason and would eventually find their way here from further up mainland Shetland. This unlikely option would quickly resolve itself. The third possibility was that a body, or part of the yoal, would be washed ashore somewhere locally, offering proof, something that would allow families to mourn a definite loss. But here the sea was wild and it could well be that no further trace of boat or body would ever be found. For the women, the wives and mothers, this fourth eventuality was always the worst option; the everlasting agony of doubt. It had happened before and no doubt it would happen again.

This evening had a very different mood as the men made their plans. Tonight there was no jollity. They would have to return home before too long but would spend another day searching before taking the news back to Fair Isle. If the others were anywhere on Shetland they would surely arrive by the following day. Apart from anything else, they could not expect the weather to hold much longer, and if they did not take their chance now who knew when they would get the next break in the winter storms. The local minister arrived on his small pony to pray with them, which may have put the seal of recognition on the event but gave little comfort. The men must now convey the bad news home. There was nothing a minister could do to make that task easier, particularly if he was not coming with them.

In the morning, along with the rest of the community, the yoal's crew went out once more to search, but when the light faded they decided that there was little hope left. They would complete their business with the merchant that night and set off before first light the next day. Farewells were made, thanks given and promises made on both sides to communicate if anything did turn up.

The journey back seemed endless. Although brought up to hard lives, none felt ready to be the bearer of such awful news. As they rowed in automatic unison each brain tried to assimilate loss and process grief. In such a small community all would be touched by this relatively small loss of life, with so many folk related by some degree or other.

At the end of the day, coming into Kirki Geo, they saw them outlined along the shore. With ten men away of course there were people on the lookout by now and the sighting of one boat would raise hopes for the next. How did you do this? Hard weathered hands drew ever more slowly as each man tried to put off the moment. What were you meant to say?

Strong turned his head to the side so that no one could see his eyes fill up. Men did not weep. Or at least they did not weep in public.

"Hold back a bit."

The friends in the boat were quick to respond to his command, resting their arms for a moment and leaning forward to look down into the boat as if there was some help to be found down there. None of them wanted to see who was standing on the shore. No doubt there would be children who would now be orphans, or women who would be widows. Perhaps some in the crowd might have surmised that, after a longer period than had been expected, one lone yoal inferred that there could be a problem. But not the youngsters. No one would have warned the youngsters.

"Ach, I canna bear the thought of it," Jerry spoke all their thoughts.

"Do we say that we think they are all dead?"

"We don't know for sure that they are."

"Aye we do. You all know we do. We just don't have the proof."

Strong felt that, as nominal leader, he had at least to be honest. This was not a time to raise false hopes, however tempting. They had to be honest. Folk at least deserved that. "We should send boys to get Stewart Wilson and old Cheyne. They'll help us do it right… and Tom Wilson. The factor has to tell people, write it down, let the master know."

"He's John Wilson's brother."

"So he is. Man, I'd almost forgot."

In the midst of such a burden of horror, it became easy to forget. Tom Wilson, so often the butt of their frustration as factor, had lost his brother. He must tell the laird, but more importantly he must tell his father that he had lost a son, and his sister-in-law her husband. That job no one would wish to take from him.

Stewart Wilson was the Methodist lay preacher as well as being a fisherman and crofter. He was a steady man in any crisis and well respected by both sides of the religious divide. Of course he would help them, and so would Cheyne, the teacher. James Cheyne had been with them for many years now and, although not an islander, he was almost one of them, doing a bit of crofting when he wasn't teaching. He knew all the families through their children.

There was no resident minister, since there was neither the money nor the congregation to justify one. Occasionally the Church of Scotland sent someone to check up on them, but unless the teacher had also qualified as a minister the community looked after itself. They dealt with their problems, shared their burdens, bore their children, looked after their sick and buried their dead, only needing a minister for marriages and christenings once a year, when it was hoped that someone might come from the mainland. Although the teacher's job was to see that they all knew the catechism, few came from the mainland to listen to their answers. Rural and island parishes that covered wide areas all had the same problem when it came to religious leadership. When arguments arose, the factor, the Methodist preacher and the teacher mediated, only appealing to the laird if a problem was insurmountable. So they would together deal with this disaster, as they did with everything else life threw at them.

When the yoal finally made it to land, figures came forward to help them pull it ashore, mainly cheerful faces, asking how the trip had been.

But before they could ask twice, Strong barked out orders to three of the older boys. "Away you to the schoolhouse as fast as you can go and bring Mr Cheyne here, and you to Springfield for Stewart Wilson. You, get Tom Wilson from Gaila. Now!" Then he faced the assembled crowd and said, "I'm saying nothing more till they arrive, so don't ask me."

The lads had run off like sheepdogs after a quarry. Given the faces of the men, such orders were unlikely to portend good tidings and suddenly they too had a part to play in whatever story would unfold. Boys shivered in anticipation as they helped the men silently haul two kists of meal ashore. Two kists in one boat said it all. By now the silence was oppressive, but Strong wanted to say this only once. He could not trust himself to repeat it over and over to different relatives. It seemed as if his crew had been struck dumb too. They sat around on the rocks, staring at their feet, defying anyone to speak to them. It had become clear that Armageddon came with the second kist.

Stewart Wilson was first to arrive. Although not a Methodist himself, Strong Eunson had never been so glad to see the man's weather-beaten face. Stewart had stopped to put his Sunday jacket on over his workaday clothes. He was here as a man of God because he had a feeling for what had happened. There was no need to pretend any more. By now the crowd was large and still folk came from all directions, with Tom Wilson hurrying down and old Cheyne appearing in the distance too. They almost had the required quorum.

"Well, boy. What's to say?" Stewart Wilson came straight to the point as soon as he arrived.

Strong quietly asked him if they could wait till Cheyne arrived.

"Aye. Of course. I take it we have bad news."

"Aye."

"We'll wait then."

Tom Wilson nodded in agreement and moved nearer his two nephews from Taft, as if his proximity might help. John and Lowry felt the discomfort of fear such as they had never known before, forcing their hands deeply into pockets to stop them from shaking. The lack of words spoke volumes, but they wanted to know. And then they did not want to know. John held his head high and kept his mouth closed, readying himself for the onslaught, while Lowry took his lead and tried to keep himself from shivering, for suddenly the day seemed very, very cold.

Some of the women began to moan quietly and there was a little muttering about all this waiting being cruel, but Strong would not be moved. Children stood with tears glistening on their faces for they knew not what, except that clearly this had been an ill-fated enterprise. Finally James Cheyne arrived, heaving at the effort of haste.

Strong took a breath to steady himself and began. "When we landed at Grutness there was no sign of the Wilson boat. We searched and the people there helped us, but all we could find the next day was their kist in a geo. We searched all that day and the next, but found no wreckage, nothing that we could say was theirs. They may be fine, picked up by a passing boat, or blown off course for some reason. But we looked and looked and found nothing but the kist and thought it best to come home to tell the story. The folk at Grutness will come over if they find anything."

By this time women's sobbing filled the air, as aprons and shawls were held to faces to withstand the flow. Children wept too, adding to the clamour, and there were questions asked by everyone, to everyone, to which all began to respond at once. But answers only made more questions and there were no real answers, only doubts and fears.

Finally, Stewart Wilson intervened. "Look here! It's dark now and these men are tired. They've had a terrible journey with dreadful news and it's our turn now to do our bit. God knows that they have done theirs. I have no doubt that they did their best to find our sons, brothers, cousins and friends. We do not know for sure that our neighbours are lost, so I want you all to join me here in prayer and then I want you to let these men go home to their families. We who are here will go to the homes of those who need to know. These men have done enough. Tomorrow, if you do have questions, go to them and ask, but for now let them find some rest. They have told you all they know. They have done their best."

And there, on the beach at South Harbour where the lost ones earned their living, Stewart Wilson prayed to God for the saving of bodies, if that was still possible, and the saving of souls if it was not. His cousin John Wilson was well to the fore of his mind.

It was then that exhaustion took hold of the travellers. Physical tiredness was something they all knew and could deal with, but two days of emotional trauma had taken its toll in a way most had not known before. After they handed over the responsibility, each man relaxed just a little and then a weighty fatigue swamped them. Friends or relatives put arms round their shoulders as they struggled home. Now, others would deal with the wives, children and parents. It had been the thought of all of these people that had unnerved them. More than one had silent tears coursing down their faces as they let themselves be led home.

Tom Wilson took it upon himself to go to Taft to see his father, sister-in-law, nephews and nieces. John's two older boys were quite stunned, so he put his arms around them and slowly guided them up the slope to the croft. He would help them to tell their mother and grandfather, he told them. They must all go to Taft now, before Jeannie and their grandfather heard it the wrong way. As he walked with them up Taft Brae he thought to himself that there was in fact no right way, and dreaded the scene he was about to cause, wondering if his father would survive the night. Jeannie would be heartbroken, but she was strong. His father was an old man. And then there was the rest of the family – the children, brothers, sisters, cousins, aunts and uncles – all to be told, shocked and grieved.

The three of them stopped at the door of Taft, horrified about what they must now do. It was their uncle who stepped forward, knocking heavily on the door before lifting the latch to go inside. Perhaps the heavy knock would act as a warning. Tom wanted the family to understand immediately that this was no social visit.

They did. From the moment they saw his face, Jeannie and old Laurence knew. It took the younger ones a little longer to understand. The old man sat transfixed, feeling that he should show some leadership, exhibit an example, but quite unable to move a muscle. Jeannie also seemed frozen, until Jane shrieked, "No!" in a long, chilling wail.

Then it was a maelstrom of sorrow and disbelief. Tom and his nephews stepped forward to hug and to hold, but nothing helped. It was all quite awful and seemed to last forever. Even when the women arrived, Tom's wife and sisters, then the other Methodists, it still seemed like a nightmare. In truth, there was nothing that anyone could do or say. All they could do was to offer support.

Four other families would also grieve that night. Stewart Wilson had volunteered for Quoy, to tell young Aggie that she was a widow and Ann Wilson that her brother Tom had died. He would organise people to tell the rest of Willie Mather's family.

Cheyne felt that he must go to North Break-a-Wall, with some of the women to help him, for Janet Leslie was so alone and with four young children under nine. Her eldest two were girls, not boys who could soon be able to fish. How she would manage he had no idea, but he would get his wife to stay with her tonight if John's family were too distraught.

Magnus's brother said he would take his friends to help break the news to his family, while Andrew Wilson went off to tell his sister-in-law that her young children were, in all likelihood, orphans. Friends and relatives followed, willing to help if needed and ready to disappear if not. The noise of the wailing women broke your heart. It was to accompany the families for months to come, a steady reminder of shared sorrow.

True, there would be practical things they could do, since both men and women have well defined roles after a death in any society, things that help you to find a purpose in the short term. There was plenty of talking, not that talking helped those who were immediately involved. Only time would help them, but the practicalities like cooking and getting in the peat and the water, or looking after small children for a bit, might be of some use. Of course, in the end there is nothing you can do for those who grieve except bear witness with them in their desperation and anger. Sadness permeated the fabric of the entire society over the next few weeks, as people gradually absorbed the dreadful loss. On such a small island there was no escape from the pain.

Each household dealt with the tragedy differently. Magnus had been a young man full of promise, one whose mother would never recover. Tom Wilson left a very young family, where small boys struggled to become men overnight. Janet Leslie knew complete despair with four young children. At Quoy, young Aggie broke her heart, while Ann echoed her despair for her brother Tom. William Irvine began to feel his family was plagued, with the younger generation to be no luckier than he had been himself. He was heartbroken for Jeannie too and all his Taft grandchildren and tried to do and say something useful. For a man who had never learned to express his feelings, he found this time extremely hard. Yet with two daughters in such an extremity of pain, he wanted to do or say something meaningful.

As the days passed at Taft, still Jeannie could hardly believe John would not come in the door and explain that it had all been a mistake; that he had been picked up by passing ship instead of drowning. It took her a long time to accept the truth, years rather than months, but there were all these months still to endure. Like all the wives she went on, but with a terrible knot in her stomach that never went away. Old Laurence was quite shocked. Had it not been for young Lowry he had not thought to make it through the night, but the boy needed him. Lowry was thoroughly broken.

All the children were devastated of course, except perhaps for the very little ones who didn't really understand. This father, as so many appear to their children, was of heroic worth and thus they could not imagine their future without him. Young John was as despairing as the rest, but felt that he should be made of sterner stuff and coldly put his mind to keeping the Wilsons afloat, wasting little time on tears and talk. He became fixated about returning the family to its previous balanced state, toiling until exhaustion made him sleep at night and reading the Bible when there was any spare moment when he was not working. He read the Good Book till he began to know much of it by heart, its poetry filling part of the deep void in his life. But it would be a long while before young John would again waste a day scavenging along the beach with friends. However absurd it might be, he found it disgusting to think that he went beachcombing while his father was struggling for his life.

Lowry did all he was told. He fished, farmed and generally worked as hard as a true Wilson should, but he could not suppress his sorrow like his brother and found it hard to focus on the future, any future. To make things worse, their yoal was lost. The long struggle to build up sufficient funds to buy materials for a boat must start all over again. Taft became a sad, inhospitable place for a while, as each sought their own way out of the tragedy. Had it not been for old Laurence, coming to bear witness with them day after day in the midst of his own suffering and staying with them when he felt it was needed, it would have been harder still. The old man's presence helped them, his dignified support offering a crutch to each and every one who needed it, although few realised that old Laurence needed his grandchildren to give himself a reason to live. Lowry benefited most from his presence, finding he could speak with his grandfather in a way he could no longer do with John. His elder brother's way of dealing with grief was to wall himself off from it. This created a barrier between them that would last for the rest of their lives, for on the day his father died, John withdrew from people and focused on the way forward for Taft.

So Laurence found that with Lowry there was still a purpose for his life, a reason for living. Lowry was pleased to talk out his pain as the two worked together at small tasks around the croft. Jeannie, though immersed in her own grief, was grateful that Laurence was there for her son. She knew that the family needed all the help they could get to survive the disaster. And the uncertainty remained, for the men were not dead, just 'presumed dead'. It was always the case when fishermen failed to return. In modern parlance the families lacked closure, for without bodies there was no funeral, no official mourning, no final closing of doors.

# Chapter 4

# The Legacy

It was quite dreadful throughout February, when hard, dark winter weather and meal shortages further dragged down the morale of grieving households. Then March shambled in, endlessly cold, wet and windy. Food was for everyone a gnawing worry, even after a small gift of grain from Orkney had been organised by the laird in recognition of their loss. Turf roofs that had survived the winter began to develop drips, so that there was even less comfort to be found inside the houses. Children stopped their games and laughter when certain adults were about. It seemed inappropriate and no one had to tell them. Children also began to wonder about their own fathers. Would they come home tonight? They had always assumed so. Perhaps they too could become orphans. The spectre of death now walked the island, threatening parents, siblings, wives and children alike, a recurring fear in the darkness of the night.

And still the women wept.

For James Cheyne, the schoolteacher, March 30th, 1851, would be a hard day.

When the First Statistical Account was finally gathered together for publication by Sir John Sinclair in 1798, it provided an insight into the way the people of Scotland lived, and became a yardstick for church and state to measure progress. Over the years it was agreed that this was not necessarily an independent survey, since the people who were charged with answering the questions were all ministers. In 1798, ministers knew that their position depended on the patronage of the landowners and heritors who appointed them, so that a good report was imperative. Indeed, some of these men had large, widespread parishes and did not know how their parishioners lived. Many had to be cajoled into making a response and did not answer all of Sinclair's 160 questions, so that the results were extremely varied. The outcome was that the majority of Scotland's people were described as being both 'sober and industrious' and 'peaceable and contented'.

The Reverend Mr Barry, minister of Shapinsay in Orkney, gave the account for Fair Isle, possibly because by this time the Reverend John Mill of Dunrossness was in his eighties and no longer able to travel to his parishioners. It is not known how well Mr Barry was acquainted with the island, but true to form he found the people to be '*sober, prudent and industrious... The proprietor, sensible that their money is scarce and indeed almost unnecessary, receives his rents in the articles they can best spare. He furnishes them with those (things) they stand most in need of.*'

Barry noted that '*almost all could read and many could write*' and '*all were content with their lot.*'

Mr Barry's bucolic account of Fair Isle contrasts with some of the other Northern Isles' submissions, like that of the Reverend Thomas MacFarlane of Bressay in Orkney, who said of his flock that '*many services, the sad marks of slavery, are demanded of them. They must fish for their masters, who either give them a fee entirely inadequate to their labour, or their dangers, or take their fish at a lower price than others would give... and are (thus) often deep in debt. Why not let them have leases on reasonable terms and dispose of their produce to those who will give them the best prices?*'

It would be some time before issues highlighted by the Reverend MacFarlane were addressed throughout the Northern Isles, but the First Statistical Account did stimulate the government to ask its own questions about its populace, by means of the national decennial census that began in 1841. This document never managed to encompass the range of questions set by Sir John Sinclair, but it did provide an honest record of who was living in Scotland and how and where they were employed. As the decades passed, additional questions would provide more information.

So on the night of 29th March, 1851, James Cheyne tossed and turned restlessly, until Elizabeth snapped at him. The tight space of a box bed left little room for squirming. "Be still, for goodness sake. What on earth is troubling you? Are you ill?"

"I wish to God I was. Then I could maybe put off tomorrow."

"Why? You've done it before. I know it's a different form this time, but you will manage. It's just a form after all. Go to sleep and let me get my rest."

"It's not the damned form that's worrying me, woman. It's all those people."

Elizabeth's irritation was rising. The older she got, the more she valued her sleep and riddles from her husband in the middle of the night were infinitely less alluring than they might have been forty years ago. "What on earth are you talking about? Which people? Have you been at the drink when you were down at the factor tonight?"

"It's the drink I'll need tomorrow night. I've been thinking of the number of crofts that lost men."

Now, in the dark silence of the box bed, his wife understood. There would be widows to register, rather than wives. The horrible gaps in families would have to be written down for the government. Elizabeth's husband would have to ask all the questions to be sure he wrote the right thing, even though he already knew the answers. The instructions were quite clear about the questions.

"Why not do the ones that lost the men first? Get it over with. Then you can do the rest of them. I know you like the chat. You can have a chat with the later ones." Elizabeth was trying her best to offer some resolution to her husband's plight. She was not, however, saying the right things.

"There's more to the census than chat woman. You have to do all the houses in order. It's important to the government that it's all done in some sort of order."

James now sat up in bed, furious at his wife's apparent lack of understanding. "I can't just fill in something as important as the census on a whim. It's got to be filled out in an orderly manner so that someone who doesn't live here will understand it, in Edinburgh, or London even. You know how difficult it was for us to figure out what all the relationships were when we came here, with nobody staying in their right house half the time and everyone married to their cousin and all with the same names from one house to the next. So I have to do it all in order and that means seeing the widows in a methodical fashion. Anyway, however I do it, it'll bring it all back to them and then they'll cry and I'll have to say something and I never know what to say! Now see what you've done."

Angrily the man threw off the covers. "I have to get up and pee."

And with that he opened the doors of the box bed and let in an icy damp draught before he slammed them shut again. It didn't take much nowadays to get him up in the night at the best of times. It seemed to Elizabeth that no sooner than you got the babies out of the habit of waking you at night, than your husband took over. It appeared that the good Lord didn't want women ever to get a proper night's sleep.

But she understood about the census. Last time, the first ever, it had been a day of great interest and excitement for everyone on the island. The government had wanted to know who they all were and where they all lived and her James was given the responsibility to see it was done right. It was amazing to think that just as her husband was doing his bit here in Fair Isle, all around the country other men of status were going from house to house, undertaking the same task.

She did wonder what on earth it was all for, since nothing had changed over the last ten years except for the laird dividing up the common agricultural land into individual working farms and that was nothing to do with the government. Perhaps some time in the future the information would be of use to someone. She couldn't quite see how, but there was a lot she didn't understand about the world and James had said that this year the form was more complicated. Perhaps this would make a difference.

Elizabeth was a modest person, a midwife who was with women when they needed her help to deliver their children, someone who could run her own home and deal with all the practicalities of life. Her intuitive skill with women had been inherited from her mother. It wasn't anything out of the ordinary really. She left all the clever stuff to her husband, the teacher, and was proud when last year he had finished the census in his lovely copperplate writing, proud that he was trusted to do something for the government down there, wherever 'there' was. She understood that in a country where not everyone could read and write well, or indeed at all, you needed someone trustworthy to complete such an important form. Even if nobody ever read it, she thought quietly to herself. There were some thoughts she didn't share with James. Then her husband pulled open the doors of the box bed once more and brought his cold feet back inside with him, along with another icy draught.

He continued to speak as if he had not stopped. "It's not just the five crofts either. It's all the rest of them. Every house has its own sad story for me to hear about their brothers and nephews and sons and even if they don't speak of it, we all know it's there and I have to intrude. There's barely a house where it won't be the same thing. We'll write about the living and think about the dead!"

Elizabeth reached over to comfort her husband. Seldom had she known him so moved by one of his tasks. He was a highly practical man who did his best as a teacher for all those who wanted to learn, but lived along with the rest, making the best of every opportunity he could to make a living. The main difference between James and the other men was that he didn't fish and he received £15 a year for his teaching, as well as a free house, so he never had to search for a rent and would always make a profit of sorts. Like all the rest he grew some vegetables and kept a few sheep on the hill, as well as a couple of Shetland ponies. Then there were the gifts of fish from folk who felt they owed him something. The Cheynes were by no means rich, but they were more comfortable than many and had lived happily in Fair Isle for almost thirty years.

The midwife was no stranger to death since not all babies survived a confinement, along with quite a few of their young mothers, and you attended each birth with an awareness of that fact. You did what you could to save people and you mourned with them when you failed. Elizabeth's experience of life and death gave her knowledge you wouldn't find in a book and like most midwives she had developed a pragmatic attitude that protected her from sorrow. You could be worn down by sorrow. Her husband needed to understand that.

"You just have to do what you can. It's simply another job. Just don't say to people that it was God's will. In my experience people don't want to hear about God's will when young people die. God is supposed to help folk, not punish them, whatever the church says. I sometimes say the 23rd psalm when babies don't survive. It helps me when I have to wrap up someone's dead baby, or a young wife."

James knew that his wife was trying to understand, but there had been many changes in ten years. In 1841 there were 232 people to register, but even before the recent disaster there had been deaths, while other people had chosen to seek a better life elsewhere. By writing down who was there, James would be reminding people about who was not, all the lost siblings, children and parents. Although there were 280 names to record on the day, a mini population explosion with great significance in such a small place, loss was always a painful aspect of island life.

So the day was quite as difficult as he had imagined it would be. He was, in the end, simply glad that it was over. The government would get its statistics but the faceless bureaucrats would never understand what pain surrounded them, for there was no place on the form for a measure of tragedy or loss. He went back to the schoolhouse tired and depressed, took a small keg of brandy out of a kist and poured himself a large measure. Without a word, Elizabeth placed a plate of food in front of him. There was really nothing left to say.

And so the winter dragged on. Spring is always late in the far north but surprisingly quickly the days do become longer so that people know there will be another summer, even when the weather does not seem to change. Food was still in short supply, however, and the fishing had not yet begun to yield that much of a reward. People worried about surviving. Morale was low. Still the women wept.

Eventually, as the days lengthened further, the land began to take up more and more of their time. The cattle were let out and it was time to clear the byre of its accumulated muck, spreading it on the fields along with the mountain of dung that had gradually built up at everyone's front door. A little normality returned, along with the sun and light. Life went on, but the shipwreck, which people already called the 'rocking cradles disaster' (because there were so many small children orphaned), would leave its imprint on minds for years to come.

Families who had not been directly affected continued to do their best to give support where it was needed, but it was difficult when you were so near the edge yourself. Janet Leslie at North Break-a-Wall was in the most desperate of straits. Her children were just too young and she had one of the poorest pieces of land, even though John's brothers and sisters kept an eye on her. Other women took to sending youngsters with a bit of something they had cooked, if they could possibly find the way to stretch any dish, saying that they had made too much and it would just go to waste. As if anyone could imagine food going to waste in Fair Isle! It was never much, but it helped a little. Tiny bags of meal would be dropped off when folk passed by from the mill and fish would arrive at her door in the hands of beach boys, who as often as not were unable to remember who had sent them on their errand. Pride was something people in Fair Isle could only have in small measure, but no one wanted to rob Janet of any fragment she had left. With the help of the community she worked her fingers to the bone to keep her family fed and clothed so that she survived, but only just. In the event the laird helped too, by not hounding her for rent he would never get.

By May the fishing was in full swing, with all the men working at full stretch until the end of the year when fish and weather together would bring the season to an end. Saithe was the main export from Fair Isle. The men caught other fish of course, many of which were of higher value, like haddock, cod, or even halibut. However, since Fair Isle suffered from a problem of communication with the outside world, or to be exact the lack of such communication, most other kinds of fish could not generally be sold at market. Saithe could be dried, salted and kept until a boat came to take it from the island to Leith, or Ireland, or Europe, depending on market needs. In 1851 the saithe season's start was never so much desired. Everyone wanted to move on somehow and leave the desperation of winter behind.

At Taft, Jeannie once more felt the terrible nausea. She retched in the byre as quietly as she could, certain now of the cause and aghast at the reality. Just when she had thought there could be nothing worse, this had happened. First there had been that terrible night when Tom had come to tell them that John had disappeared and was probably dead. Jeannie had played that night over and over in her head, her worst nightmare, one she had never expected. John was so strong and clever she had thought him to be invincible. At first she told herself that he was just lost and that he would come back in a week or two. Well, she had been wrong there. The weeks had passed and now, unless there was to be a miracle, she had to accept that she was a widow.

The three older boys tried so hard to be men that it broke her heart just to watch them, the younger two taking their lead from John. At first the girls had howled and howled while the wee ones had joined in with them in sympathy, as Jeannie struggled to hold the family together. It was so difficult to see any way forward when you were swathed in black thoughts and sometimes she could hardly bear to get herself out of bed in the morning and face another day. Old Laurence was the only one that understood the depth of her suffering. He had been a tower of strength, just when he was hurting so badly himself. The young had their future to live for, but Jeannie felt that she had nothing. Nothing would make her feel anything again she decided, as she went through her days mechanically, ticking off the boxes of tasks till it was time to go to bed, to toss and turn through another dreadful night. There was nothing to blur the pain, nothing that anyone could say that helped. In reality, she did not want to cope. She wanted to climb Malcolm's Head and shout from the very top for everyone to hear, "I'm not coping! I've had enough!"

Naturally, she didn't do anything like that. Like any other respectable woman she just got through the days. Then there were John's things to think about, the clothes and some small personal things, for like everyone else they had very little. It distressed her to look at his pens and his few books and Sunday clothes. But should you give things away if you are not sure someone is dead? It seemed like abandoning hope. In the end she gave some things to John and Lowry to use immediately and packed all the rest in the bottom of the boys' kist and tried to forget about it.

Then there were the people to deal with – her fellow Methodists, her family, John's family, friends and even those who were not. They all felt they had to say something but didn't always know what exactly. Should they encourage her to hope, or be coldly realistic? Either they tried too hard, or they tried to ignore John's absence completely in case she cried. Either reaction caused her pain, a dark fog of suffering that now seemed to separate her from everyone.

Even her sister's plight left her numb. You would expect her to have some fellow feeling for Aggie, so recently married and then widowed, but she did not. Aggie just had to manage her own loss. Jeannie felt little for anyone, so engulfed was she in her own black depression. Finally, when she began to accept the truth, she hated it when people drew her into conversation because she could not be bothered. John was dead. He had gone away and left her to manage on her own. At times she hated him for leaving her alone, but there was no one at all to whom she could unload that terrible thought.

Jeannie simply wanted to get through every day. Alienated by the loneliness of death, she turned away from everyone who might be able to help, speaking less and less, avoiding eye contact as much as possible and getting on with the daily grind, just as she had done for years. She was there and she would do her duty, but she embraced a solitary road that increasingly isolated her family. To the children it seemed that they had lost not only their father but also their mother. And only when the nausea became really serious did she figure out what had happened. John was gone, but he had left her with a child in her body. The thought filled her with all the emotions, from grief to hysteria. How could she cope with another child now? How could she tell her family? She was forty-five, with seven live children and no husband. What did she want with another child now?

Even the practicalities overwhelmed her. John had always told the boys when a new baby was to arrive, while she had mentioned the fact to the girls quietly, so that they could help her more. It was never something for a big public announcement, something she made a fuss about. She told John and a few of the women and that was it until the birth. There was never time for mollycoddling a pregnant woman in Fair Isle, unless it was the first time of course. People made a bit of a fuss the first time. Later, only just before the baby arrived, the mother was allowed a little ease if there were older ones or relatives who could take the strain. Since everyone knew that a birth could be tiring, or even dangerous, no one spoke of this. You didn't want to frighten the young ones. It was just something you got on with, alone.

But this was different. This was horrible. She didn't want another baby if she didn't have a husband. This was even more of a punishment. And she was too old. What was God thinking of? Had she not suffered enough? And what if something happened to her this time? How would the younger children manage then? It wasn't as if she had done all that well with young Stewart the last time. This was a memento of John she didn't want, but then she knew that was a terrible thing to think. Desperate thoughts made her feel even more sick, in spirit as well as in body. The baby, now she was sure that one existed, absorbed most of her days and part of each night, but she could not share her dreadful secret with anyone.

Any irritation she showed was put down to grief. The older boys were busy with the fishing and the land and even the girls were crying less now. Old Laurence persisted with his visits, trying to share his grief but failing, for the last thing she wanted to talk to him about was his son. He puzzled at her aversion but, since he was old enough to let things be, he spent time chatting with the wee ones and talking to Lowry, who seemed to need his support. John would have wanted his father to keep trying, of that he was sure, so he would just keep on going to Taft until he was ordered to stop.

Then one morning Jeannie set the house to rights and told Jane she was off to Quoy to see Aggie and watch the wee one perform whatever new achievement was her mother's joy. Aggie had sent a message the day before that she wanted her to come over to Quoy, but she simply had not had the energy. Her sister liked to talk and cry with her, but Jeannie did not want an invitation to cry. Aggie had her problems, that she allowed, but crying together did not mend anything. If only it did.

Bereft, and with no future except looking after her old father and uncle, her sister had decided that her life was over. She had renamed her baby Williamina after her dead husband, not necessarily the best of ideas Jeannie had thought, realising that Aggie was young enough to marry again. A new husband might not relish such a vivid reminder of his dead rival for her affections. But this she could not bring herself to say and it gave Aggie solace in the meantime. Aggie had so hoped that marriage would open a door to a more promising future. Now, there she was, aged thirty and still at Quoy, just as if she had never been married, only now with a baby.

Jeannie walked quickly up the road to her old home, nodding at folk she passed but not pausing to talk, so that no one had the opportunity to say something that might cause her any upset. She had found that if she walked fast she could avoid quite a bit of casual chat. Stewart had been clingy when she left and she wondered what his reaction would be when he discovered he was no longer the youngest. No doubt it would not be good news for him, but it was not the best of news for anyone so he would just have to find his place and get on with it.

It was a bright May morning and after a cup of tea and a bannock at Quoy she was happy enough to join Aggie for a wee walk with young Williamina before returning home. At least the bannock had settled her stomach for the moment and Aggie had not cried yet. As they walked and Aggie babbled on, Jeannie puzzled that this everlasting sickness was more wearing than it had ever been before. Perhaps there was something wrong with the baby? Or perhaps she was just too old to be having babies in the first place?

As they walked up the track, Jeannie was managing in the main to ignore Aggie's repetitive listing of the difficulties she had to endure: her loss of independence, her loss of the love of her life and her loss of status. Who would want to take on an old widow with a baby? Why did she have to be a widow anyway? What would become of her if her father died and Uncle John married? How would she support Williamina? On and on she went, as if Jeannie too had not lost a husband and had problems to face. Finally Jeannie felt irritation and bile rising in equal quantities and wondered if she might just be sick right here, out in the open. Surely not! Not at her age! How embarrassing! Desperately, she tried to hold the nausea in check.

"You don't know how lucky you are. You have the boys to fish for you and the girls to look after Stewart. You are sure of your place at Taft whatever happens. You can't understand how I feel. I've lost everything. My life is over and Williamina will be alone with me forever. Who knows what will happen when faither dies! He's seventy and won't live that much longer. You are so lucky to be so settled. You've no idea what it's like to be me!"

It wasn't like Jeannie to lose her temper, particularly with Aggie, but to feel as she did and to be lectured on her good luck! Finally, this was too much. "Well, my lady. I'm to have a baby in the autumn. I feel horribly sick and I don't know how I'm going to tell my family. So now do you think I'm the lucky one, me at forty-five years of age and having a baby with no faither right from the start? You at least are young enough to marry again. Count your blessings, my girl. You might just have a future. Perhaps you could think of others for once."

With that she retched most terribly, losing her stomach contents out in the open for everyone to see. Then she stood up, wiping her mouth on her apron. The two women faced each other, both rooted to the grass by her words. That Jeannie was having a baby shocked Aggie out of her self-absorption.

She grabbed her sister to her bosom in an effort to provide some comfort, hugging her sparse frame tightly and valiantly ignoring the stench of sickness. "Oh, Jeannie, I'm so sorry. What will you do?"

"There's nothing I can do. I'll just have to manage. And hope that when John marries it's to a girl I like, for I'll have to stay in Taft with them forever. But that's not all. My problem is how to tell folk. What will the bairns think? What will other folk say? How will I manage? I just don't want anyone to know."

The last was spoken in a panic-stricken wail, for finally she had voiced all her fears and found them just as shocking as she thought she would. Tears came. She had been keeping them at bay for weeks now, but finally they threatened to overwhelm her. Was it not enough she had a husband to mourn without another mouth to feed? People would gossip and she realised that it was gossip that she feared as much as anything else. In a small community there was no privacy, and even if the chatter was sympathetic she didn't want to be the topic for other people's nattering. Jeannie kept herself to herself and gave no one the opportunity to talk about her if she could help it. She hated it when you could feel people whispering about you after you walked away. Now they would all whisper, and there was nothing she could do to stop it.

Eventually Jeannie sank to the ground and began to sob terribly as she recounted her litany of woes. It was all too much. By this time she had no idea of where she was, or what was happening. Jeannie was finished and didn't care who knew, even if she was making a public spectacle of herself.

It was the rasping sound of her sister's sobbing that turned Aggie around. Her big sister had always been there for her, comforting, helping, caring for everyone from the day their mother had died. Now she needed help. Aggie pulled her up and began to lead her back in the direction of Quoy, for a walk was the last thing Jeannie needed. You could see from her face that she was at the end of her tether, pale, and thinner even than usual now that Aggie finally thought about it. Jeannie's clothes were falling off her, for goodness sake. Why had she not noticed? Why had no one else noticed?

With her arms round her sister she led her back to the house, voicing mindless platitudes to do with new babies being a gift, fully appreciating the emptiness of this sentiment to the older widow. But she had to say something. Aggie's mind, which had been frozen in grief, now whirled in an effort to think of what she could do to help. Surely the first thing was to tell folk, for that seemed to be absorbing Jeannie as much as anything else. Once folk knew, they could all rally round and stop her feeling that she was having this baby on her own. When she thought about it, the baby was a miracle, a reminder of John, although she had the sense not to say that now. Jeannie was not in a state to consider God's gift in a normal way, not if she was feeling sick all the time and not when she was missing John so badly.

When they got back to Quoy their father was there, seated in front of the house checking his fishing lines. He too had been rather preoccupied with his own issues since Willie Mather's death, thinking that he would just have to keep on fishing forever to support Aggie and the baby. He nodded at the two women as they came into view, surprised that it was Jeannie this time who was crying. Before he could say anything however, Aggie decided to start telling people right there and then, without consulting her sister. Jeannie liked to control everything but this was different. God knows the old man had dealt with a pile of his own problems over the years. He would know what they should do next.

"Jeannie has a problem, Faither."

Jeannie turned to her sister, furious that her secret was to be shared without either her agreement or input. And her father was not necessarily the first person she wanted to tell.

But Aggie was not to be stopped. She ignored her sister's frantic shushing and went on. "Jeannie needs you to tell her boys that she is to have another baby in the autumn. She doesn't know how to do it and it's upsetting her."

"Well now, do you tell me that?"

The old man lifted his rough fingers from the task in hand and looked at his two daughters. At his age there was nothing left that surprised him, nothing that could really upset him. Jeannie had done well, gone up in the world even. He hadn't thought she would ever need his help again. A man who had buried three wives should have known better.

She was getting on in years for a baby, but that was hardly the end of the world. She was fit and had delivered all her other children without any problem he had heard of, and some women had bairns when they were even older than Jeannie. Perhaps a baby would take her mind off things. He had noticed she was looking worn but had never thought that this was the reason. Pregnant women were always a bit of a taboo subject and now, because of her circumstances, everyone would gossip about her condition. Well, he would see that his grandchildren at least would deal with this matter in the best possible way for their mother. It was not often he had a chance to help Jeannie, but he would do his best for her now.

"I'm pleased for you, girl. Despite what you might feel at the moment, this is good news. Now away inside with Aggie and get a cup of tea while I think best how to do this. No!" The old man waved his hand in the air. "Don't tell me. For once, you do as you're told and let folk that are older than you deal with things. I'll come in once I've put all this away."

Best he didn't talk too much about a subject that would embarrass them both. It had been quite a while since William had taken such a position with Jeannie and for now she was more than happy to follow Aggie inside and leave her problem at the door for someone else to sort out. She had handed over the responsibility to her father and suddenly it was not her problem. For now she was just a tired, sad woman at the end of her tether, one who was more than pleased to sit by the fire and sip tea quietly.

A moment later her father came inside, picked up his jacket and refused a drink. "Now, you're to stay here for a bit till I get the telling over. I'm away to Gaila to see if Laurence would like to speak to your boys with me. He'll be happy for you, I tell you that. It will give him something positive to think about. We all need to feel we're helping and you feel that less when you're older. Anyway, two grandfathers will do the job better than one. I'll send Agnes at Gaila over to tell the girls at Taft and then to Springfield to let them know as well. Hannah Wilson can see that the other Methodist ladies are told and Stewart will spread the word too. Before you know it you won't need to speak of these things to anyone. Good news travels fast here," and he smiled as he said this, to underline the fact that the coming baby was not a problem. They all needed to look to the future.

It had been a long time since Jeannie had needed her father to be a father, but today she was happy to let him help. She spent the rest of the afternoon being spoiled by the women at Quoy, playing with young Williamina and talking of anything other than dead men. It was a short escape from her daily routine and a surprise, the day the sorter of Taft was sorted by others. Aggie had bucked up too for she had something to worry about other than herself, for one afternoon at least. Jeannie felt an intense relief now that she could be honest about her sickness, for not only was she worried about coping with a new baby, cooking had become a nightmare, made worse by the re-appearance of fresh, smelly, oily fish in the diet.

The daily fare in Fair Isle came not only from fish, but during the season from its by-products of which there was a surfeit. This meant dishes like slot, where fish livers and roes were crushed and beaten into a paste before being boiled in hot water. Muggies were stuffed fish stomachs, much of the stuffing also being livers, while crappin was fish livers, flour and oatmeal, all stuffed into the large head of a saithe and then boiled. There were other variations on these themes and although all this fish offal was very healthy and much enjoyed by those bored with the constant winter diet of salted and dried fish, no one could deny that there was a strong smell associated with its preparation and that it was a messy, stomach-churning business if you thought about it. Thus, once the family had been warned off, Jeannie was allowed to avoid cooking, at least until she regained her normal appetite.

She was relieved when with June came the return of wild birds' eggs to the diet. A dish of caadel (scrambled eggs) was easy to stomach, and the boys all took it in turns to bring home fresh eggs for the next couple of months so that Jeannie could build herself up for the birth.

Fair Isle is today famed for the range and complexity of its ornithology, but in the 1850s the birds who came to breed on the island were simply seen as a welcome supply of food; May, June and July being the most rewarding months for eggs and then young birds, which were generally tastier than their parents. Wild birds were caught with snares and nets, but men and boys also risked their lives to climb down cliffs with a basket tied to their back, which they then filled with eggs that they carefully picked out of nests. Sometimes a man would hammer a wooden stake into the ground above a difficult cliff face and let himself down with the aid of a stout rope. Guillemots, skuas, shags, razorbills, kittiwakes and puffins were all on the menu. Puffins, or tammie-nories as the locals call them, live in burrows at the top of the cliffs and a stick with a hook on the end was often used to pull them out. A gloved hand might also suffice and, if all else failed, you accepted the bite and put your hand down uncovered, retracting your arm with an angry puffin fastened to the end of it.

Today, we see puffins as captivating, engaging, inquisitive birds, an utter pleasure to study even when you are not an expert. It is impossible to spend time watching their antics without smiling, so it is harder for us to imagine viewing them as food, but that is what they were to all the people in the Northern Isles. They were plucked, gutted and set in rows over a gridiron (an iron ribbed set of bars on four metal feet that could be placed over the fire) to roast for a meal. It would be 1880 before any steps were made to introduce the protection of wild birds during the breeding season and many, many more before they received the protection that they have today. For poor and hungry people in the 19th century, sea birds were simply free food and it was inconceivable that they might fail to return year after year.

When young James was born that October, he was a much-celebrated child, a miracle in so many ways. Of course there were sad moments, but since the older boys were well able to take over the fishing at Taft, John's death had not threatened the family's ability to keep going. Thus John's memento was the focus of a lot of attention in a croft that was, relatively speaking, thriving. Poor Stewart, who had felt ignored for so much of his early life, was now quite superfluous, replaced by a baby that everyone seemed to love even before he was born. Like all children in big families, Stewart just had to learn to put up with it and pick on his younger brother when he got the chance. That was how it was. James was the only joy that came from the rocking cradles disaster.

Perhaps it was because he was destined to have so much extra attention, that James had always the sunniest of natures and enjoyed his special status without ever really understanding it. With his elder brothers being so much older, they became his male role models, his father substitutes. His mother and sisters doted on him, his brothers protected him, and the wider family found time for him, in memory of his father. Of course there was never enough fussing to make any Fair Isle child feel spoiled, but there was no doubt that James experienced a life slightly easier than most.

The effect of the disaster resonated for many years to come, but all the widows continued to live on the island, if only through the generosity of neighbours and families. Both sides of the religious divide came together at times like this, common humanity superseding religious differences.

When John Lewis brought Methodism to the island in 1824, he was driven by his belief that men's souls could gain salvation '*by grace, through faith*'. The man was on a five-year mission to Shetland to persuade people that '*all need to be saved, may be saved, may know that they are saved and may be saved to the uttermost*'. His message was so powerful that he often found that those listening to him responded emotionally, men and women moved to tears as they considered and accepted this wonderful new version of Christianity.

Lewis spent just over a week in Fair Isle, preaching at least nine times and visiting people in their homes where he handed them tracts and prayed with them. During that time he converted a small group to his new, enthusiastic version of religion (mostly Wilsons) and taught them how to support one another on this new path, one that required no formal minister. There would be visits over the years from ordained Methodists, but this contact would not, in the short term, be regular. People must read the tracts and their Bible and try to follow the new path as a group. Lewis noted that the island had not been visited by a Church of Scotland minister for three years and had thirty-four unbaptised children, so one can understand why there might be an opportunity for a new vision of God, one that seemed to care and, more importantly, offered salvation.

In many ways Methodism was ideal for Fair Isle, since it offered a framework where people met together in small groups to discuss religion and examine their souls, before meeting in larger groups on a Sunday, led by a lay preacher. It was, like so much on the island, a self-help structure. The Church of Scotland had based its new religion in 1560 around ministers and elders, forgetting that this system only worked well if the minister had a small parish. All the old rituals of the Roman Catholic Church were replaced by the sacrament, which required a series of preparatory actions and tests. Without a minister the sacrament could not be taken, and without ready access to a minister the elders could not entirely fulfil their role either.

In Calvinism there was a great deal of emphasis on God's anger, the need to repent and punishment for sin, with no certain knowledge that you would be one of God's elected few, for only God's elect would go to heaven. It was not clear how God chose his elect, only that you might not be one of them. Methodism offered a different spiritual road, one that seemed to offer a more reliable route to salvation. Of course, it took a lot of confidence to leave the official church in a country that was still run, to a large extent, by its rules. There were those in Fair Isle who would always feel that Methodism was not a real religion at all and this schism would cause some heartache over many years, particularly when people married. When four women lost their husbands, however, the community came together, for all knew that tomorrow God could take more husbands of either denomination.

It has to be said that some women found life difficult even when they had a husband. At this time Robert and Helen Mather, like many others, had been forced to settle for a home built on a relative's croft, a small house at Stackhool without any land. Robert came up with a more imaginative solution than most for surviving his difficult circumstances. He resorted to smuggling, an occupation where he found limited success over several years. He did not become rich but he earned enough to survive.

At one time Lerwick had been a major centre for smuggling, but by the 1850s the trade was conducted on a reduced basis, with foreign ships unloading brandy and tobacco into small boats that each had its own small following of clients. However, smuggling became increasingly difficult as time passed and Robert was finally caught by one of her Majesty's ships and detained in Lerwick at her Majesty's pleasure for three months. Helen was now another island wife struggling to survive, suffering terribly until Robert was set free. Many of those who helped her during this time had been customers of her husband, so a small sense of obligation accompanied their support. When you were surrounded by boats of many different nations that were mostly replete with untaxed liquor, smuggling did not have the same sense of law-breaking as it did in London or Edinburgh. For men like Robert, who had no land, there was little alternative in Fair Isle, and as soon as he was offered the opportunity to emigrate he took his family to Canada.

Even when the Royal Navy stepped up its offensive against smugglers there was always some contraband hidden in small corners and ledges on the island's many cliff faces. No one would remove anyone else's cache and no one would dream of reporting such matters to the authorities. Despite the church's warnings about the demon drink, it would always have its followers. The amounts were probably never large, but since no one spoke of it, who would really know?

# Chapter 5

# *Change and Tradition*

I t took time for everyone to accept that the men were dead, but after the first year of anniversaries, families had to acknowledge their loss and move on. By the time the worst of the potato blight was overcome, life for some was improving. Progress was usually measured in small steps and was, of course, never universal. Any level of prosperity depended on how much land you were allocated, how fertile that land was, how healthy your animals were, how fertile your wife was, how healthy your family was, if you had enough men to fish, and how lucky you were. Additionally, some people would always work harder than others. Success is never a simple equation.

Illness was always a threat to any family's efforts to improve their lot. In 19th century Scotland, medicine was primitive even for the wealthy, and symptoms such as fever, coughs, headaches, stomach pains or vomiting had few genuine remedies. Although smallpox was largely defeated by this time, diphtheria, dysentery, typhoid, tuberculosis and cholera were still to be found, while whooping cough, measles and scarlet fever could take scores of children when these ailments arrived in a community. Fair Isle men and boys had the opportunity to catch a range of diseases when they travelled to Shetland or boarded a passing vessel to barter, and there were both visitors and shipwrecked strangers who could bring disease. Isolation protected people, but it also prevented them from building up resistance to ailments for which there were few remedies. There were always those who specialised in the preparation of salves and potions, but most illnesses simply ran their course. Throughout Scotland it was still common to believe that when an outbreak of sickness arrived in a community it was a visitation from a wrathful God, who had a tendency to punish sin in a variety of unpleasant ways. Prayer was a comfort in such difficult times, not least because it stopped you feeling helpless.

In 1855 the government began to collect official data on births, deaths and marriages, a task that increasingly overwhelmed Parish Records in Scotland. As the 1800s progressed, the agrarian and industrial revolutions encouraged more and more people to relocate to find work. Additionally, between 1845 and 1851, thousands of desperate Irish arrived on the 'floating bridge' of ships that helped some of them to avoid starvation during the potato famine. Glasgow's sudden influx of people meant that it became so overcrowded that it was known as the unhealthiest place to live in Britain. As the state grew in power, it realised that it required statistics if it was to manage its growing and changing population.

So in Fair Isle the teacher had another responsibility, that of official Registrar of Births, Deaths and Marriages. His first recorded death was in January 1855, a lady of sixty-three who died of tuberculosis. Since this disease was a long way from being understood, far less cured, it was a regular presence in crowded, unventilated croft houses in Shetland, just as it was in small, cramped homes throughout the entire country. Mary Brown was not particularly old, but she had five adult children and it was felt she had endured a life comparable to most. Her family mourned, but in an accepting way.

Then at the end of March 1855, a young sailor suffering from measles infected a boy on a bartering expedition. It was more than a week before the child developed the fever and cough and later still before the spots gradually began to spread over his body. As a precaution, Mr Cheyne closed the school, but such segregation was too late and all too soon the virus had begun to affect many families. By this time the first boy had developed a deep and frightening cough. Gradually, more children succumbed. The women did their best, bathing hot foreheads and covering small limbs in potions, but the illness took its course. Soon there were little people lying in box beds throughout the island, covered in the dreadful rash and coughing terribly when it spread to their lungs. Pneumonia was the killer.

At Taft, Jeannie's children were ill along with all the rest and she sat up night after night, bathing and soothing her brood. Aggie was the most affected and for a time she thought she might lose her, but she turned the corner just when James began to feel hot and tired. By this time Jeannie was exhausted, but still she insisted on sitting with him night and day, forcing sips of water through parched lips and willing him to live. She was sure that this would be God's final punishment for her sins and this feeling grew as each day passed. James was her favourite. He was the image of his father and she had spoiled him. Now she would be punished for her weakness. The older boys came home every day from the fishing afraid that he might be dead, and terrified of what this might do to their mother. Jane occasionally persuaded Jeannie to let her sit with the child, but never for long, since Jeannie felt that only she could pull him through. Despite the severity of his illness, James survived. To the family's delight he gradually regained his strength and, better still, he suffered no long-term consequences.

Others were not so lucky. One child was left with damage to his hearing. Others died. Most did so in April and May; nine babies and toddlers up to the age of two, all desperately loved and missed. Then nine-year-old Williamina Wilson from Houlaby died. By now, mothers were distraught. With so many deaths over such a short period of time a desperate fear and sadness permeated many crofts, and the community mourned with those who had been worst affected while they worried about those who thus far had missed the contagion. Was it waiting to strike, or would they be spared? Not knowing made everyone nervous.

It was not just children who caught measles. The outbreak took to the graveyard 19-year-old John Irvine. Then two young mothers followed, each of whom had carefully nursed their family only to succumb themselves when finally exhausted. Agnes Wilson of Leogh left six children while Jacobina Eunson of Brews left three. And in this tragedy Thomas Wilson of Leogh lost both his wife and sister. When a young mother died, people had to step in immediately to help with the children, so with these two deaths other mothers took stock of their families and shuddered to think of what would happen to their brood should the hand of fate decide to point at them. Finally, the epidemic waned and disappeared.

Despite such outbreaks, the population continued to grow too quickly for the size of the island and children continued to marry and produce more offspring. Increasingly, this meant that young couples had to share their parents' two-roomed croft house, or build a new house next to the family home. Such makeshift housing solutions did not answer the desperate land problem, for without land you could not grow crops and feed your new family. Slowly and relentlessly numbers rose, but no one came up with a solution. Although the most prosperous managed to survive, those at the bottom of the scale increasingly found it difficult to keep body and soul together. Those most under pressure were the very people who did not have the means to move somewhere else. James Stewart (who owned Fair Isle) lived in Orkney and as he grew older he became less and less involved with the island and its problems. Now, there was no word of a move to Orkney to work on his land there, an option that had been made available in the past.

～·～

July 1857 saw Taft back on an even keel. In fact, celebrations were in order and Jeannie found herself preparing for another major change in her life, probably the greatest upheaval that would occur before she died. She moved gently in the box bed on the night before the ceremonies, trying not to disturb Aggie, who lay deeply asleep by her side. It had been a hard and difficult day of preparation for the morrow and the poor girl was totally fatigued, although despite her exhaustion and the lateness of the hour, Jeannie herself could not get her brain to switch off. The last few days had been a ceaseless round of cleaning and tidying, washing and drying, visitors and cooking. There had been endless lists of things to do before the big day and even now she was not sure she had done everything. This afternoon everyone had more than the usual, ritual face rub. She had forced the older boys down to the sea with the younger ones for a dip and washed almost everything they owned in the meantime, despite all their grumbles.

The girls had used the time without the boys to wash themselves all over in the safety of the house. For weeks they had all been pingling away whenever they could find the time, each trying to fashion a new dress, skirt or blouse from material that Jeannie had ordered from Lerwick. There were even some pretty ribbons that John would no doubt have tut-tutted over, but they were good lassies and she didn't think that a few ribbons would turn their heads completely. Anyway, it was all done now. The place was swept and everything was at its best. There had been no time to sit and think about the changes that the morrow would bring and perhaps that was for the best. Tomorrow evening, it would all be done and dusted.

The Church of Scotland minister from Shetland made his annual visit to the island this week and both John and Lowry were to marry. As was so often the custom at this time, each was marrying another Wilson who was also a cousin. John was to marry Barbara Wilson of Springfield, the daughter of the Methodist lay preacher. Of all the girls that he might have chosen, Jeannie was thrilled that John had settled on Barbara, for she was a strong lass, one that would keep him on his toes and not be dominated by his strong character.

Lowry would leave Taft to stay in Quoy with Ann Wilson, who had continued to live there with Jeannie's family. Quoy had seen more changes than Jeannie might have imagined over recent years and she found it strange to think that one of her sons would now be added to the mix. It was still an Irvine croft, but one without her father. It had been a difficult thing to accept, Quoy without William Irvine.

Of course, you might have expected William's four girls to marry and leave home, but his boys gradually oozed away too, so that he was increasingly dependent on his nephew John after Willie Mather perished in 1851. However, now that there was no other young man in the house, John found that his position was elevated to that of 'heir apparent' and he found himself attractive to the ladies, or at least one of them. Ann Wilson of Quoy had a sister, Isabella, who now found more excuses to visit, so that in the midst of the 1855 measles tragedies, 48-year-old John Irvine was moved to take a wife. At the time Jeannie had been too involved with her children's illness to give the matter much thought, but the whole balance of Quoy had been irrevocably changed.

First of all, William's remaining girls didn't get on with Isabella. They felt she was a bit slack in her housekeeping habits, which meant that the burden of work fell on their shoulders. When Isabella had a son less than a year after her marriage to John, she made it quite clear that she felt that this was the start of the next dynasty to inherit Quoy, little thinking that her brash confidence bruised the feelings of those who already considered it to be 'their' home, particularly while their father was still in residence. Not that Isabella's husband raised the topic, for John Irvine was a quiet soul who basked in the enjoyment of his unexpected late marriage and did not dream that his satisfaction might cause distress for others.

Croft houses are not pleasant places to be when there is tension, particularly over the winter when small homes can be claustrophobic. By the time Lowry (Isabella and John's son) was born in April 1856, Aggie Irvine had reeled in Willie Eunson, whose wife had died in the 1855 measles epidemic. Aggie insisted that they make the difficult sea crossing to the church in Dunrossness, lest she might have to wait some unknown length of time for a minister to visit the island. Early disappointments had encouraged Aggie to take charge of her life and make the best of what was left of it, both for herself and Williamina. Since her new husband came with three children, it was as well that she started the new union with a positive outlook.

Aggie and her child relocated to Brews, taking William Irvine with them since he now needed more care and attention. The old man must have been disappointed to leave the house he had built with such hopes for the future, but old men have little choice but to go with people who are willing to undertake their care.

There would be a third marriage tomorrow, one that meant yet another change at Quoy, for Jeannie's half-sister Bina would marry Thomas Wilson of Kennaby, the second widower from the measles outbreak. With six children already in the marriage, Jeannie didn't envy her half-sister, but the man needed help with the younger children and Bina wanted her own home now that she was almost thirty years of age. Of tomorrow's marriages, Bina's would be the most challenging.

The vacuum created by Jacobina and Aggie's marriages enabled young Taft Lowry to find a place in Quoy when he married Ann, who by now regarded the place as her home and found Isabella less difficult than the Irvine girls had done. That was how it was: one generation inexorably followed the next, although not always as you had imagined. At Taft, Jeannie would find it hard to give up the reins to young Barbara Wilson and another woman in the croft would make everyone watch the length of their step for a bit. There would be a new regime, for a new wife would make sure of that if she was worth her stuff, but Jeannie had known Barbara since she was a baby and knew that it was her time to step to the side. Life altered with each birth, death and wedding, and everyone moved over to accommodate their changed position.

Jeannie was particularly pleased that her two older boys would start their married lives in separate crofts. Lowry had gradually become as strong-minded as John and increasingly stood up to his brother when there was a disagreement. The boy had gained confidence from Laurence's support after his father drowned, and when the old man had died last year she had been glad that Lowry's involvement with Ann had helped him get over his grief. Aye, there was a good chance it would all work out. If they had all lived at Taft, in what would have been quite a crowded home, the boys would certainly fight about something and John would always have the upper hand in any disagreement. Lowry would be more likely to make a peaceful life living with John Irvine at Quoy.

The day went well, all sporting new finery, and after the ceremonies most of the island visited the new couples. Jeannie went to Quoy and Brews, before returning to her own home where already she felt different, possibly a tad insecure. But she looked on the bright side of the change. Barbara was a strong young woman, a good foil for John and they would work hard to make a life together. With the rest of her children healthy and still at home, Jeannie felt she had much for which to be thankful, despite all the struggles of the last few years. She had kept her family together and they had retained the croft, despite the haunting fear that some of her brood would leave. You wept all the more with those who waved sons and daughter off to brave new worlds, when tomorrow it might be you. There was a real fear that finally you would be left quite alone and the issue got worse every year. Now, the islanders' ability to live to an old age might be considered a curse.

On 3rd October, 1860, the *SS Edinburgh*, a steamship sailing from Leith, was lost off Fair Isle with all hands. Some of the men spotted her going northwards, a ghostly shape just visible on the horizon through murky weather, but soon the illusionary silhouette disappeared. The islanders realised that there had been another tragedy when flotsam began to gather on the edge of the tide – batons, barrel staves, great spars of wood and all sorts of smaller stuff. As usual they salvaged what they could for Fair Isle's everlasting recycling project. On an island without trees any scrap of wood had to be saved and carefully stashed away for future use, along with anything else that was found. When the name of the vessel became clear from the wreckage, the factor sent word to Lerwick so that the ship's owners and the families of the deceased could be informed. They understood here that it was better to know the truth rather than spend the rest of your life in agonised conjecture.

As the 19th century progressed, year on year the shipping lanes around Fair Isle were becoming increasingly crowded. Britain's inventiveness, its skilled workforce, its spectacular industrial development and easy access to raw materials, meant that the country had become a dominating force in the world of manufacturing. It exported all manner of textiles, iron goods, crockery, cutlery and instruments (mathematical, musical and medical). Glassware, toys, watches and clocks, furniture, machinery and raw materials all added to the manifests of increasing numbers of ships on the horizon. Then there was the human cargo, the endless stream of emigrants from all over Europe, people who sought a better life somewhere else. Britain haemorrhaged citizens over this period and many of them sailed past Fair Isle. Shetland alone lost 8,124 people between 1860 and 1880, a quarter of its population! And Britain was hardly the only country to be involved in this international trade in humanity and goods. All over Europe people were hearing about opportunities in the New World, so that Fair Isle witnessed a seemingly endless procession of sails on the horizon.

Then there was the growth in fishing. Encouraged by the British government, new harbours were built to accommodate fleets of ever-larger boats all around Britain's coast. A bonanza of vessels, including those from foreign ports, came to fish in Shetland's waters and as the years passed the islanders wondered aloud about how they could benefit, apart from salvaging wrecks. What they needed was a decent harbour, one that would allow them to accommodate bigger boats. Perhaps they, too, could become a focus for the growing trade.

Sea captains navigating to and from Europe, or simply from the east coast of Britain to the west, chose the broad passage between Orkney and Shetland rather than hugging the northern mainland of Scotland where the Pentland Firth was notorious for its tidal races and rocky inlets. The route between the two sets of islands was about fifty miles wide and relatively safe, provided you understood the tides. All you had to do was keep an eye on the weather and keep clear of Fair Isle. Somehow, this proved to be a challenge so that year on year the number of shipwrecks grew, along with the loss of life and money. Minds further afield than Shetland discussed the need for a lighthouse that would warn ships of the danger that this small island presented. Governments, merchants and ship owners, together with those who encouraged European emigration, all voiced a keen interest in the subject of a light.

The responsibility for lighthouse building in Scotland had been focused on the Commissioners of Northern Lighthouses since the 18th century, when the Stevenson family began to dominate the field. Gradually, the Stevenson name had become synonymous with lighthouses and they were famed for building lights where no one had thought it possible. A land mass as large as Fair Isle would not present the authorities problems like those at Muckle Flugga or Skerryvore. Although the 1850s and 1860s saw a surge in lighthouse construction around the Scottish coast, demand always outstripped the ability of the Commissioners to fund all the nominated sites. Just when the need was greatest, the 1870s and 1880s would see bureaucratic and political difficulties slow down the building programme in Scotland. It was particularly galling that this occurred when technological advancement was producing better lights and new fog sirens that would offer mariners greater protection.

Robert Louis Stevenson visited Fair Isle with the lighthouse steamer *Pharos* in 1869 (at the time when his father Thomas still entertained hopes that his son would follow in the family's engineering footsteps). Stevenson junior found the isle to be '*the wildest and most unpitying coast of any place yet visited. It is a conspicuous example of matter in the wrong place*'.

When he considered its weather and the strong tides to which it was exposed, he commented that it was '*one of the most dangerous spots in the North Sea,*' but even with the weight of the Stevenson family behind the project, there was no funding. A Royal Navy report in 1877 would recommend not one, but two lighthouses, but with no money, the litany of wrecks carried on unabated.

For those on shore, winter continued to be the most challenging time. As the shortest day approached and islanders lost much of their daylight, heavy grey skies and coastal fogs could make things even worse. With an ever-growing population and pressure on supplies, food was now firmly managed as the women prayed that it would last. Of course, some houses managed this time of rationing better than others and the increasing numbers of landless families were forced to fall back on family bonds to make ends meet. Winter dark and cold could make some people's moods as unpredictable as the weather, particularly when hunger stood at the door. If it was fine the men found outside tasks to occupy them, but regularly it would pour with rain, or fierce gales would make outside work too dangerous so that the men busied themselves with rope work or carpentry, while the women knitted between bouts of housework. Small, crowded croft houses soon became claustrophobic so that small irritations could quickly attain monstrous proportions. Particularly after the turn of the year, when the harshness of the wind ate into your soul, winter was hard. It was difficult to remember that spring was not so very far away.

To break the monotony people took the chance to visit neighbours, most likely relatives, who were usually glad of a diversion to while away an hour or so. Everyone moved up a bit, made room and listened to recent gossip and stories from the past, for the old people liked to recite yarns much older than themselves. Some were simply embroidered tales of daring do, but, especially when the more religious were not around, old women told superstitious tales they had from their mothers. The church may have discouraged such stories but the young of both sexes were happy to listen to them through a dark winter afternoon and evening. Smaller children sat round-eyed in wonder while they heard of the old good luck customs that were supposed to ward off the other sort of fortune. There were stories of scaly trows, frightening fairies and fantastic mermaids, all of which scared the children half to death. As the old people remembered the past, they quoted poetry, rhymes and riddles, so that they too could be preserved. All these words from the past would only be preserved as long as they were spoken and remembered, for no one thought to cast them into print.

It was agreed that during the darkest days of winter the line that separates the underworld from the upper regions weakened, allowing a variety of strange and unusual creatures to emerge from shadowy haunts and take advantage of those in human form. All around the country, ancient local festivities surrounded these beliefs, along with superstitions that had existed over untold centuries. And all were best appreciated sitting round a smoky fire on dark, cold nights.

By December people longed for the return of the sun and focused this longing on the Yule festivities that long predated the Christian traditions, celebrating the winter solstice and using ancient rituals to assure people that the darkness would shortly be overcome so that the ground could once more become fertile. There were many different rites and customs, including those where young girls divined ways to conjure up future husbands. Despite the power of the church, there was a lot of fun to be had from the old ways. Grandmothers spoke of omens and ancient beliefs relating to nature that affected people, cattle and even the weather. Young children absorbed all the stories, never daring to question what they were hearing. All the small observances had their place and they helped people to make it through the long, dark months. Sometimes the deeply religious questioned the old habits, but in an isolated community the church often learned to live with the old ways. For those who kept these traditions alive, they were talismanic, providing an ancient type of protection that helped people get through to the spring.

# Chapter 6

# *Emigration*

I t had been hard for some people to celebrate Yule as 1860 moved into 1861, for food shortages did not make for a merry time. That spring the census revealed that 380 people were now living in Fair Isle, and there were five men away at the fishing. This was a 35 per cent increase in just ten years, which everyone could see was unsustainable. In ten years another such increase would take the population to more than five hundred! Everyone was suffering from this pressure of numbers, although the people who felt the greatest pain were the landless. While all recognised the dilemma, what were poverty-stricken people supposed to do? Move? Where would they go and how would they get there?

The laird, James Stewart of Westray, died in 1858, unmarried and childless. The land was then held in family trusts, until finally Fair Isle was willed to the presbytery of the Church of Scotland in Orkney, with no real attention being made to its tenants. By now the relationship with Orkney was increasingly slender despite the fact that the people still had to pay their rents. Historically, the Orkney Stewarts' means of solving the ongoing population issue had been to encourage struggling families to move to some of their more prosperous land on Westray, or Stronsay. But in 1861 there was no word from anyone in the Church of Scotland about a reassignment of tenants and the most needy islanders were too poor to move without help. While they still had family and friends to give some fragile support, the poorest could see no option but to stay in Fair Isle.

Despite the fact that the presbytery of the Church of Scotland seemed willing to ignore the issue, there was discussion by the authorities in Shetland when they received the census results and realised that the situation was now critical. Worthies from the Church of Scotland and John Bruce of Sumburgh, the son of a wealthy Shetland landowner, met to discuss what could be done to enable the people of Fair Isle to avoid a crisis. This involvement was not entirely altruistic, since paupers who might move to the Shetland mainland might become a call on the local Poor Law funds, a fact of interest to anyone who paid the Poor Law rate in Shetland. It has to be said that Scottish Poor Law relief at that time was meagre and harshly meted out, at a lower rate even than that accorded to the poor in England.

When the potato blight came to Scotland, lessons learned from the Irish tragedy had helped to prevent great loss of life. Whereas in Ireland up to one million people died, in Scotland the population was not left to starve and relief funds were set up to collect donations. Cash came from a range of charities, religious and secular, along with individuals motivated by the popular Romantic Movement to feel inspiration for all things Scottish. Important people like Sir Walter Scott and Queen Victoria encouraged the establishment to support the cause and, naturally, many Scottish emigrants contributed. The Central Board for Famine Relief was set up to administer the resulting funds and this quickly divided into two sections, each of which was allocated responsibility for different parts of the country. The Edinburgh board included the Northern Isles in its remit and John Bruce played an important part in ensuring that aid was brought to Shetland during this time.

Sadly, since many board supervisors knew little about the lives of the poor in rural Scotland, they were not particularly sympathetic either to highlanders, or islanders. Views ranged from those who felt that such people simply needed to be more industrious, to others who thought that they were racially inferior. While there were some who delivered the assistance in a kindly manner, others were less than sensitive in their philanthropic efforts. This charity tended to be minimal and often required recipients, starving people, to do a day's work in return for their small bag of meal. When the worst of the famine was over, the board continued to help people in rural areas, particularly those places where life appeared to be no longer economically viable. Subsistence farming had become a problem throughout the Highlands and Islands, as the population grew beyond the ability of the land to support growing families. Fair Isle was not alone in its suffering.

One saving grace was the newly formed Free Church of Scotland. The Disruption of 1843 resulted in a new 'free' church breaking away from the established church, producing a group of new, passionate, evangelical ministers. They were willing to question the status quo and keen to find answers to the many problems that plagued northern areas of the country. While some established churchmen had become less sensitive to the physical needs of their flock, many of these new men were pleased to become involved in the lives of the poor. With a burgeoning Scottish population, during a time of momentous economic and agricultural change, there were more than enough people on the fringes of society in need of their help. One of the more popular ideas that gained credence was to help desperate people to emigrate, since many who wished to change their circumstances in this manner did not have the means to do so.

The Free Church supporters threw themselves behind the idea of funded emigration for entirely the best of reasons. It was not to be forced on people, but offered as a practical solution for those who were desperate. This was not coerced emigration by absentee landlords, with the motive of changed land use that occurred in some areas of Scotland. The objective here was to offer the poor, the children of the poor, orphans, unmarried mothers and other needy groups, the ability to join wealthier Scots who were choosing to seek a better life somewhere else. For many, it was sufficiently challenging simply to move to the south of Scotland or England, but others were willing to seek opportunities much further away. With the New World crying out for settlers, it was thought sensible to give the poor a chance to flourish elsewhere. America, Canada, Australia and New Zealand were primary targets.

With the possibility of external funding from the Board in Edinburgh, talks about a large Fair Isle emigration scheme were initiated, both in Edinburgh and Shetland. With guaranteed funding in place, John Bruce the Younger of Sumburgh agreed to visit the isle with the proposal in 1861. The Board of Supervisors would assist 100 adults to emigrate to New Brunswick in Canada, travelling as a group. Two children would count as one adult when families came to work out the detail of the numbers. The islanders themselves could choose to leave or stay, but they were asked to appoint a leader to act as an intermediary with the authorities. Fares would be paid and on arrival at New Brunswick, each adult would receive ten shillings (and each child five shillings) to help them to begin their new lives in Canada.

This news caused many a sleepless night in many a box bed, as people tossed and turned, weighing up the opportunities for success or failure. Despite their poverty, most rural Scots were passionately attached to their land. All were aware that there was no guarantee of success in a new land and that it would be a move from which there was little likelihood of returning. The journey itself was a huge undertaking for people who had never left their own limited environment and Fair Islanders understood better than most the dangers of a long sea voyage.

Then there was the destination and what they might expect from it. John Bruce produced a map that showed where New Brunswick was, but there was little assurance about what it would offer when they got there. They were told that it would be colder in winter and hotter in summer and the area offered opportunities in fishing, sawmills and shipbuilding. There were forests, an alien sort of environment certainly, but there was also farming and a variety of opportunities in small towns called Chatham and Bathurst.

There was a lack of certainty, but there was also the suggestion that in Canada there was the possibility for improvement.

Every family considered the move, only some more than others. People who had almost nothing to lose, particularly those with less productive land (or indeed none at all) showed most willing. Worn down by the fight to survive, some of the men believed that almost anything would be better than another winter worrying if you might starve, or lose the right to the hovel you currently rented, for rent arrears had become a recurring problem. The British and Canadian governments were supporting the offer so they would be made welcome, surely. How could a father face hungry children when he had the chance to improve their lot? For some it was not a problem, simply an opportunity.

Since the loss of so many people would cause prodigious change, the topic was on everyone's mind. Overnight, the island would lose one third of its population! Even those not tempted to go found the topic absorbing. Some people could not sleep for excitement while others lived in a constant whirl of indecision. Older folk felt the everlasting dread that their son, their daughter or their grandchild would make that final goodbye.

Jeannie Wilson wondered if any of her brood would go, but she kept her own counsel. The decision was for the young, not old bodies like her. Lowry was the most likely, but of late he had seemed quite settled at Quoy. Then there was Jane. She had married Thomas Wilson from Springfield, Barbara's brother. Thomas was a weaver, who sometimes talked of leaving to find somewhere his skills would offer him more opportunity. She would miss Jane terribly. William, her third son, already lived in South Shields. He had written once to say he was marrying and a second time to tell of a child. Then there was only the occasional, very short letter. William had never been much of a writer. He was a memory, one to be cherished and mourned and she never thought to see him again and now Jerry was talking of joining him when he was old enough. So when the subject of emigration arose, Jeannie said nothing. She did not want to stop the young ones from improving themselves, even if she dreaded them leaving. She wanted the best for them all and if that meant leaving Fair Isle, she must simply live with it.

Jeannie herself would stay on the island till she died, for John would never leave Taft and she would always have a place with him, a certainty that she cherished. She was fifty-five now, not really an old buddy, but old enough. Aggie, James and Stewart were too young to go, so she could be sure of keeping them for a while, but she sympathised with all who worried that their children might leave. Every weekend when the Methodist families gathered for their meetings the subject dominated the conversation before and after the services. No doubt she was not the only one who always had it on her mind, rather than concentrating on words from the Good Book.

When the decision was made, there was not a single Wilson on the departure list. It had long been rumoured that the Wilsons kept all the best land to themselves and this might well have been the evidence to support that claim. Laurence Johnston, the new teacher, set about vaccinating all the emigrants for smallpox and by the spring of 1862, 137 adults and children were ready to leave. Things would never be the same again. When a third of a population leaves such a small place on the same day, those who are left are destabilised. If so many can leave on one day, why should more not leave the next? Mass emigration is not a simple activity.

Of those who were leaving, the children were aware only of the greatness of the adventure, while older folk who had decided to go with their families were quite dazed. For everyone, there was a panic of preparation. Luggage had to be found or made, to take what few clothes and possessions these folk had, so the men built kists, identified a few tools, fishing lines and bits of ironmongery that they thought might be useful and made sure they had a good pair of shoes. They then set about selling their animals, all trying to get the best price, since every single penny would be useful in the new land.

The men mainly worried about their ability to support themselves. It is as well that they did not know that in the New Brunswick newspapers some of the existing residents were worried about such a large influx of poor people who lacked formal skills. They are coming to a town, some of the Canadians said, not at all the right environment for country folk. New immigrants should be young, they said, with skills to bring to Canada. They were not at all sure that they wanted poverty-stricken families with no skills to offer except as fishermen.

For the women, the business of preparation involved a lot of worry about clothes. Poor they might be, but they wanted to appear as well presented as possible. Even those who had not had a new dress for more years than they could remember made efforts to improve their wardrobe, and many Shetland people, including the inhabitants of Lerwick and Bressay, collected money to assist the travellers. It seemed important that the people of Fair Isle should not arrive as absolute paupers.

The sewing served as a distraction, as those who were leaving were aided by those who were not. Knitters worked as hard as seamstresses, for most wanted to offer a useful remembrance to friends and family they would never see again. Finally, there were some extra clothes to pack in the women's kists and, of course, their knitting wires, belts and wool, along with small bits of china, porridge spurtles, darning mushrooms, needles, threads and buttons; anything that might be useful in this unknown abyss into which they were about to jump. Some persuaded husbands to pack pots and pans along with spinning wheels and hand carders, for they could not imagine life without their wool industry.

Emigrating can be wonderful, but no one will deny that the departure day is always quite desperate. The boat that finally came to take the families from the island was ironically called the *No Joke*, a small vessel that was quite inadequate for such a large number of passengers and their belongings. It had been understood that it would make two journeys, but when he arrived the captain announced that all must travel at once. The ship would now be overloaded. More than familiar with the ways of the sea, some of the men wondered if they would even make the first leg of the journey to Kirkwall, but by now they were resigned to their fate. If it was meant, it would be.

Over the slow course of that final morning, families of Stouts, Mathers, Irvines, Browns, Leslies and Williamsons all made their way on board. They were taken to the ship in yoals by the men who were remaining. George Irvine of Greenaby was under particular pressure, since not only was he taking his wife and five children, but he had been appointed spokesman, a role which seemed to mean that he was expected to answer everyone's questions about anything. People who had no part to play in the departure stood along the line of the shore watching from different vantage points. It was pitiful to see families making what they knew would be their last farewell, with mothers, sisters and grandmothers crying freely. These were people you had known all your life and many were relations, so that even the men found themselves at first choked with emotion and then finally with tears running down their leathered faces. No one could fail to be moved as they listened to and watched the personal grief of so many and it all hurt more than anyone had imagined. Women on the shoreline sobbed, aware of each different individual tragedy as it was enacted before them. Some of the old folk had to be supported where they stood. It was quite awful.

Yoal after yoal made its way out to the ship, men heaving up kists, parcels and children, along with women encumbered by long skirts and a need for decency. Few of these women had ever left the island before and this hideous scene was not what they had expected. When finally they were under way, they wept unrestrainedly, trying to keep their eyes on family and friends as they disappeared into the distance, imprinting this final image on their minds for the rest of their lives. Given the slightest chance, some who were leaving would have changed their minds and stayed. Blinded by tears, those left behind waved and waved till the ship was a mere speck on the horizon. Old folk were helped home. There was a terrible, awful sense of loss amongst those who had been deprived of family.

Once the emigrants arrived in Kirkwall, the excitement of disembarkation into a town (albeit a small town) and the counting of all their packages, kists and children on the quayside was the first step to recovery. For the young, sorrow was already less acute and they began to realise that an adventure had begun. Just thirty miles from home there was so much to see that was different, so that excitement soon overcame some of the pain of separation. A sense of fun and adventure that was quite alien to the adults' normal lives began to take over. By the time they boarded the *Prince Consort* for Granton, near Edinburgh, they had left more of their sorrow behind and here there was a much bigger town to absorb, one with tall buildings, huge ships and seemingly endless numbers of people. From Granton they travelled to Glasgow, where they boarded the *Olympia* and faced the final leg of their journey to New Brunswick. By now all were tired and inspired by the new experiences.

Since more than half the passengers on board the *Olympia* were Fair Islanders, people felt confident and supported on the voyage. For those normally denied any formal medical support, they were impressed that a qualified surgeon was accompanying the ship. Emigrating was perhaps not such a difficult endeavour as they had imagined. The journey was long and tiring and the food must indeed have been poor, for written complaints were made about lukewarm tea, cold, salty soup and small portions.

The success of the event was glowingly reported in the *Edinburgh Review*, but in New Brunswick opinions were still divided about the reception required by such a large, poverty-stricken group. They were at first held in quarantine in St John's old Poor House and then the local St Andrew's Society, and some Presbyterian ministers came to their aid for they needed help to find their feet. The essential problem was that £52-10s was hardly enough to settle 137 people in a new land, and there had not been enough thought given by those who had arranged the journey to what happened once the group arrived.

A charitable collection of clothes and other items was felt to be necessary and the New Brunswick government was persuaded to donate £100. The New Brunswick *Morning Freeman* reported that '*These Fair Isle emigrants are very poor and the Glasgow paper properly described the women and children as emaciated looking. They appear to be intelligent and gentle but they require counsel, direction and aid.*'

This the people received from Scottish Canadians, but there must have been some distress during these early days.

For some of those they left behind, the departure was a day of opportunity. It is said that no fire was allowed to go out in any house that was vacated, for their homes were quickly taken over by those in need of the space, which was in truth the purpose of the enterprise. But for those with nothing to gain, it was a day of personal loss that would remain with them for the rest of their lives. At first there were letters telling of new land, new experiences and new lives. Eventually there was less contact and the letters spoke of children they would never know and places they would never see.

They were all incredibly positive. When you have made the effort to leave, you justify this by overcoming any doubts you might have, the homesickness and setbacks that are part of any new life. Emigrants are famed for their ability to send only good news and after a while there were lots of exciting new experiences to report. They had been taken to different towns, much further apart than many had imagined so that they lost contact with some of their old neighbours once they arrived. Most discovered some Scots in their new locations, people with similar habits, religious beliefs and expectations, folk who were happy to welcome and support newcomers from 'the old country'.

The women wrote home about roomy wooden houses with hardwood floors and no animals kept indoors to dirty them. They all had iron cook-stoves with chimneys to keep out the smoke. There was food in abundance in the Promised Land, including many things they had never seen before, like sweet corn, beets, green peas and red cabbage. Buckwheat, they found, made a very acceptable alternative to bere. Gardens grew in such abundance that in the autumn you could hardly pick the quantity of produce. Canned goods were available in the stores. Canned goods! Want and discomfort, it appeared, were things of the past in Canada.

The men told of a regular weekly wage, one that they could spend as they wished, even if it was largely spoken for before they got home on payday. Many of them worked around the ports as fishermen, or in lumberyards. Some were saving to set up farms. Land here was cheap and in some parts of Canada they heard it was free! They spoke of fishing for Atlantic salmon for their families, not for the laird. There were hunting trips that provided a multitude of game for the pots. There were folk from many lands in New Brunswick, including black slaves who had escaped from America and French folk with entirely different ways. Canada was exotic and all had work and security. At any rate, no one came home.

The emigrants forgot to mention the cold, hard winters and the oppressive heat of summer, when the stove was a hindrance rather than an asset. They didn't tell of the flies, beetles, moths and ants that came with the territory, for people were not the only things to flourish in summer heat. There were other minor irritations in their new lives, although seldom alluded to, for when you emigrate you have to justify giving up the past. You do this by completely embracing your new and perfect life when you write home.

Letters were always widely read, handed from relative to friend, to be worn thin as the years passed. Over time many more people would emigrate, not only to Canada but also to America, New Zealand and Australia. Emigration became a constant dribbling drain, resulting in a stream of letters that continued to unbalance the status quo.

Life was better for most of those who stayed behind, if only because there was less pressure on the land and more crofts to go round. Men like Lowry Wilson were thrilled that they could for the first time fulfil their desire to be head of their own house, even if this new croft came with a tiny parcel of land. Despite the fact that having your own hearth was an improvement, this was still a central fire on the ground in a house with no chimney, no running water and no sanitation. The byre was still an opening off the front door, with a rank dung heap piled outside.

Elsewhere, people were improving their lot. In the occasional newspaper that made its way to the isle there were stories of the common man fighting for his rights, from the factory floor in Manchester to the American Civil War. But in Shetland nothing seemed to change. You continued to be tied to a master who regulated how you earned, how you were paid and how you bought the necessities of life. Once a year in May the factor told you what you had earned and what you owed the laird for rent and purchases during the last year. This was the only month in the year when you might see cash for your efforts. And there again, you might not. Too often you suspected you were being deceived and that the landlord was nothing more than a racketeer, but you were powerless. The men did not have paper records about the fish they landed and some did not document what they bought from the laird's store. After all, not everyone could read and write. Thus it was quite possible for a tenant to show no reward at all for an entire year's work when the year's accounts were read out to him. To break even was a sort of success, but hardly an ambition. The arrangement was not exactly slavery, but neither was it exactly freedom.

Much of Shetland remained an almost cashless society at this time, its people bound by the disadvantageous truck (barter) system that the landlords controlled. You fished for the landlord, you paid your rent to him in produce and you bought from his shop, settling up at the end of a year. Since money was not exchanged and good records were not kept, it was difficult to estimate the value of your work or produce. Proprietors disallowed any access to a free market, where a tenant might obtain a better price for produce. You were also required to sell your cattle or sheep through this system, which extended even to the knitting, when the laird could access this.

In Lerwick, merchants would offer at least some of the value of any knitting brought to them by local women for goods or tea, rather than cash. During the 1860s, as the power of advertising increasingly made itself felt, the 'curiously knitted goods' from Fair Isle became popular elsewhere in the country, though how much of this came from the island is difficult to gauge. Shetland women had their own skills, producing fine, intricate lace shawls, but Fair Isle emigrants had taken their accomplishments with them, continuing to make and sell 'Fair Isle' garments and handing on their techniques to others. Tea had become a regular type of payment, indeed a form of coinage for Shetland's poor, for the women were usually paid at least in part in tea, which they then used or bartered. The issue was that if coin of the realm was not given, it could not be freely used which, by the 1860s, was an outdated, unfair system in Great Britain. For many years the topic of truck had been decried in parliament. Laws had been passed to outlaw its use, but decisions made in London took a long time to percolate this far north and without pressure, those in power in Shetland did not feel the need to change.

In Fair Isle, the power allocated to the Wilson family became an increasing irritant to many. In the 1861 census, the Wilsons made up 26 per cent of the island's inhabitants, but when no Wilson joined the New Brunswick exodus they then made up 41 per cent of the population. Wilsons tended to intermarry and almost all were Methodists, adding another level of suspicion to the mix. When two religious groups live in such close quarters, one will always suspect the other of ploys to further their own ends. Not only did they worship separately, both the Church of Scotland and the Methodists recognised fast days, where prayer was embraced and work eschewed. Clearly, if these were not on the same day and one group had to watch the other fishing when the sea was bountiful, irritation was rife. Even when there were common fast days, one group of men from 'the other side' might be tempted to abandon their fast to take advantage of God's bounty, encouraging more negative feeling. Of course, the main problem came not from religion, but rather that these people met and gossiped separately, often marrying within their own religious group. Because of family ties, related men usually worked together.

John Bruce senior bought the island in 1866 for, it was said, 'the good price' of £3,360, which was well over the £2,500 asking price. Interestingly, it was this man's son who was instrumental in arranging the New Brunswick emigration four years earlier. Bruce senior was a man who expected to make a profit and one imagines he was not carried away by some romantic notion when he paid quite so much for his new investment. His son, who would take over the lease from him in 1872, was already much involved in Shetland's politics. It is said that William Strong, a successful Dundee merchant whose family had historical links with the island, was extremely disappointed when he was outbid at the sale and it was felt that life could have been easier under his lairdship. Although Fair Isle might have been viewed as a Victorian status symbol, the Bruce family does not give the impression of being over sentimental. For the islanders, the initial effect of new ownership was that old ties with Orkney were supplanted by new ties to Shetland. In his initial efforts to improve his purchase, Bruce set about increasing the storage area for dried fish and building a goods store, from which he sold staples to islanders.

Initially, the tenants saw little immediate change in their daily lives. There was still the fishing with all its different stages and there was the land, which required attention from the spring to autumn. The animals still had their needs, along with the grain mills, the ditches and the croft houses, which required to be examined every summer so that they could be returned to a state that would survive the next winter. Even the new homes that were built after the land was planked in 1845 needed to be examined, for they were known to be 'imperfectly built of stone and clay', so that rain and strong winter winds damaged and penetrated croft house walls and roofs.

New turf roofs were required every few years. A special spade was used to cut the turf so that roof turves were shaped thicker in the middle, to allow them to over-lap cleanly and smoothly, preventing gaps. When the turves (or pones) were finally laid on either side of the croft house roof, a further layer of coping turves was set down along the roof ridge. All this had to be done with great skill and care so that the structure would cast as much of the rain to the ground as was possible. Men twisted two-strand, straw simmens (ropes), many metres of which were needed to help in the construction of a roof. Bundles of straw were laid on top of the turf pones and twisted into a good shape so that the rain could run smoothly off. A wooden smoke hole was carefully worked into this, while more rope and long wooden pins held the whole creation in place.

Finally, thatch was cut, trimmed and tucked in at the thick gable edge of the roof and then heavy stones were slung over the top. These held the straw down during winter gales and were slung carefully along the ridge from a variety of long and short ropes. It took three men and a boy some days to complete a new roof, but it was vital work if families were to survive the winter. Some were more skilled than others at this craft, but all fit men had a part to play once it was decided that the current roof would not last another winter. It was a regular and time-consuming task.

*Chapter 7*

# *Jeannie's Dilemma*

James Cheyne had retired as Fair Isle's teacher in 1853. His son, who had trained as a tailor in Aberdeenshire before deciding to teach there, now returned to the island to take over his father's job. By this time not only was the population growing and the number of children multiplying, but the cramped school building was beginning to show signs of age. For some reason James Cheyne junior did not settle, moving to Foula in 1862 and taking his newly widowed father with him. Since Cheyne did not settle on Foula either, it may be that he was not suited to teaching. He then moved to Edinburgh, where he reverted to tailoring.

The new schoolteacher, Laurence Johnston, was not in the least impressed by the physical condition of either the school or his living quarters and thus he did not tarry. '*The accommodation is unacceptable*,' he wrote to his employers in explanation of his departure. The Scottish Society for the Proliferation of Christian Knowledge was still in charge of the island's teachers and their remuneration at this time. They replaced Laurence Johnston with the Reverend John Craig, who also wrote to the society to complain about the lack of teaching accommodation, before leaving. The school was officially suppressed in 1864.

A new teacher/missionary was dispatched in 1866, the Reverend Andrew MacFarlane. The SSPCK school inspector, John Kerr, visited Fair Isle that same year and reported to his superiors that the school was in ruins and had been disused for sixteen months at least. Kerr found the islanders to be in a poor state, the children badly clothed and the women thin and particularly sickly. Given such poverty, it was difficult to assess the extent to which parents could send their children to school for any great period of time, although without a school, it was difficult to see how any teaching could be done. Kerr's 1867 report on Shetland's schools stated that Fair Isle still lacked a school and fifty children there were in need of education. What he refrains from saying is that by this time the factor, Jerome Wilson, had taken over the schoolhouse as his home. Clearly, without both a school and suitable accommodation for a teacher, it was necessary to reconsider the teacher's position in Fair Isle.

The Reverend Andrew MacFarlane was finally asked to leave in 1869 and although he seems to have had little devotion to his vocation, he wrote to the SSPCK in November of that year to explain that it was too difficult for him to quit the island. He did not manage to take his leave until early in 1870, so that yet another academic year passed without much, if any, education.

In the autumn of 1870 the Reverend Alexander Arthur arrived to take up the post, reported terrible accommodation and left, despite promises from Bruce to build him a new house. Since Jerome Wilson was still living in the old schoolhouse, it seems that new teachers were expected to live in what was by now a fairly derelict Haa. Certainly, the Reverend Arthur does not appear on the 1871 census, so we know that another academic year had passed with little teaching, just at a time when the concept of universal education for Scotland was dominating the news.

Further advertisements for the job of teacher/catechist in Fair Isle were placed in the press. It is sad that the SSPCK, who had provided an acceptable level of education in Fair Isle since 1732, was unable to maintain this record at this important time. Many of the parents were extremely distressed by the fact that their children were denied the opportunity to learn skills that had been available to them, but there was nothing a mere fisherman could do to alter this situation.

Of course, fishing was for many of the boys more important than any book learning they might attain. It was a hard and difficult craft to learn and the work was arduous, even for beach boys, who split, salted and dried the fish, laying them out on a specially constructed stone beach and piling the carcases into stacks covered by hides when it rained. Their work was relentless but vital and although saithe was not a high value product, it was readily available and, more importantly, readily processed on the island. Older men on the beach boiled down fish livers, which were sold by the laird to an outside market as 'cod liver oil', whatever their origin.

As the 1860s wore on, the island continued to be a magnet for ships bent on destruction. A derelict came ashore near Malcolm's Head in 1865 with a very welcome load of timber, to be followed by the *Gazelle* in 1866, which ran aground with a full complement of crew and 310 emigrants. Fair Isle men helped the crew to undertake repairs so that the ship could continue its journey to America. The men were sent £100 by the German government to thank them for their efforts. Sometimes no discernible ship came ashore after a big storm, just a slick of pathetic detritus, strewn over large areas of sea: debris that washed towards the island's shore and then out again, as the tides decreed. At least when a wreck did come on shore there was a chance of retrieving something you could use. Bigger ships carried bigger cargoes of food and drink, and there could also be furniture, material, toys or tools, particularly if the wreck lodged itself on shore for a while. Often it was simply timber on the beach and rocky pools filled with bolts, screws or other bits of ironwork, a hint of the disaster rather than the full knowledge.

The *Lessing*, which wrecked itself on the isle on 23rd May, 1868, was, however, quite a different matter. This was an emigrant ship on its maiden voyage, carrying 465 Germans to America with a crew of twenty and a mixed cargo, and it was to cause Jeannie Wilson more heartache than anyone could have imagined. The ship's master was overconfident of his chart-reading skills, so despite a thick fog and heavy seas he sailed directly into the island at Clavers Geo at the south-west, wedging himself firmly into this deep, narrow cleft in the cliff side, from which there was no chance of escape. After the force of the collision, the passengers ran on deck to discover terrifying circumstances: tall sheer cliff sides that soared high above them and the dreadful noise of grating timbers that threatened the disintegration of the ship as the sea battered it. Once you have witnessed the fearful power of the seas around Fair Isle, you realise that even if you can swim relatively well, you stand no chance at all against such an awful force of nature. It is humbling to view from a place of safety, but quite shocking when you are at its mercy. Anyway, few of these emigrants could swim and there were many women and young children.

The crew of the *Lessing* launched boats from the stern, which were quickly demolished by the waves. A feeling of panic engulfed crew and passengers alike, for it was quite clear that they could not dislodge themselves, while the cliffs offered no landing point for even the fittest amongst them. Shouting for help seemed a useless effort, but that is what they did and when an islander heard the noise and ascertained its reason, the entire population was attracted to the cliffs above the luckless vessel. It was immediately clear to the fishermen that any attempt from the sea at the stern of the ship would result in the same misfortune that had destroyed the lifeboats. This must be a land-based rescue.

The men set off to carry yoals from South Harbour to the cliff top, which were then lowered carefully down to the beach at Hesswalls. This was an exhausting operation, contrived by stalwarts who were determined to save as many people as they could before the ship broke up, for no one knew how long it would last in its current resting place. Yoals may be light enough to be dragged up to a noost on a beach, but it is quite a different thing to carry them any distance so it took every shoulder to ensure that the task was accomplished as speedily as possible. Meanwhile, those on board the ship could only panic quietly, growing colder, wetter and more desperate by the hour. The rest of the island watched from the cliff, praying that no lives on either side would be lost.

Given the wind's strength, it was challenging to lower yoals and men safely down to the beach, but that was finally accomplished. To reach the ship the fishermen had to travel under an archway called Sheldie Cave, through which the yoals could easily manoeuvre during calm weather. This day was anything but calm, however, so that huge swells would fill the cave to the top and then foam away, leaving the men to sail through when the swell was receding. They then loaded the boats with people, waited until they assessed it was safe and rowed like blazes back through the archway, before it once more seethed full of waves. Given the size of the yoals, the force of the swell and the number of passengers to be taken off, the entire endeavour took some considerable time to complete and involved everyone on the island.

Once through Sheldie Cave and on the beach, the exhausted passengers found themselves faced with a climb up a challenging cliff face to reach safety. Like all emigrant ships there was a cross section of society on board the *Lessing* – elderly parents, pregnant women, young children and small babies, not all of whom were by now in the prime of health. Ropes were lowered and those at the top of the cliff shouted encouragement, but the fear and panic engendered by the shipwreck and the ensuing lifesaving trip in the yoal, ensured that the most frail were in shock by the time they reached safety. By now both islanders and new arrivals were wearied, but even this was hardly the end of the affair. A crew of twenty and 465 emigrants had to be taken to safety, found accommodation and in some cases given rudimentary health care. Yet Fair Isle hardly had sufficient room for its own inhabitants. Few crofts boasted extra space, but everyone was wet and shocked to varying degrees, so all must be made (and kept) warm and dry. More importantly, on an island where food supplies were not abundant by the spring, five hundred additional mouths had to be fed. It seemed like an impossible predicament.

Yet the elders of the community rose to the challenge with remarkable ingenuity. The yoals were carried back to South Haven and one crew was chosen to make the trip to Shetland as soon as the weather subsided. In the meantime, everyone else on the island who could make a bit of space did so; the very old, and young mothers with babies and young children being the primary targets for shelter. There were also the injured, who needed a little more care whatever their age. Shock was one of the most pressing problems, accelerated by the fact that for the emigrants, English was not their first language. Whatever progress they had made in assimilating this new tongue for use in America, Fair Islanders spoke a dialect that was difficult to align with what they had learned. Communication was an added difficulty on a day that already had sufficient problems.

Every building on the island, including the church and chapel, was pressed into use and every stock of food decimated. The factor shared out all that was available in the laird's store, but this was hardly sufficient for such an influx. Luckily, the weather subsided the following day and a yoal was sent for help. Outbuildings were filled with folk and for those denied the shelter of a building, tents were fashioned from old sails attached to the sides of buildings. Finally, some sort of covering was found for everyone. Toilet areas were marked out. Sheep were slaughtered, fires were lit and all who were mobile were sent to scavenge round the coast for firewood. The men and boys took some of the visitors with them to search for birds.

As soon as the yoal arrived at Lerwick, the schooner *Ariel* was sent back with supplies. The *Ariel* gradually took passengers off, over a period of several days and by the 4th of June all the newcomers were gone. The city of Bremen, from whence the emigrants came, was grateful and sent £100 in thanks, to be distributed among the poor of the island at the laird's discretion. The laird decreed that the men and the boys should share the money, excluding the widows and spinsters who had carried children from the beach and provided food and shelter in their homes.

At Taft and Quoy, as elsewhere, women had worked extremely hard. Beds had been given up, treasured sheets torn into strips for bandages and every scrap of food used to keep people alive. Jeannie Wilson was one of the many island ladies sufficiently roused to write and complain that the women's efforts were not recognised. After all, it would fall on women's shoulders to replace the sheets and food so that families could return to normal. This was, however, still a time when equality of effort was dismissed, as was their claim. There is no evidence that the men and boys felt under any pressure to share their spoils, not even with the widows.

But the fallout from the *Lessing* was far greater than an unfair distribution of rewards. The wreck was advertised in newspapers and a sale was duly held in Fair Isle, where Williamson of Lerwick bought the ship for salvage. The laird, through his factor, let it be known that he had imposed a condition on the sale that no local labour could be employed on the wreck. Thus local men, who had risked their lives to save the emigrants, were now forced to watch outsiders making cash out of what they regarded as 'their' wreck. Despite the laird's ruling, many men and boys offered themselves up for hire at one time or another, while some did so regularly.

One of those to renege was Thomas Wilson of Springfield, the weaver husband of Jane Wilson, Jeannie's daughter. Thomas normally augmented his weaving earnings by working on the beach and doing other jobs for Bruce, as the factor instructed. He was always looking for additional work and did not feel that his relationship with the master prevented him from working at the *Lessing*. However, Jerome Wilson, who was currently the master's voice on the island, said that anyone who worked for Williamson would be asked to leave and made it quite clear that all Fair Isle men were forbidden to work for him. With such temptation in such a close community, he felt that he ought to show no weakness, lest everyone stop fishing completely.

"But I wanted to work for him, and I did," Thomas was to say later. It was a simple issue for the weaver, who felt he was a free man since he was not a fisherman and his only responsibility to the master was to pay his rent and look after his family. The *Lessing* work would help him to do this. He was young, and with a wife and family he had ambition.

His punishment was to have some of his beach boy earnings for the year withheld, so that despite having earned the sum of £5-15s from beach work, he was only paid £3. For Thomas, this was the final straw. Life on the island was hard enough, without losing earnings which were your due, so he now felt that it was time to look for employment elsewhere.

Thomas had taken in two Shetland men as lodgers when the *Lessing* was stripped and discovered from them that Williamson, who had bought the wreck, would sell him meal much more cheaply than he could buy it at the master's shop. On all sides, Thomas felt he was being hounded by the laird, so he made up his mind to leave Fair Isle and seek work somewhere else.

Lowry, brother of John Wilson of Taft, was not exactly a firebrand but he had become increasingly outspoken about the unfairness of life under the laird. Despite any progress that he and Ann had made, still he was unable to make any real difference to their standard of living. So Lowry, too, decided that he was not going to pass up the chance to earn real money when fate landed the *Lessing* in his back yard. However, unlike Thomas the weaver, Lowry was a fisherman and bound by the rules of his lease. He insisted that when he went to work for Williamson it was at a time when there was not much work at the fishing. Indeed, he was not fishing for Williamson. He said that there was nothing in his lease preventing him from working on the wreck, only Bruce's desire that he should not. He was the first of the fishermen to take regular work from Williamson and the first to earn a daily wage.

Those who were not quite as brave hesitated, but were nevertheless jealous of the fact that he was earning cash while they were not. Others joined Lowry, at least for some of the time. Thus, those who went fishing got full recognition of their catches, but others got cash for each day's work and people doubted if their alleged recognition for a day's catch was equal to Williamson's daily rate of pay. After all, no one really knew what a day's fishing brought them at the end of the year. Gradually, more men were tempted to join the rebels. In the end many men worked on the *Lessing* irregularly, while some worked more than others. Lowry and Thomas had become the focus of a small revolt.

From this time, everyone Lowry met as he went about his business told him he would be warned off his croft. The factor had written to Bruce, he was told. The factor was writing to tell him to leave, he was told. The factor would be round tomorrow with the paperwork. Ann became a nervous wreck, waiting at every creak of the door for Jerome to appear, shaking his fist. John came up from Taft to try to get Lowry to consider his position. Was it worth risking all for a few days' gain? Lowry sent him on his way. He was his own man now, not his brother's junior.

But the incident of the *Lessing* drove home the extent to which they did not control their lives. The Shetland incomers had been openly shocked at the price of the few staples that were kept at the local shop. Lerwick was supposed to be dear, they said, but it was infinitely cheaper than the Fair Isle store. So when Thomas decided that he would leave in the spring of 1869, it only took a few days for Lowry to announce that he would join him. The factor did not tell them to leave their crofts, but since the pressure of rumour had pushed open the door, escape they would. All questioned their decision, but such questions only strengthened their resolve. Ann was happy enough to take her chance with Lowry and although Jane worried more about leaving her family, she felt that her husband was right. Anyway, they were not the first islanders to go to Kirkwall, although this combined decision to leave set off arguments throughout the isle. It was always thus when people moved away. Those left behind felt insecure and obliged to justify why they accepted the status quo. Those who decided to leave became increasingly sure they would find a promised land. Such conflict does not make for a tranquil life.

Jeannie found herself listening to all the arguments with dismay. Was it better for Jane and Lowry to leave, or to stay? Everyone shared their views with her at the least opportunity. It seemed as if no one spoke of anything else as soon as she put her head round the door. John, who increasingly saw himself as a man of consequence, continued to advise Lowry to be cautious. Although he could see his brother's point of view, he would never jeopardise his relationship with the laird for a pipe dream.

Lowry made it clear that he wanted more for his family, emphasising that this was 1869 and there wasn't even a decent school for his children. For a while the two men argued whenever they met, but finally they agreed to differ, for their mother's sake. Jeannie was upset enough at losing Jane, Lowry and the grandchildren without John falling out with any of them. John set about making Lowry a kist for some of his belongings, to show there was no ill feeling.

Although she understood, Jeannie was bereft. They were only going to Kirkwall, they told her. They might as well be going to London she said, for she would never travel to Kirkwall to visit them. It had all been going too smoothly. Barbara had proved to be a lovely girl to live with, one who worked hard and produced another child every couple of years. She included her mother-in-law in any decisions around the croft, so that Jeannie felt that Taft was still her home.

Although she had been spared when none of them went to New Brunswick, Jerry had left to join his brother in England and last year Stewart took himself off to Canada. There had been a letter from a place called Sault Saint Marie and then only irregular correspondence. Stewart had always been unsettled. Jeannie sighed when she thought of Stewart. She had tried to do her best for them all, but with him, perhaps she could have done a little more. Now she was to lose two more of her children. She understood why they were leaving, but understanding didn't help her at all. What was the point of learning to love all these new grandchildren if they were just to be taken away from her?

A black cloud descended on Taft as she tried to get through the days. Certainly she still had three children here, John, Agnes and young James, but in the silence of the night she wept quietly. John was annoyed at all the upset, but could think of nothing to help her. The atmosphere at Taft became thick with dissent and sadness. Thomas was Barbara's brother, so she too was distressed, as were her parents.

Then it got harder. Jeannie's daughter Aggie had married Willie Stout and when he put his head round the door one night, Jeannie knew without asking what it was he had come to say. His face spoke for him. He could barely look her in the eye as he stood there like a delinquent child. Aggie had not dared come to her. She knew what all this was doing to Jeannie, but her place was to follow her husband. The man wanted to better himself, he told his mother-in-law. As Jeannie sat in her chair, poker faced, Willie continued to stand in front of her, twisting his hat in his hands and looking for the right words, all the while sweating under his jacket, since he had put on his Sunday clothes for this task. He could not find anything to say that would help, however. Willie had to tell his own family next and had started with Jeannie, thinking that this would be easier. He was either wrong, or his day was about to get much worse. Telling Jeannie made him feel like a traitor. But going as a group to Kirkwall meant that the family would help each other till they got settled and Aggie would have her sister and brother nearby. As he saw it, they could only improve themselves. But he wished it wasn't so hard on his mother-in-law. He could see she was taking it badly. God alone knew what his own mother would have to say.

John too heard him out, then cleared his throat to make a pronouncement when Willie finally ground to a halt, but Jeannie made him silent with one biting look and a commanding lift of her hand. She would have no interference from him, no religious platitudes and certainly no false hopes for the future. The man was only doing what he thought was best by his family. That was his right. She was to lose three of her children and so many grandchildren. Well, if she was a young one with a family she too might grab at a chance somewhere else. The good Lord knew that things here left an awful lot to be desired.

So Jeannie's world turned upside down and for once John was sensitive enough to let her be. Finally she rose, unable to speak or to make any noise that would disturb the silence that filled the room. She felt all eyes on her, but if she tried to say anything it would come out as a wail. Patting Willie on the arm to show that she was not angry with him, she took herself to bed, shoulders drooping under the weight of this new burden. As she climbed in, her stomach turned and she felt quite sick as her mind tried to absorb this dreadful reality. She had borne all these children just to lose them. However much she understood the reasons, it would still hurt terribly never to see any of them again. It had been a privilege to teach the peerie girls to knit the complicated patterns now she had time to be patient when they dropped stitches and made mistakes with the counting. Well, this privilege she would lose. Three of her boys had already left and she had lost any chance of seeing either their children, or their wives. Now she would lose her girls, her beloved girls, as well as Lowry. All she would have was Taft and James, with John and his family to keep them company. Perhaps she was selfish, but it didn't seem enough.

The next morning she rose with only hard and terrible thoughts in her head. Nothing Barbara could say diminished her dreadful feelings of despair, but she felt sorry for the lass. Barbara was doing her best, but there was nothing that anyone could say that could possibly lift her spirits. The chores took a long time and Jeannie found herself snapping at the girl for no reason at all, until eventually you could cut the atmosphere with a knife. They all tried to ignore the spectre in the corner, but the day was going to be long if no one did anything to make it better.

It was Jeannie who relented first. She stood up and packed her knitting. "I'm off to see Aggie at Brews," she announced. "The walk will do me good, and you will benefit from my absence. I'm sorry to be so upsetting, but I'm fair higgered by it all. I don't know where to put myself. Maybe Aggie will help. We've seen a lot of bad days through together, my sister and me. At least you'll get a rest from my ill feeling."

"Take your time, Mither. I understand. John doesn't really understand, but I do, truly. I look at mine and wonder what they will do and what I will feel if they go away. I can't imagine it, so I can't see what to say that will help you. But children leaving is going to be the thing, unless something changes life here. It's so sad for you though."

"Lassie, on this island the women are meant to weep. If I know anything, I know that. I've wept for my parents, my husband and my children, not to mention a whole lot of other folks as well. I've sat through illness, blight, death, shipwrecks and shortages. I keep telling myself it will get better, but if this is better, I'm not sure we should not all get up and leave the place tomorrow. Och, I'll be back by the evening. Hopefully I'll be in a better mood."

And with that she made her way up to see Aggie. Sometimes she felt that her sister was now the rock that kept her from foundering. With time, their roles had altered, so that it was increasingly Jeannie who leant on her sister. They had been through so much together, losing their mother and then their husbands, worrying over their children, sharing their food, and looking after their father before he died. Aggie understood. Her second marriage had not been easy, because they had Brews with almost no land and Willie's youngsters took some time to get used to both her and Williamina. Then there had been three new children to find a place for, so Aggie struggled. She was sure that talking to Aggie would help.

But Aggie was no comfort at all. She made it quite clear to Jeannie that this was not the end of the world. Nobody was ill. Nobody had died. Nobody was starving. Kirkwall was not a million miles away. True, neither of them had ever been there, but it was not a million miles away. And the children would have a better chance surely, better than they had here. There wasn't even a school here on a regular basis. They all knew now that things were changing elsewhere, but in Fair Isle things never changed. What's more, Aggie and Willie were going too.

The silence in the room halted Jeannie in her tracks. She should have realised immediately. Aggie too had avoided eye contact. Aggie had been waiting for her. Her sister's diatribe continued. Now that their father was dead there was nothing to tie her to the island. She and Willie had three lots of children. It was not a big family, but she wanted better for them than the life she had here, never knowing if they would eat from one week to the next, never knowing if the children would learn to read and write. She couldn't afford even a candle some of the time and she was sick of trying to keep the children shod and covered on a pittance. It never got any easier. Did she want Williamina to marry a fisherman who would die like John and Willie? No she did not.

Both of them were in tears at the end of all this, for Aggie had run out of ammunition and courage in equal measure. She felt that she was letting Jeannie down, but Willie had persuaded her that it would be the right thing and when he spoke of it, the idea had simply seemed entirely logical. Now it seemed like betrayal.

Jeannie sat pole-axed. Never for a single moment had she expected this. All the way up here she had been anticipating Aggie's sympathy, Aggie's support and Aggie's understanding. But she was going as well! Jeannie would be at a complete loss if Aggie left. Panic began to overtake the fear and sorrow. A week ago her position on the island had been secure. In just a few days, it was in tatters. Not since the night she heard that John had died could she remember such desolation.

"Aggie, I have to go. I need to think. I'm lost. I'm quite lost. I don't know what to think any more."

She shook off her sister's arms and pushed past her, out the door, setting off for she knew not where, wanting only to be alone to think. She felt old and abandoned. For once Aggie did not follow her. There was nothing she could say that would help. Her path was quite clear. She and Willie had to leave, whatever distress it caused her sister. If only it did not cause so much pain.

Jeannie stumbled round the track that led northwards. She needed to be alone. The last thing she wanted was to meet anyone, as she could neither carry on a coherent conversation about trivia, nor voice the unbearable thoughts that she must now endure. Jeannie needed to think. At least the day was fair she mused, as finally she found a grassy hollow out of the wind in which to encase herself. She sat deep in the corner and wrapped her shawl close to her body as she squatted, totally alone and hidden from view. It was hard to be alone on the island, but now she needed to be solitary to take all of this in. She backed into her small haven, like an animal trapped by a hunter, facing the sea and watching the waves endlessly drive towards her.

At first she wept. Then, when her face was sore and swollen, she sobbed, great racking sobs that made her feel sick. To lose so much all in one go was insupportable. The one thing you had in Fair Isle was relationships, but these would be severed when so many of her family left. How could Aggie face the challenge at her age? It's not as if Aggie was all that young, or all that brave.

On the other hand, the young were taking a chance to improve themselves. Things were never going to get better here as far as she could see. Perhaps they were right to take a chance for their children, if not for themselves. Perhaps life would be much better for them in Kirkwall. Perhaps the young had a right to expect things to be better. Who was she to deny anyone a better life?

Time passed and the day moved on. Occasionally she heard someone going about their business, but quickly drew back further into her small space to avoid detection. Jeannie felt no hunger, no cold and no consciousness of her daily routine with the family. She just tried to sort all this out in her mind, for she knew as soon as she returned to Taft, John would start to tell her what to think. With the passage of the years he had become more and more sure of his views and never held himself back from telling other people what they should think and how they should act. John did not feel he was being untoward with his judgements either. He knew what was right and it did not occur to him that other people might not appreciate his thoughts. To him, dissenters from his credo were obtuse, stupid even.

Over the years, Jeannie had begun to realise that just because he could sit and argue the scriptures with old Stewart Wilson, this did not enable him to know how other people should live their lives. Gradually, she began to understand that his arguments with Stewart were an intellectual game, one that the pair of them basked in all the more because only a few folk knew how to play it properly. But being able to play games with words was not the same as knowing how to play the game that was life, for that seemed to have no rules. Staying away from Taft and John was the only way she could work out for herself how she was going to deal with this new situation. She needed to ignore her feelings and try to understand how the young ones felt, so that she could help them with this, as she had tried to do with all their other problems. The longer she sat the calmer she became, and the calmer she became the more she could rationalise. In time, she arrived at a possible way forward, not one that resolved all the issues that so deeved her, but one that made her feel less of a victim.

Back at Taft, Barbara had become worried about the non-appearance of her mother-in-law as the day drew on. Surely there was nothing wrong, or at least nothing more than there had been this morning. It was not like Jeannie to stay away from the evening meal. Everyone else was home and had been fed, but still there was no sign of her. Although John was not really disturbed by his mother's non-appearance, James picked up Barbara's disquiet and said he would take a stroll up to Aggie's to see if his mother was ready to come home yet.

James was now a strong young man of seventeen, already working with John on the boat, but also learning from his brother-in-law Thomas about weaving. When Thomas had several orders, or was busy working for the factor at something else, James could take over. He was not sure he wanted to become a weaver full-time, since like most of the boys his age the fishing seemed a more vigorous occupation, but he liked to have another way of earning money. Now he would miss both his uncle and the extra work.

James had enjoyed an easier life than many, an upbringing slightly less severe because his father had died before he was born. The young of the island did not enjoy boots until they were older and went either bare-foot, used clogs bartered from a passing Dutch ship, or wore rivilins, home-made shoes fashioned from hide and laces. Your first pair of boots was a milestone. When James was twelve, a cousin made him his first boots and he was so enamoured that when he went to bed that night he insisted they be placed where he could see them from where he lay. Although his mother left them in his line of sight, when everyone was asleep he got up and moved them over a fraction, so that he could see them better by the light of the peat fire. Pride in his new possessions was to be his undoing for, sadly, he moved them too close to the fire and by morning one of the boots had dried out until the leather was hard as stone and quite unwearable. Any other child would have been forced to run around the isle for another year in rivilins but, like everyone else, his cousin had a soft spot for James and made him a new boot within the week. It was no more than the boy expected.

Thus he lived quite happily in Taft, his mother's favourite at all times. Being the youngest in the family was never the trial it had been to his brother Stewart, for it meant in his case more attention rather than less. Anyway, after John married there was soon another generation of young ones running around to look up to him, so that he never felt the youngest really. But he adored Jeannie and found her disappearance vaguely disquieting this evening. It was certainly no trouble for him to make his way up to his aunt's croft to see that all was well.

Once there, he knocked at the door and shouted "Hello," to whomsoever was inside, lifting the latch as he entered. "Hello there. It's me."

"Oh, James, what a relief to see you. Tell me. How is Jeannie now? I've been so worried about her since this morning. I almost came down to see her but Willie said I should leave it till tomorrow, when she would have calmed down. Is she all right?"

James was nonplussed. What on earth had happened that morning? And more importantly, where was his mother now? "I'm here to walk her home. When did she leave? We've not seen her all day. We thought she was with you. Why was she upset? What happened?"

Aggie immediately panicked, blaming her husband, since he was in the room. She had been worrying all day and she had been right. Where was Jeannie? Where could she have gone? Aggie knew she should have obeyed her instincts and taken herself down to Taft earlier. "I'm so sorry, laddie. I told your mither that we were going to Kirkwall with the rest of them and she got a bit of a shock. She just walked out. I thought she had gone home. Where on earth can she be? Willie, what's happened to Jeannie?"

The last was delivered in a frightening wail that did nothing to calm either her nephew or her husband. Willie had just come back from talking with some of his own family about leaving and had found the reaction as upsetting as he had suspected. You would think he was betraying them all, instead of looking after his own. Now there was this fuss with Jeannie Wilson to be dealt with. Sighing heavily, he got up from his chair and began to put his jacket on. Some days never seemed to come to an end.

By this time Aggie was panicking, waving her hands around distractedly and beginning to gabble, as her voice tried to keep up with her mind. "What if she's desperate? What if she's done something stupid? I should have been with her. I shouldn't have let her go off like that. I should have told her in her own house. Why did you not let me? What if she's thrown herself off a cliff!"

This last, shrilled out like a banshee, was the ultimate fear in Fair Isle, that someone might fall or let themselves fall into the sea from a cliff when they were disturbed. When people went out in a frantic state you always worried that they might not take the care they needed.

"Woman, calm yourself. A person less likely to throw herself off a cliff than your sister I've yet to meet. Aye, she'll be upset, but we're all upset just now. She'll be with someone. Stop your noise and let's just find her." Willie could see that James was becoming perturbed and wanted to calm him too. However, by now Williamina had joined his own daughters in the tumult and the younger ones had come through from the ben of the croft house to find out what the noise was about.

It was all getting like a madhouse. He had to do something for his own sanity, never mind the rest of them. "Right, Willa, you get your shawl on and get off to Springfield. You speak to the Wilsons there. Aggie, off to Leogh to ask Willie Stout if they've seen her. Andrina, away you to Lowry and Ann. She'll be with one of them, mark my words. And come back here and send word to Taft when you've found her, so we can all stop looking and I can sit in peace by my own fire. You, my lad, come with me and we'll search around in case she's just off to have a think. Aggie! Stop howling. Your sister will be fine. She's upset at the way you told her. You'd have been the same yourself. Come away everyone, let's be getting on with it."

So Willie and James set off into the darkening twilight towards the north of the island, while the girls all went running down to the southern crofts, from which tiny shafts of light were now showing in the growing darkness.

Willie tried to jolly James along, between bouts of shouting hopefully into the night. "She'll be fine, lad. I give you my word on it. Jeannie's not the type to do anything foolish... Jeannie! Jeannie!"

"Mither! Mither! Where are you?"

Their voices rose skywards until they lost themselves, gradually dissipating into nothing. Occasional birds were surprised out of roosting places and the odd sheep turned to stare, but there was no human response. Time made them anxious, so that they gradually increased their pace, stumbling and staring in the gloom until finally they heard her, a tiny voice that came from a small hiding place.

"Hello. I'm here, James. I'm here."

Suddenly, the boy could see his mother struggling to her feet out of the small corrie she had found to shield herself from the wind. At first she stumbled, for she was sorely stiff from sitting so long, but she was calm and totally in charge of herself and clearly not the desperate woman Aggie had inferred. Both men sighed with relief and then James ran up to her and hugged her off her feet until she beat him away, laughing at this unusual show of emotion. Willie, always reserved, just stood and watched, his shoulders slowly relaxing from their unnoticed tension. Thank God, was all he thought. Although he had not really believed the worst, in Fair Isle the worst was so often what you got.

"Are you all right?"

"I'm fine. I'm a bit stiff from sitting but old bones don't do so well with this sort of caper, I'm finding. Ah well, old age doesn't come by itself. Give me your arm, boy. Willie Eunson, why are you out looking for me?"

"Me! I think you'll find half the island's on your trail by now, Jeannie Wilson. Aggie got us all wound up about not knowing where you were and Barbara was quite disturbed at Taft. I imagine they'll be wound up at Springfield too, so you'll have some explaining to do when you get home. Aye, and Willie Stout and Aggie will be on the warpath as well, so you can expect a visit from them too. Wouldn't be surprised if they'd lit the beacon on Malcolm's Head to warn folk in Shetland." Willie laughed in relief that all was well.

"Aye. Well, it was a surprise to hear you and Aggie were leaving. When I found out that you two were going along with Jane and Aggie and Lowry, I just needed a bit of time to take it all in, to mull it over. I wish you all well mind, but it's a shock. It was always going to be a shock."

"Thanks, Jeannie. I know you must be upset, but I've got to take this chance for Aggie and the family. Who knows what they all might become in Kirkwall. As it is, Willa and my Aggie and Andrina will marry a lad from here, just like me, and I can't see where that's going to take them, the way things are now. Then there's young Willie. Who knows what he might be if he gets a chance. Jeannie, I'd like my son to have some options in life. We might not do any better of course, but as far as I can see, with Brews not able to support us, Aggie and I can't do much worse. God knows we all work hard enough. Honestly, have you asked yourself what all this has gotten you?"

"Aye. It's gotten me a lonely old woman, that's what it's gotten me. When you all leave that'll be the case certainly. You away to Aggie and put her mind at ease. I had no intention of upsetting her. And send word round the rest of them before I become the talk of the island. You know how much I'd hate that. This one will see me home, but we'll be slow. I'm stiff. It's terrible to be old, you know."

"You'll see a good few years yet, Jeannie Wilson. You Wilsons have to be shot before you finally lie down and die."

They all smiled at this island joke against the eternal tribe.

As he disappeared into the gathering gloom, Jeannie smiled gently at his back. "That one hasn't had to look for his troubles either. It would be a hard person who would deny him a chance to better himself. He knows I believe that. So does Aggie. It was just such a shock, coming so soon after Willie Stout. Did you know about our Aggie and Willie?"

"I'd heard that my sister might be leaving, but not my auntie. But no one was sure, so I didn't want to worry you for no reason. I know you're sad, but I'll stay with you, me and John. We won't ever leave you. Perhaps we could visit them all in Kirkwall when they are settled."

This was a slender hope, but he felt he had to offer his mother something. She was not old she told him, but she was sixty-three now and when you are seventeen, sixty-three seems very old indeed. Jeannie had worked hard to bring them all up, cleaning and cooking, working at the peats and on the land, pulling the harrow and digging the fields every year, just as all the women did. He understood a little of what she was feeling, for women like her seldom left the island. Once they left, she would never see any of her family again, so James decided he would never leave. However tempting the outside world was, he would stick here with her till she died. She deserved that at least.

"James?"

Aye, Mither."

"James, have you ever thought you might like to go to Kirkwall, like your brother and sisters?"

The boy stopped on the path and turned Jeannie round to face him. "I promised never to leave you. Don't you worry, I won't go."

"Oh, you say that, but what if I went too? Would you come with me?"

The boy halted in his tracks, not sure what it was he had heard, not sure if his mother's mind was wandering after her day on the scattald without any food. Surely an old wifie like her would not think of leaving Taft?

"What is it you're saying, mother?"

"I'm saying I think it is time for me to leave Fair Isle. I'm saying it might be time for you to leave too, and that the only thing that might be keeping you here when your brother and sisters leave is me. I've spent the day thinking about what Aggie said about all the children having a better chance in Kirkwall and about it being easier if there was a family group. Well, I'm willing to give it a try for you, James. Perhaps you could have a better future in Kirkwall. What do you think?"

The boy looked at her, making sure she was all right, hesitating for a moment to take the chance he was being offered, but only for a moment. "I'll be packing my kist tonight."

"What kist, laddie?"

"The one our John's going to make for me, though for the love of us all I can't think where I'll find enough to pack in a kist. But folk who leave always take a kist. Maybe we'll just share one. Aye, Mither, let's go to Kirkwall, and if we don't like it we can just turn around and come back again."

The light-hearted enthusiasm and innocence of youth made her smile, although she wanted him to be realistic, or as realistic as a young lad can be. He needed to think on it. Or perhaps he had been thinking on it already. Perhaps that was why his response was so sudden. Or maybe it was just that the weight of years made you over-cautious.

"Well, I want you to sleep on it anyway. It's a big move. Don't say anything to John tonight. Just think and pray, for that's what I'll be doing. I don't know how we'll manage, James, with me an old lady and you just a laddie, but we can give it a try. One of the girls will take us in at the start. What with Auntie Aggie and three of your brothers and sisters going, we won't lack relatives. So if you still want to, we'll tell John in the morning. But think seriously, mind. This is an important decision and I don't want you to regret it. Now, come on and let's get me a cup of tea. I'm fair gasping for a hot drink."

The return to Taft was emotional and noisy. Barbara was both glad to see Jeannie and sad for her new burden. Aggie going too, the sister she had loved so sincerely over the years. It would be such a wrench. Barbara fully understood why the old lady had gone missing for the day and could only sympathise and make a fuss over her.

John was surprisingly disconcerted by the news. His aunt and Willie Eunson were fine where they were. What were they thinking of at their age? All this moving was just over-reacting and silly. No wonder his mother was completely thrown. Three of his brothers and sisters leaving must have been a terrible shock. No wonder she had gone off by herself, though he hoped this was not the beginning of the senility that sometimes afflicted the old. Her eldest child saw himself as the head of a clan, but his clan was deserting him and now his mother might be losing her mind, rambling away on her own like a mad thing. It took so little to upset the equilibrium. John spent more time than usual reading the Bible that night, searching for guidance before he went to bed, hoping that it would all be resolved in the morning. His mother would just have to come to terms with her loss and the sooner the better. Earlier than usual they all retired, even though nobody slept much. Everyone in Taft had something to contemplate.

The morning did not bring resolution for John, however, for his brother and mother were up first. Jeannie looked at the boy, who nodded and smiled in response. They were going.

Jeannie decided that it was only fair to tell John immediately, so that he could deal with it as best he could. She knew it would be a shock. "John. Barbara. I want you to sit and listen for a minute. James and I have something to tell you. We are going to Kirkwall with the rest of them. James will have more of a chance there and I'll have four of my children near me, as well as my sister. I'm sorry I haven't discussed it with you. I only realised yesterday that we could go and I think it's the best thing for James."

An awful silence met her announcement. John and Barbara were flabbergasted. Jeannie leaving the island! At her age! The world had gone mad, surely. John would now be the sole member of his father's family left in Fair Isle, with no one left to lead except his own children. How had this happened? His father had built Taft and Jeannie had brought nine children into it. Now, he would be the sole remnant of the Taft Wilsons. The world was turning on its head.

～·～

"Are you sure, Mither? Are you quite sure! Have you thought this through properly? How could you of all people leave Taft?"

"Taft is your future John, not mine and certainly not James's. You have your own family to take care of now. Anyway, it's people that are important, not places or things. I'll lose you and Barbara and the children. Don't think that won't hurt, for it will. But I'll have the girls and Lowry and James and my sister and all the grandchildren. I have to think of James, you know. He's my responsibility, not yours. I think he will have more of a chance in Kirkwall and we won't be alone. My time here is finished, for I was here to support my children and your father. Well your father's dead and your brothers and sisters are leaving. You and Barbara will manage fine. Barbara's folk at Springfield will always be here for you. And you have aunts and uncles and cousins still on the island. You'll be fine, John."

James stood close to his mother, saying nothing but ready to step in if John should start to argue. This was the longest speech Jeannie had ever made and it got the respect it deserved. She had drawn herself up as far as her tiny stature allowed and her look defied John to argue. James was there to take him on if he did. He had been brought up to respect his eldest brother, but suddenly his future did not lie here. Now he was emancipated and thrilled to anticipate new and exciting prospects. James could barely contain himself. At seventeen you can take on the world. At seventeen you do not feel the ties that bind.

John, however, was not seventeen and felt every one of his thirty-nine years. It was as if he had not kept up with the future and its possibilities and now even his mother had overtaken him. Instead of being the leader, he was at the tail-end of his family, the last remnant left in Fair Isle. Out of the blue, he must now reassess his position as the family's leader. Was he wrong to stay, to try to make his own family's future here? So very recently he had no doubts, but now they were there. Now, even if he stayed in Taft until he died, it would never be the same. Without his family he would be a different person and the island a different place, so deep in his mind some doubt would always exist. It was unthinkable, but should he, too, leave?

Over the next few days he complained sporadically to Barbara, but she told him firmly that he was here to support his mother, whatever she decided, so that was what he did. Barbara seldom spoke up against him and he respected her views. She understood how difficult it was for Jeannie to leap into the unknown, but she would do the same if there was ever such a choice to be made. For James, Kirkwall would offer untold opportunities and with the rest of the family there to support them, Jeannie and James would survive. So John built a new kist for James, a small one, sufficient to the boy's needs and he gathered some of his father's old tools to add to his baggage, so that the father he had never known would in some way go with him to Kirkwall. He never voiced any thoughts of leaving himself. He could not do so.

There was much to be done and once more the women were supreme, knitting and sewing like the very devil, to ensure that those leaving would not arrive in their new town as paupers. At the last minute, Stewart Wilson of Busta, Lowry's brother-in-law, decided to take his family too. Stewart was married to Agnes, his father's youngest sister, so now John added an aunt, uncle and cousins to the litany of family members deserting him. As many noted, for the first time those leaving were mostly Wilsons. Perhaps their superiority was fading? Perhaps this was a sign of better things to come for those who stayed? Or perhaps the Wilsons were showing evidence of the perception that had guided them to better things in the past? Only time would tell, but whatever the case, their absence would be felt in many homes.

Although he had watched the people leave for Canada, it was only now that John fully understood the depth of pain you could experience. Right at the end, just when you thought it was fine and you were in control, emotion overwhelmed you. Of course the sobbing and distress of others weakened your resolve terribly, for you felt their sorrow and then added it to your own. But through all the farewells his mother maintained a stiff set smile, her shoulders firm and her head held high. Although she was scared and terribly sad, she knew where her future lay and this was a choice she had made. She would not make it worse for John and her grandchildren by crying. Her generation was made of firmer stuff, she told herself. Stewart and Hannah Wilson also stood by stoically, waving to Thomas their beloved son, along with Jane and their irreplaceable grandchildren. Barbara had her arms round her mother's waist to support her, until finally, she too was weeping and needing comfort.

As the ship that had paused to pick up the passengers finally made way, all the families stood on deck, watching and waving, unwilling to move until they lost sight of the island completely. Only then did Jeannie allow herself to cry.

James put his arm round her, just as the other men were pacifying their women folk and trying to find words that would help. "It's horrible, isn't it? It really hurts. But Orkney is not so far away and, you never know, John might be the next one to leave." James tried to sound as if he believed it.

Jeannie smiled at him through her tears. "John will never leave. You know that as well as me. He's married to Taft as much as he is to Barbara. But let's look to the new land, my boy. Let's make plans for Kirkwall. We've made our decision so let's make the best of it."

The old woman drew her coat back into order and touched her hat to make sure it was straight. "And for goodness sake try to stop Jane crying. She'll make herself ill over all this and it's upsetting the children. You come with me, young Stewart. Let's take a wander round the ship and see what there is to see, and you too Babs, come along."

Jeannie took her grandchildren by the hand and looked into the future with them. The pain might be abrasive to the soul, but Jeannie had endured worse. They must all look forward and try to make a success of Kirkwall. She would die there she supposed. It seemed strange to think of that now, but what did it matter? After all, her John wasn't buried in Fair Isle, so why should she be laid to rest there? No doubt they had graveyards aplenty in Kirkwall.

For John Wilson the summer of 1869 was one of the most difficult he would remember. He would make out a shape in the distance and respond, but just as often he was wrong. Ghosts may have remained, but the people had gone. He found it hard to take in and spent many an hour with old Stewart Wilson, talking about what had happened, trying to persuade himself it was God's will. God's will, John was now finding, was not always easy to understand.

Fewer people meant more space of course, but this time it did not result in any great improvement of opportunity. The world was changing elsewhere, while Fair Isle found it increasingly difficult to compete economically. The yoals that the men used to fish had to stay the same size, for their landing places could not entertain bigger boats without a proper harbour. Saithe remained the primary fish the islanders could sell, for they could conserve no other. Without a harbour they could not attract the newer, bigger fishing boats that could stay at sea longer and then take white fish to the mainland. Of course, herring was now the fish of choice for the poor and there were plenty of poor out there ready to buy, but without a harbour, neither could they attract a processing plant. Fair Isle was never considered by the British Fishing Society for improvements, so like many other remote communities, the men struggled to find a place in a changing world that questioned their economic viability. Natural harbours with ease of access were the primary targets for the burgeoning fishing industry and Fair Isle did not fit these criteria. The laird was loathe to spend his own money on an expensive project that might not bring an adequate reward. After 1869, those who remained tried desperately to bolster one another's belief that fishing opportunities would develop and life here would improve.

Although Fair Isle remained a close society, its people encompassed all the human frailties that were exhibited on the mainland and indeed throughout the rest of the world. Not everyone on the island led an equal life, whether they were Wilsons or not. Many valiantly tried to live respectably, with due reverence for the Good Book, while others swore, argued, cheated, fought or stole, just as elsewhere. Even those who conspicuously flaunted their religion were occasionally blind to their own weaknesses. Perhaps it was an indication of increasing stress on the isle that petty theft was by 1869 on the increase (not that people had much to steal). But if you had struggled to dig and transport a pile of peat to your croft, when some of it was taken by someone else you were annoyed. When you had a good store of cabbage, corn, potatoes or fish, it was to feed your family, not someone else's. And if you collected a particularly good piece of wood from the sea and dragged it home, you expected it still to be there in the morning. It only takes a few people to develop a light-fingered habit for everyone to be thrown into dismay, for on an island you cannot blame an itinerant gypsy or beggar. It had to be a neighbour, someone you knew, a relation even.

After a small flurry of disturbances, suspicions were voiced and finally complaints were communicated to Bruce, through the factor. In due course Bruce appointed two local men as bailiffs, or ranselmen, to bring folk to order. These were Laurence Irvine of Hool and Thomas Wilson of Kennaby, and the pair let it be known they would not stand for any continuation of petty theft or unpleasantness. In the main they were sufficiently respected (or feared) to encourage the perpetrators to desist.

Whether it was because there were now ranselmen charged with keeping the law, or whether people were simply more aware of their rights, 1869 saw a court case raised in Lerwick concerning an assault on the island. Mary Leslie and Jane Leslie had been at the hill, loading their horses with peat to carry down to the crofts, when an argument broke out between Jane (from Barkland) and Mary (from Pund). Their fathers were brothers. The argument was a silly squabble over whether or not Mary's brother Charles had thrown a stone at someone, but it escalated until Jane was throwing large stones at Mary. The two then grappled and punched in a decidedly unladylike fashion, until Mary was sufficiently bruised and hurt to require to be helped home and put to bed. When George Leslie returned from the day's fishing to find Mary lying in her bed, sobbing, bruised and bloodied, he lost his temper and stormed over to Barkland, where he grabbed Jane by the hair, hit her and threw her to the ground. Of course, Jane's father and brother rushed to her aid, so that they too became involved in the hullabaloo. The ill feeling was sufficiently strong to take the case to court. Whatever the legal outcome, the families' relationships were forever damaged. From their two pulpits on succeeding Sundays, two preachers had little trouble finding a topic for their sermons.

Meanwhile, for those who went to Kirkwall in 1869, life was challenging. The men found jobs easily enough, since there were already some islanders there to show them the ropes and give references. The women quickly found rooms to rent, since Kirkwall was a fast-growing town where people were always on the move. The families lived close to one another, enabling them to discuss and compare every new benefit and problem. There was much to discuss.

Kirkwall was a solid little town, dominated by a large medieval cathedral that had high, delicately carved sandstone walls; an edifice totally alien to everyone's previous experience. It had huge pillars, statues, a splendid vaulted roof and of course a bell tower, which the men all chose to climb. Secretly, Jeannie wondered if there was something sacrilegious about using such a fancy building as a church. She was grateful when they found the more modest Methodist hall in which to worship.

The streets at first seemed infinite, narrow and overshadowed by high buildings, with some of the fancier homes boasting big ornamental gateways. New building was in process in several areas, evidence that the town was prospering, with the magnificent Commercial Bank in Albert Street exhibiting all the splendour and confidence that you might expect from Victorian Britain. There were hotels, shops, public houses, banks, schools, offices, stables, warehouses and even ornamental gardens with flowers and trees, a truly novel idea for islanders who had only thought of wild flowers as decoration. An impressive iron pier dominated the harbour, which was generally busy both with fishermen and travellers arriving from all the other islands, as well as from Scotland's mainland. Some of the foreign fishermen dressed and spoke quite differently. Everything was on a scale they had never imagined. Surely, in such an environment, they would all prosper.

The men still worked at the fishing, but with the promise of real money they could manage themselves. Education was not free, but at least there were teachers in Orkney. The new homes may not have been much bigger, but here they no longer shared their houses with beasts and the fire was on an end wall, with a chimney to take the smoke out of the house. Floors were wooden, rather than earthen. Windows were bigger. Box beds, of course, still had to be shared, but no one expected anything different. The women continued to knit, bartering their wares with local merchants. Most importantly, the boys now had a range of opportunities when it was time for them to work. In a town you could train in a multitude of skills, undertaking an apprenticeship that might lead to success and security.

Jeannie shared a home with Jane and looked after her children, while James found work as an apprentice tailor and Thomas quickly found work as a weaver. Of course, they all missed the island on a lovely day in June, or when they thought of the companionship of family, but they were closer than ever to the family they had brought with them from Fair Isle. Jeannie always wondered about the wee ones she left behind in Taft. Did they forget her as soon as she disappeared? Did they think she had abandoned them? John wrote regularly and well, telling how Barbara and the children were managing, but Jeannie was glad that she had made the effort to leave. Above all she prayed that James would stick at the tailoring he had chosen as a career. If she wanted anything for James, it was that he made a success of life on land.

Over time, bits of gossip from the island filtered through to the group. Young Stewart Wilson, who had taken over the weaving from his brother, was also taking over more work from his father at Springfield. However, if the old man was waning physically, he was still as strong a preacher as he had ever been. The youngest girl, Polly, was still at home with her parents and it must have been a comfort for the older couple to have her there, even if she was unmarried. Then Andrew Wilson, Barbara's brother, wrote to say he was going to bring his family to join them. Over the next few years others followed. Finally, the Kirkwall emigrants never had to look far for familiar faces. And after a couple of years Laurence and Thomas Wilson found themselves starring in the public domain in a way no one had imagined.

It was Fair Isle's dire weather that forced them into the limelight, rather than their own choice, for when the Truck Commission came to Shetland it could not visit the island due to bad sea conditions. The issue of truck had long involved British governments. Despite all the inequalities of life, by the 1860s there was a general agreement that a labourer was worthy of his hire. The only doubt for most employers was the extent to which that hire was worth. Those who practised truck still argued that if this system was altered, the men who worked for them might not be able to manage their money, insisting that their labourers continue be paid in kind (at least in part) rather than in coin of the realm. Often, they regulated how these wages were spent. Successive acts had been passed by parliament to try to ensure that truck was outlawed, yet in 1870 it was deemed necessary to restate the principle, because some trades were forced to endure reduced wages and enforced purchases at company stores which sold goods at inflated prices.

The 1870 Act of Parliament once more stated that people should be free to be paid regularly and reliably in coin of the realm and that people should be free to spend their money where they wished. Truck system supporters still claimed that it was wrong to interfere in the relationship between an employer and employee, even while others reiterated that the truck system was *'free trade for the masters, but robbery of the men'*. So even after the 1870 Truck Act, parliament noted that there was still *'systematic infringement in certain areas that required further investigation.'*

This statement resulted in Commissioner William Guthrie being directed to conduct a separate inquiry into truck in Shetland in 1871. The fishing industry was not included in the trades referred to under the Truck Act, but the connection between renting land and being tied to fishing for your landlord, together with the enforced sale of fish and other items to him, was an anomaly that the government wished to explore. They were also aware of the situation that surrounded the merchants who 'bought' knitting from local women, but paid them in tea, rather than cash. Commissioner Guthrie was particularly capable and exacting in his remit, a champion of the truth and he quickly found that he had been sent to a society where those in charge cared little for the situation of the vulgar poor. There was bound to be conflict.

Public notices on printed bills were exhibited everywhere he visited, while circulars were sent to clergymen, schoolteachers and landed proprietors, so that they too could become involved. Guthrie interviewed fishermen, merchants, lairds, knitters and shopkeepers. Ultimately, his report told the world that in Shetland people lived in turf roofed stone houses, with holes in the roof for smoke to escape. A dunghill stood at every door and the byre was part of the main house, sometimes with beds and furniture the only means of separation between man and beast. Floors were of clay, with the fire on the centre of the floor, but to his surprise he found the houses more homely than those he had visited previously in the Western Isles, and the people intelligent and industrious.

His research showed that all over Shetland it was the habit for fishermen to pay their rent in fish and also to hold an account at the landlord's shop. Guthrie noted that the level of fish money paid to men stayed the same all the year round, whatever fluctuations occurred in the market. Accounts were settled at least a year in arrears, which made it difficult for the men to argue about what they were paid at any given time. Furthermore, he found that the fish merchants met to agree what the prices should be, so that it was hardly a free market. Landlords claimed that under their system the tenants were protected, since they were not thrown off their land immediately if they found themselves in rent arrears. They also stated that if the current system was abolished and people became homeless when times were bad, they would then be a call on the poor rates. The current system was claimed to protect men from wasting money, since they did not have access to cash!

Guthrie found that the fishermen's accounts were settled in a very '*loose manner*', with men being read a list of what they had spent over the last year and being told what they had earned, with little proof of either sum. He also found that meal, tea, cotton and tobacco were all much more expensive in Shetland than on the mainland, and that landlords dissuaded other traders from selling to their tenants at more competitive rates so that they gained as much profit as possible from their shops.

John Bruce was not just the laird of Fair Isle. He owned considerable land on Shetland, where he saw himself as a pillar of the community. He had about two hundred tenants, mostly people with large families, so that he had responsibility for a large number of individuals. In January 1872, he gave evidence concerning his tenants in Fair Isle, admitting that no one had any choice about whom to sell their fish to, for all were tied to the same landlord. He agreed that the men had no security of tenure and any lodgers were expected to have the same obligation to him as the tenants themselves. When it was stated that men were paid for saithe at 10 shillings a ton less in Fair Isle than Shetland, it did not worry Bruce in the least. Why would it?

He went on to argue that he needed to have all the shop trade in Fair Isle to justify maintaining an establishment on the island, although he admitted that items like soap were charged at double what he had paid for them. In Dunrossness, too, all the shops were connected to the fish trade, so that truck was the means of 'paying' for most goods there. In Fair Isle his tenants all fished for him, but his mainland tenants were also expected to work on his land during the voar and hairst (springtime and harvest) for free. Certainly he would evict any men who worked for anyone else. He also claimed the right to control the sale of all his tenants' animals.

Bruce finally admitted that, '*there are no doubt many things in the Shetland system of trade which might be improved, but the system has been of long growth and is so ingrained in the minds of the people that any change must be very gradual. A sudden and sweeping change to free trade principles and ready money payments would not suit the people and could produce endless confusion, hardship and increased pauperism. Abolish the system suddenly and I am afraid that our Poor Law rates would be unbearable and nothing could save the country from depopulation.*'

Once he had completed his research on the Shetland mainland, Fair Isle was to have been Guthrie's next port of call, but when the commissioner was disappointed to find that he could not travel there he went instead to Kirkwall, where he heard there were recent émigrés who would to speak with him. Free from pressure, both Laurence and Thomas Wilson's words would now be set down in perpetuity.

Springfield's Thomas Wilson gave his evidence first, stating that all goods bought on the island became dearer after Bruce senior acquired the land in 1866. Prior to Bruce, other people would bring their boats to trade, but he discouraged such practices. Local men had to sell all their fish to him and a man came to the island to settle the accounts on 1st May, for the previous year. The accounts were read to the people, as few had passbooks so you had to trust the laird, which they didn't. They were given cash only on this day and only then if they were told it was owed. It was possible, if you had bought much from the shop and it had been a hard year, to discover that you were due nothing at all. Some people were constantly unable to buy things, except on credit. One trader, a Mr Rendall, sometimes set up a booth on the shore to sell a variety of commodities, the shore-line being held to be outwith Bruce's jurisdiction. Cotton cloth, tea, sugar and meal were much cheaper at Rendall's and Thomas stated that everything was much cheaper in Kirkwall. This was why the families left in 1869. People managed to survive the winter by fishing off the rocks and in the main they lived on fish, tea, porridge and oatmeal cakes.

"I left," he told the commissioner, "because meal was so dear and wages were so low," adding that since he left he had been better off, with better food, better wages and less work.

Lowry Wilson was then called and he reiterated Thomas's views. He also stated that he felt threatened by Bruce's insistence that tenure on his farm would be at risk if he tried to improve his family's life by earning money at the *Lessing*. He told his listeners that prices at the shop in Fair Isle were higher than anywhere else, and there were no passbooks for accounts so you had no idea what you owed at the end of the year. He did not feel that he got true value for the livestock he sold to Bruce when he left. In his opinion the people on the island should be free to sell their fish to whomsoever they pleased and pay an annual rent for their crofts. He also told Guthrie that some islanders were in arrears and could not leave, but not being in arrears himself, he could bring his family to Kirkwall.

It was empowering for these two men to spend so long in front of such an august figure as Commissioner Guthrie, who ensured that every word was recorded. It was a moment much appreciated by all the emigrant families, particularly when it was reported in the national press. Times were surely changing when ordinary men were given a pulpit from which to voice their grievances.

It should be noted that Guthrie went further than simply recording opinions. He took samples of goods sold in the Shetland shops back to Edinburgh and called in local shopkeepers for their opinions about quality and price. These men left him in no doubt that all the goods he had brought from Shetland were over-priced, even with carriage costs being taken into consideration. Additionally, they were all of a very poor quality. People in Shetland were being cheated.

Sadly, although it was clear to Guthrie that the Shetland system was grossly unfair to tenants, he did not feel that the system was legally encompassed by the definition of truck. The only definitive example of truck was the knitting that the women did on the Shetland mainland, where they had no choice but to sell to local shops run by local merchants, who regularly forced them to accept tea as payment. Even when 'pay-lines' were offered, many shop items could not be purchased except with cash.

Guthrie found that the system in Shetland made the tenant insecure and made them weak in any negotiation. Some tenants had been unwilling to speak, fearing that they might suffer from raised rents, or worse. Lowry and Thomas Wilson could be honest, only because they had already left Fair Isle. Sadly, since the fishermen's situation was not entirely within the definition of truck, it was not entirely against the law. What happened on Shetland was bondage, a terribly unpleasant way for men to live, but truck was what he had been sent to examine. Guthrie wondered if the 1854 Merchant Shipping Act could be used to lay down different regulations for the employment of the fishermen. He was frustrated by the outcome. If the people of Shetland must rely on the law to protect them from their lairds, they must find a different law.

It would be a very different type of law that altered all their lives, although it came too late to help many who lived there during the 1870s. The Crofter's Commission would visit the island in 1892, some twenty years later. By this time ordinary people had a different view of their rights and felt more than free to express themselves.

Jeannie had worried about Lowry and Thomas speaking their minds with the Truck Commissioner and had tried to talk them out of it in case there were repercussions, even though young James had laughed at the very idea. That was the thing about Kirkwall, James told his mother. You were free to be yourself, whether it was changing your work, or speaking up to support your views. Jeannie was not quite sure about some of her youngest son's ideas about freedom. Before his twentieth birthday he had found himself a lass and all too soon they seemed to get very serious. Jeannie had only just pointed out that a tailor's apprentice could hardly support a wife, when the boy got himself a job as a weaver, earning a man's wage.

"I could have cut my tongue out," she told Jane. "He's too young by far to settle down and have children. He's not really stopped being a lad himself."

But Jane just laughed. "Well, you were the one who wanted him to be free. He's not a child, Mither, even though you kept him close to you. I suppose we all keep our youngest close for as long as we can. But better he marries her than dallies with her. Let him be a good lad and do the right thing."

Jeannie sighed. In Fair Isle a man tried to see he had some opportunities before he married, for there it was difficult to find a place to live and the means to support a family. But Kirkwall was not Fair Isle. James had a good wage and could pay for a small home, so the young couple married on 25th January, 1872, at the height of the Commission excitement. James was just twenty-one and Isabella twenty-two, but they were happy. Soon there was a child.

Jane and Thomas now had six wee ones, while Agnes had four and Lowry eight. Everyone was settled, and with regular money coming in people could manage fine. After all the years of struggling, it was a relief to know that they all had a penny or two put by for a rainy day. As long as they kept their health, all would be well. Jeannie now had no doubt that they had all done the right thing to move, and when she heard that there had been a meeting in Fair Isle to discuss a mass emigration to New Zealand she was not in the least surprised, for here in Kirkwall waves of folk moved into the town from all around Orkney, while further waves lined up to catch a boat to take them somewhere else. Yet Jeannie was not really surprised to hear that Fair Isle's mass emigration had not occurred, for there were many like her John who would never, ever consider leaving his croft. Whether his children would stay was a different matter and Jeannie understood that her son had still to learn that he was not in charge of his family in the long term.

Then, just as they all began to feel quite confident, there was an outbreak of measles in Kirkwall. It was of course the youngest who died first. All the mothers cleaned and cleaned, and when that did not seem enough they prayed, and the old ones quoted words from the past that would keep the trows from their houses. The young ones had no time for the old bits of verse, but anything that might help could not be ignored, so they kept quiet when the old women whispered over their bairns.

Aggie's youngest son William became hot and girny one day late in October 1874. Jeannie rushed round to help her daughter, reminding her that she had nursed them all through the illness in 1855. It would be fine. They wiped the boy's head with cool cloths, but as the rash emerged his temperature rose. They called the doctor, but he had little to offer. The young ones were sent off to live with an older widow lady, away from home and away from other children. For ten days Aggie and Jeannie took it in turns to nurse the boy, wiping him with cool cloths and trying to get a bit of liquid past his lips. But the cough became deeper and deeper until it was that of an old man and finally the exhausted bairn was unable to lift his head from the pillow to clear his drowning lungs. He passed away on the night of 25th October. Aggie could not be comforted. Willie was heartbroken. Aggie had taken up midwifery, helping other women bring their children into the world. It seemed so hard that she could not keep one of her own.

After the funeral the family came together to support the couple with their three remaining children. It seemed hard that the pair with the smallest family should be the ones to lose a child to this dreadful scourge. It took a bit of time before everyone relaxed again and stopped over-reacting when children had a sniffly nose or a spot or two. Measles, whooping cough and mumps forever eddied around young ones at this time and luck seemed the only talisman. One by one, Jeannie's other grandchildren caught measles until she feared that she would never get away from sick beds and worry. None of these children died, however, and the rest of Aggie's family was spared, so after the turn of the year Jeannie hoped and prayed that they had put the measles well behind them.

Then one night in February 1875, Willie Stout came home, hot, bothered and unwilling to eat. He threw himself into his bed in the kitchen. Aggie was not unduly worried, until the rash appeared. Then she began to panic. Her husband was a big strong man, but in forty-eight hours he was reduced to a shivering wreck who hardly knew her. The children were kept away from their father and again Aggie and Jeannie bore witness round the clock. The doctor was called. By this time the cough was there and the lungs were thick with phlegm. The doctor came, shook his head silently and refused payment. In less than a week, Willie Stout was dead.

To lose a child to measles was terrible, but to lose a husband as well! Aggie did not know which way to turn. The three children tried to be good, and tried to help, but she did not heed them. All the time she wondered, was this a punishment? To be left with three children and no husband was a terrible challenge. How would they survive? Her mother moved in with her and all the other folk from the isle tried to help, but Aggie could not respond. The preacher from the chapel came and lectured her on faith and

God's will, but Aggie sent him away with a flea in his ear, not caring if she went to chapel again, ever. Jeannie was worried sick about her.

In June, young Andrew caught the measles and died. It was harrowing. During the long summer of 1875 they watched Aggie and her two remaining children with fear and worry, lest something happen to the children she had left. Then, in November, Jacobina followed her siblings to the grave. By now friends and relatives were beside themselves. How was one person supposed to cope with all this grief? The loss had been drawn out and bitingly painful. Aggie was now a thin shadow of her previous self. She went through the motions of life, but you could tell she felt nothing. No comfort was found in the church, with relatives, or well-meaning friends. She lived with the knowledge that in 1855 she had survived the outbreak in Fair Isle. Whatever happened now, she alone was inviolate.

"At least you still have James," they all said. And she did. She watched over her five-year-old darling with a suffocating love. She would not let him out of her sight and certainly not to play with other children. The wind was not allowed to blow on him. It wasn't healthy, everyone thought, but what were you supposed to say? You had your family, so in the meantime all you could do was watch and pray with Aggie till she came out of it. The women helped by sitting with her of an evening as they knitted, watching to see that she was never alone. Fair Isle friends whose husbands were fishermen brought her fish, and anyone who made soup or any other dish that could be eked out brought her a bowl. Aggie barely noticed. All she had eyes for was James.

The Yule celebrations came and went before James became ill. He lasted for almost three weeks with Aggie's careful nursing. Finally he developed bronchitis and then pneumonia before he died.

They all expected Aggie to fall apart after this final blow, but by now she was numb. She answered them when they spoke to her, did all her tasks and ate what they put in front of her. Eventually she began to deliver babies again, but she was to be found every Sunday at the graveyard by the Cathedral, talking to William and the children.

Aggie did not go mad. She made a new life. She lived a long life. But she was never the old Aggie for as long as she lived. The Lord had seen fit to give and then to take. When her family died, so did her dreams. Aggie was destined to live in Kirkwall until she was ninety, delivering other people's children for much of that time, welcoming the kindness of family and friends, but she never recovered.

## Chapter 8

# Feeding Fair Isle

The saithe fishing started in May, but before that there was plenty of preparation to be made. Once the season began the men needed to focus on catching as much fish as possible, to enable them to build up sufficient credit with the laird to pay their rents and make purchases at his store. Saithe, although a low value catch (whose main market was by now restricted to Ireland), was abundant and did not present the marketing challenges of higher value catches. When the fish were bountiful and the weather favourable, the men would sometimes go out twice a day, setting off on the first trip between 2am and 4am. Exhaustion would gradually build up as the weeks passed, leaving little time for any additional tasks on fishing days. Thus all had to be ready for the trials of the season and not just the boats themselves, for ropes, sails, oars, and bait lines and tubs must also be in the best of condition if the long days were to go smoothly.

Bait was collected by women and children, who heated the shellfish in water and loosened them from their shells, so that their men's hands could stay dry, hard and calloused. Men painstakingly set the baited hooks round the edges of wooden tubs, till each was filled with three to five hundred, on lines that were baited about three feet apart if saithe was their goal. Each yoal would take two or three bait tubs to sea. Old men and younger boys worked hard at the beach, splitting, salting and drying and defending the spread of fish from marauding dogs, seabirds and rain. The routine was welcomed at the beginning of the season, with the hope that this year there would be a bumper catch and that halibut and haddock might be caught just when a passing steamer could take it into Lerwick. The very least they hoped for was that all would survive the process and be able to pay their rents.

The land also demanded effort at this time, with much of the heavy work being undertaken by the women although, as in everything else, tradition allocated each gender allotted tasks. Until the 1880s when heavy oxen made their appearance, the soil had to be dug over (delled) with Shetland spades, adults and older children working shoulder to shoulder in teams of four, five or six, painstakingly turning over the soil until each field was completed. Shetland delling spades have long wooden handles with relatively short metal blades, about 15 centimetres wide and 25 centimetres long. There is a foot peg on one side of the long handle, about 35 centimetres from the blade, to give a heavy boot leverage. The demand for delling spades was such that not only were they produced by some Shetland smiths, but the firm of Thomas Black in Berwick also produced a high quality product that many thought worthy of purchase. Delling began early in February, depending of course on the weather. On patches of particularly poor land it might be necessary to repeat, or double-dell the soil. People shared such tasks with their neighbours, so that all could be planted in time, for this far north there is a short growing season.

The seventeenth of March was the traditional day to sow the first seeds 'with the flowing tide', but only if the weather allowed. The potato ground also had to be dug, manured and planted by April. From mid to late April, the kail had to be transplanted from the crus into the fields.

When the weather was bad, you were hard pushed to complete this timetable so that all the plants had time to mature before winter. When it was wet, the mud that clung to clothes, shoes and bodies inevitably found its way into houses. A muddy family, at the end of a long, hard day, was a depressing adversary for the women.

Once the soil was deemed warm enough, the seed was sown, broadcast from a straw kishie. This was normally a man's responsibility and he would be followed by men, women and older children, pulling harrows that hung from long ropes strung round both shoulders. You plodded up and down the fields both to level the land before it was sown and to break it down into an even finer tilth afterwards.

By midsummer, haymaking saw the men sharpening heavy scythes, to allow them a strong, smooth passage through the grass, and later in the year they harvested seed crops with corn heuks (sickles), although on poor land where the crop was particularly thin it could be gathered by hand. Grain crops were gathered into sheaves, loosely tied near the top and then stacked to dry in the fields. Gleaners picked up all the loose stalks, which they tied into bundles and took home to hang in the house till the grain was dry and ready to be ground into the first new meal of the year.

Later, the dried sheaves were built up into scroos (stacks), covered by simmens (ropes) which anchored each stack firmly to the ground to keep it safe. Grain was threshed and winnowed, so that it could finally be stored in big straw baskets. Kilns slow-toasted the grain so that small quantities of corn could be ground into flour using a knocking stone, or a rotating quern. Larger amounts would be taken by the men to one of the small, horizontal, wheeled click-mills that were designed to work over fast flowing streams where they plunged down towards the sea. Covered by small stone sheds, these mills were relatively simple and cheap to construct, but water-power is vulnerable both to drought and ice, so under such conditions hand grinding at home was the only option.

Much of this work used methods that had changed little over hundreds of years, but gradually the agricultural revolution that had begun with land enclosure in England during the mid-1700s worked its way up the country. In 1845, Fair Isle had finally abandoned the wasteful, medieval open-field system, but by the 1870s many more new farming ideas had been tried and tested elsewhere, so that northern lairds understood that it was possible to extend the productivity of their land. Scientific papers regarding improvements were read and discussed, although many were controversial since they would most likely cost landowners money. Although some of these theories had to be adapted in difficult areas like Shetland, the principles were universal: better farming meant more crops, bigger animals and greater profits. Since the population of Scotland was growing faster than ever and more food was required for growing populations in towns, the government encouraged all farmers to increase their productivity, offering grants for improvements.

John Bruce junior was aware of these schemes for better drainage, more imaginative land use, new crops and improved animal husbandry, so he decided to create an 'experimental, modern stock farm' in Fair Isle. His intention was to expand the area of productive land on the island, as well as improving the quantity of produce and the quality of the animals. After some research he decided to break in new land, beyond the dyke that separated existing farmland from scattald (common grazing land), hiring a manager to organise the project.

He explained to an inspector from the Scottish Drainage and Improvement Company that none of his tenants would be dislodged by the creation of this new farm. He also told the surveyor, who was advising him on the best land to enclose, '*I quite agree that five acres is too little for a farm, but we have too many tenants and it would be hard to put any of them away*'.

So, late in 1871, Peter McGregor (who had been working for Bruce at his farm in Sumburgh) was sent to manage a model farm in Fair Isle, having been provided with plans for the project. McGregor was an experienced 30-year-old, who had previously worked on his brother's farm in Orkney and was also an accomplished builder of dry-stone dykes. This latter skill made him an ideal choice for the job since the first task was to enclose the new land with stone, to keep out the sheep, cattle and horses that freely roamed the northern area. James Anderson, an 18-year-old Shetlander, was employed as the farm servant and would act as the older man's assistant. Over the harsh Shetland winter the pair toiled at building stone walls at Gilsetter. The following year they began the difficult and back-breaking task of ploughing almost virgin soil, to produce the new park at Vaasetter.

This was onerous and frustrating work in such stony moorland, and to help them McGregor arranged for two old horses to be brought by boat from Orkney in the spring, along with a plough. At the end of 1872 these beasts were returned and resold, since their survival in Fair Isle could hardly be assured over the winter and there would have been the expense of both shelter and food to consider. Bruce also had plans to buy a new ram and bull to service his animals, since selective breeding was another focus for enthusiastic farmers who wanted to attract a better price for their beasts in the ring when they went to market. In 1872, John Bruce junior officially took over the lease of his father's estate, which did not mean any major change for his tenants' lives since he had already taken over much of the work, as well as instituting an annual inspection visit in the spring.

Labourers, including local men, were hired to help McGregor with some of the initial work for it was a huge task. Fifteen-year-old Lowry Irvine would become one of the farm's regular part-time employees, a boy who worked barefoot, cold and hungry as he struggled to keep Quoy for his family. When John Irvine had died in 1869, Lowry was just thirteen and his younger brothers eleven and nine, and people had wondered if they might lose the croft. Lowry undertook additional work at Vaasetter over the next thirty years, forming an unusual bond with its manager in his efforts to keep his family afloat. Everyone watched carefully as the work continued throughout 1873, with some wondering if all the additional effort and expense would be justified at the end of the day. However, when the new land eventually began to produce good crops in an area they had not thought worthy of such intense cultivation, people warmed to the new ideas. Andrew Stout, his wife Elizabeth and their three children, who had been living in Setter, soon found that they were relocated elsewhere. Clearly not all Bruce's tenants were to be unaffected by his changes.

McGregor did not only concentrate his efforts on building dykes and producing better crops, he also encouraged the digging and clearance of ditches so that the land would be less liable to flood. Crops were planted earlier in some areas and protected from water damage in others. Ryegrass and clovers were sown to augment the rough pasture that grew on fallow ground, providing better hay for winter fodder. Turnips were also sown.

Since stone-breaking for roadwork was another of his skills, McGregor set about organising a number of local men to build a proper road between South Harbour and North Haven over the winter of 1873. This would make it easier to transport goods when North Haven was used as a harbour. During this road building two ancient urns were found – one of steatite and the other of clay – close to some grass-covered hillocks known locally as trows' knolls, near the Finniquoy Mills. It seemed that these small hillocks were an indication of human life in Fair Isle in the very distant past. No doubt other old treasures were destroyed during this road's construction, but Bruce made sure that these particular containers were saved and taken to Edinburgh, where they were lodged in the National Museum of Antiquities. The men who dug them up found it difficult to imagine life in Fair Isle so very many years ago, but when they paused to discuss the idea over a pipe, they decided that without all their modern benefits it must indeed have been a hard time.

Despite all this progress, Bruce found that there were still issues in Fair Isle to cause him aggravation. In 1873 one of his appointed ranselmen (Laurence Irvine of Houll) was called to court and John Bruce, as a Justice of the Peace, took the chair. Marjorie Leslie of Stoneybrake was a capable, attractive young woman, with no sense of timidity when it came to speaking up for herself. Laurence Irvine seems to have been a rather over-confident young man who had married one of the factor's daughters, which perhaps explains why he was assigned to keep the peace in Fair Isle. This he had clearly not done when he attacked Marjorie Leslie during an argument about where their respective family cows could graze, assaulting her so that she returned home with red weals on her back and a torn dress. Everyone encouraged Marjorie to complain, since crofting only works if people respect their neighbours. It was also felt that the laird's appointed ranselman ought to respect those rights more than anyone else.

Laurence Irvine was found guilty and fined £1, a punishment that does not seem to have hindered him in the least, since it was reported that he left the court full of himself. This family of Irvines was known as the 'fighting Irvines', to distinguish them from the quieter Irvines at Quoy. Laurence drowned a few years later while retrieving cargo from a wreck and his wife and children remained on the island until the youngsters were grown, when all left for Canada. Marjorie Leslie went on to marry James Anderson. Perhaps it was her feistiness that attracted Anderson to her, or perhaps the couple were already an 'item' and Anderson encouraged her to take up the suit.

When the Church of Scotland came into being in 1560 it imposed strict discipline on all the people of Scotland, but over the years, and as it fragmented, in parts of the country it began to lose some of its authority. In both scattered rural areas and in the growing towns its power began to diminish. The Kirk Session still had the ability to call individuals in front of it to 'stand penance' and be publicly humiliated for sins such as fornication, profanity or drunkenness, but by the second half of the 19th century such a demeaning form of discipline was avoided in most communities. Some of the poor had stopped attending church entirely, particularly when the requirement to pay a quarterly pew rent was outwith their power. Others were just too tired, too hungry, or lacked what was considered 'suitable' church attire.

The church continued to wield power however. In 1855 the state decided to formally record marriages, bringing together all the forms of religious union that were by then undertaken in Scotland. One anomaly was marriage by declaration which, although legal and entered into by many couples, was heartily discouraged by ministers of all faiths. However, after 1855, those who did not wish a church-blessed union could still make a declaration of marriage, which legitimised their children in the eyes of Scots law. This practice was popularised in places like Gretna Green, close to the Scottish border, where people came to escape the more restrictive English marriage laws.

Despite the fact that it was still lawful to marry in this way, a formal registration of marriage by declaration became customary, so that you had to obtain a warrant from a sheriff if you wished your union to be added to the official register. The Church of Scotland in particular designated such marriages as 'irregular' and piled social criticism on those who chose this process. When you had children, or died, the registrar could note the words 'irregular marriage' against your name, but the real problem came when the registrar decided to write that the children were 'illegitimate', which in law they were not.

In Fair Isle, over time it became increasingly apparent to local residents that two of the Stoneybrake Leslie girls needed husbands. It was not uncommon on the island that some wives-to-be were already pregnant. Indeed, occasionally the child arrived before the nuptials. As long as the men embraced their responsibilities and made honest women of the girls the situation was accepted. Ministers might chide couples for not waiting for his blessing, but such things had always occurred. However, Peter McGregor was not from this community. Indeed, he was not from any of the islands and did not feel the religious pressure that had seeped deeply into the souls of his new neighbours. For whatever reason, he was one of those Scots who did not feel the need for religion. Even in Fair Isle it is not recorded with what regularity everyone attended church, although in such a small community it would have been hard to be a dissenter.

So there were two religious groups equally scandalised by 34-year-old Peter McGregor's refusal to be married by a minister. Despite all protestations to the contrary, he insisted on his right to marry his wife 'by declaration'. In August 1874, when the Reverend Martin (a Free Church minister from Dunrossness) arrived, the topic was on everyone's lips. Indeed, if you did not count the illegal 'marriage' of the tacksman in 1815, no such thing had ever happened before. Nothing the young man could say would persuade people that he was within his rights. Grace Leslie may have been upset by the situation, but the man insisted that he would stand by her. Indeed, pressure from the community only made him more insistent. He had little time for the church before this trouble and the fact that young James Anderson's match was acceptable, despite the fact that Marjorie Leslie produced a child just weeks after the wedding, was to him ridiculous. And the law was on his side.

But the Church was not. Registrars, who were often pillars of the community, regularly had little sympathy for the children of an 'irregular' marriage. Thus, without written word from a sheriff, young Margaret was noted as 'illegitimate' on her birth certificate. Peter was deeply offended and never forgave Jerome Wilson's stance. Jerome, however, was a supporter of the Methodist church and, like all Godly men, knew he was right. John Wilson of Taft took it upon himself to try to persuade the couple about the error of their ways, but like the rest of the remonstrators he was sent packing. People were blind to the fact that the fundamental point of this part of Scots law was to avoid illegitimacy, which disturbs inheritance and can cause a financial drain on the community. With no access to a sheriff, if he did not intend to accept religion, in Fair Isle Peter McGregor's children would continue to be deemed illegitimate. Finding religion is, however, a personal metamorphosis and not one that occurs because it is demanded. Particularly if it is demanded!

So the topic did not go away with the boat that took the minister back to the mainland, and when John Bruce came to the island in September 1875 he and William Laurence witnessed a second declaration of marriage by Peter and Grace. Presumably, since Bruce was a Justice of the Peace, he felt that he had the standing to regularise the marriage in law and William Laurence was the new teacher, a worldly man. Yet still this was not enough for the registrar, so that Peter McGregor decided to leave early in 1876, although he finally 'regularised' the marriage in Lerwick in 1879, no doubt worn down by Grace's worry about her growing brood of 'illegitimate' children. His early work on the roads and land remained long after he was forgotten and he worked as a mason for the rest of his life, living with Grace in Lossiemouth.

In Fair Isle, Peter bequeathed the post of farm manager to James Anderson, who flourished in the absence of his erstwhile mentor having learned many of his skills over the previous five years, although Anderson's diary, which includes McGregor's time in Fair Isle, makes no mention of the man. Grace and Marjorie Leslie were the daughters of John Leslie who died in the 1851 disaster and their mother Janet had struggled to bring her family up alone. It pained Janet to lose Grace, but James and Marjorie gave her a home for the rest of her life.

Thanks to the effects of continued small-scale emigration, the island's population now appeared to be relatively stable, so all were surprised when Fair Isle experienced its first evictions, in May 1875, for non-payment of rent by three families who had small, marginal holdings. With their wives and children, Robert Leslie of Barkland, George Leslie of Pund and Charles Leslie, also from a croft house at Pund, were forced to leave for Kirkwall, reducing the population by twenty-four. This was both a shock and a warning to those who remained, particularly when land from Pund was added to Bruce's model farm. With a resident and ambitious farm bailiff ready to absorb more land into Bruce's growing estate, it was a clear warning that all must maintain their crofts successfully, or suffer the consequences.

The islanders were encouraged in 1876 to agree that it was time to protect crops from foraging animals, so that any stock that was kept south of the hill dyke that traversed the island must now be tethered between 27th April and 23rd October. Although this would continue to cause trouble amongst those who were lazy or selfish, in the main the rule was obeyed. Regulating the number of beasts that people could keep on the hill also took time to negotiate, as it was not easy to persuade some people that having fewer, healthier beasts was preferable to having many sickly ones. Eventually wisdom prevailed and in 1878 a new stone hill dyke was built, to replace the old turf dyke that had marked the separation of hill and inbye land. As the 1870s drew to a close, there was a definite feeling of progress.

James Anderson would gradually increase the area he had under cultivation over the years. By the 1920s the laird's original five-acre holding had increased to seventy-two. With a reduction in population by this time, other crofters had also increased their holdings but to nothing like this extent. Anderson was twenty-three years old when he took over from McGregor and proved to be hardworking and ambitious. He continued to organise road improvements every spring, along with ditch maintenance. As he absorbed even more moorland under his control, he started to construct strong fences to keep out livestock. By the time he fenced the land at Rippock in 1886, this enterprise used almost six hundred fence posts, at a cost of just over £12, an expense that would have been difficult for an ordinary crofter whose rent was about £6 a year. Over time he added additional responsibilities to his role as farm manager and there were occasions when his power (and his attitude to that power) brought him into conflict with other islanders. However, no one can deny that the model farm and the innovations it brought with it over the years were a positive measure.

Sheep were a vital part of the business of survival. These Fair Isle beasts were known to be sheep with attitude, for only then could they survive on this barren, windy, treeless rock. Indeed, when James Cheyne the younger went to teach in Foula in 1861, he took his flock with him and they were said to have dominated the existing sheep until the locals became alarmed for the wellbeing of their flocks. These sheep learned from birth about the principle of survival of the fittest, their poor terrain resulting in small, sturdy, agile animals that learned how to use dangerous cliff paths and ledges to find food and were not averse to eating seaweed when the need arose.

In the summer they were driven down from the common land to be enclosed in a cru, where they were relieved of their fleeces and, later in the year, separated from their lambs, some of which were taken for sale or local consumption. The fleece, coloured white through to brown and into black, was particularly soft and easily hand-plucked (roo'ed). This could be a lively procedure with tough beasts that were not used to being handled or enclosed. The local human population was equally rugged, however, and well able to manage their flock, the younger people enjoying the tussle most, while even the most staid of their elders found it difficult to suppress a smile as man and beast struggled for supremacy.

The rooing was followed by a deal of work for the women before the wool was ready to knit, for it all had to be cleaned, sorted, carded and spun. Sheep on the hill would pick up a puckle of dirt over the year and additionally there was a variation between the length and softness of different parts of the fleece, the neck area offering the finest wool and the legs a coarser quality. Carding teased out the wool for spinning and this process was often done in an amiable family group. Every house had at least one spinning wheel and several sets of the heavy wooden carders, with their sharp metal 'nails' that enabled you to separate the softest wool, which would then be used to knit fine socks or gloves that would result in a higher reward when you came to sell them.

Anderson kept the most inaccessible flock on the iconic Sheep Rock, on behalf of the master. Sheep Rock was once part of the eastern mainland, although access had long since fallen into the sea so that by now you could only make a landing from a boat. The path up from the sea is very steep and dangerous, but the grass on top is about a quarter of a mile in circumference. Once hauled up there by ropes, the animals could be left to their own devices. The Rock was said to support sixteen ewes and Anderson regularly noted that he put the animals there at the end of May and retrieved them again in the autumn. These sheep were said to be so fat that when it came time to catch them a man did not need a dog since they fell over of their own accord! It has also to be said that sometimes the poor animals were so frightened by the unexpected appearance of men and boys at shearing time that an occasional one would leap to its death in the sea far below. The introductory trip up Sheep Rock was a kind of initiation for boys, who climbed with both excitement and trepidation. A fear of heights was not acceptable in such a society where boys must learn to scale steep cliffs to catch birds and gather eggs to feed their families.

Tough Shetland ponies had for years carried peat and other goods round the island, but they also were a cash crop that required little care. Most importantly, they were small. The Mines Act of 1842 had stopped women and children under ten years of age from working underground, where they had previously dragged large amounts of coal to the surface, undertaking twelve-hour shifts on their hands and knees. It took many years of campaigning to make people appreciate that sending women and little children underground to work amongst naked men, who beat them if they were slow or careless, might be unacceptable. Eventually these two vulnerable groups were replaced, either by ten-year-old workhouse boys, or pit ponies, neither of whom could make parliamentary representation to state a case against this particular form of slavery. For Shetlanders, the 1842 Act meant that there was now a lively demand for a product they could easily rear and export for cash.

The ponies were left on rough land throughout the year, with neither food nor shelter to sustain them except what they could find themselves. They were intelligent beasts that found refuge from the winter storms and foraged for food, eating seaweed when nothing else was available. Although they seldom grew higher than three feet, they were strong enough to carry baskets of peat and well able to haul loads of coal underground. In the spring, or when islanders had word of demand, there was a round-up to choose which ponies to transport to the mainland for sale. Loading frightened wild ponies into small boats was a challenge, but there are no stories of serious damage being done to man or beast.

# Chapter 9

# The Two Barbaras

When John Bruce junior took over the lease of his father's estate in 1872, he paid him £1,286 for the privilege. Bruce senior was by this time seventy-four and had already handed over much of the responsibility for managing his affairs to his eldest son. Bruce junior was thirty-seven and anxious to make his mark, particularly since he had recently married Mary Scott, the daughter of a wealthy Edinburgh chartered accountant. With a successful marriage and new authority, the younger man felt that he could make his presence felt even more strongly in Shetland.

Despite the fact that some people seemed to be making progress, illness, weather and luck played a part in all their lives. Andrew Eunson married Charlotte Leslie in August 1873 and a child was born that October. The young couple had been pleased to have their relationship officially sanctioned that summer and thought that this would be the end of their troubles. But sadly, Charlotte never recovered from the birth and the young man had to watch his 18-year-old wife slowly fade and die. Everyone did their best for baby Georgina, but without a mother's milk she quietly faded away. At the end of January 1874 she was buried beside her mother in the graveyard. Andrew was devastated. Both families mourned.

There was, in 1874, a proposal for mass emigration to New Zealand, but for most this seemed too much of jump into the unknown. It would be an idea that would fester in some minds, particularly when the roof leaked, the rain spoiled crops, or the master's annual reward was less than expected.

By January 1875, life was proving particularly challenging for Barbara Wilson at Taft. The early months of the year were never easy, for after the Christmas and New Year celebrations were done and dusted there was still much of winter to endure. Along the coastline great waves flung themselves over cliffs, threatening to steal yoals from their noosts on the shoreline and damaging anything that was not firmly anchored.

You had to keep the young ones firmly inside some days, lest they be blown away too. Sometimes, when the wind came right over the island, you felt it was drizzling a salty rain that permeated every breath and even the adults stayed inside, worrying about imagined damage. The wind found all the tiny cracks in the croft house walls and roof, so that you were never warm unless you were hard at work or in bed, with the doors firmly closed. Even then, drips fell from the roof.

Barbara felt every chilly draught that pushed its way into Taft whenever someone opened the door and forced the peaty smoke round the room, till she felt as smoked as the fish in the rafters. Each night she heard the wind threatening her, causing disturbed and uncomfortable dreams. The menace was still there when she woke, strong gusts worrying at her throughout the day. She was now a mother of six, the wife of one of the most settled men on the island and the daughter of the Methodist preacher, but there was no one to whom she could relate her current unease. Her parents advised counting your blessings if she complained and her friends felt she was better off than many. John had no time for imagined difficulties.

Finally, after five days of tireless rain, she felt at her wit's end, and it didn't help that with no school all the children were at home, squabbling and picking on each other in frustration. Thomas, the last baby, would not settle and Barbara began to feel overwhelmed by the mix of children, animals and wet clothes. When John set off to talk to one of his cousins she was relieved, for his absence reduced the tension, but all too soon small tempers frayed and the children began to bicker. Two-roomed houses all over Fair Isle seethed with frustrated humanity, smelly animals and damp clothes.

Over at Springfield things were not much better, for there Barbara's aunt, for whom she was named, was currently struggling with a different set of problems. Barbara had been loath to land herself back on her family when it became clear that the Shadler Wilsons no longer had need of her, but she had very little option when that family began to need both the space and food that she had been allocated over the previous twenty years. This was the lot of the unmarried on the island. They had to go where there was need or opportunity, or at worst, where there was someone willing to take them in. With so much work to do on a croft, an extra pair of hands to knit, cook, wash, mind the children or work on the land was indispensable, but as you grew older and less useful you sometimes felt in the way. Then, as you approached your seventies, you began to worry about the future.

Barbara had always been a fiery wee woman, and thus a person who found her role back in the arms of her family difficult. Not that Hannah made her feel ill at ease. Her sister-in-law was a kind and generous woman, one who lived her faith throughout her daily life. Hannah was a saint. It was just that Barbara was feeling her age. Living with a saint and a preacher was not easy. When Barbara was at Shadler, helping with the children and the croft work, she felt useful and that God had a role for her on the island. Here at Springfield she felt increasingly superfluous. Hannah and Stewart were getting older, but young Stewart and Agnes were well able to do the croft work. Polly, her youngest niece, made it quite clear that she preferred to look after Stewart's wee ones herself. Barbara might work in the fields, help in the house and knit like the devil, but as she grew older she felt that she lacked a purpose and wondered what the next few years would hold.

The previous evening she had found herself staring into the fire, wondering what would become of her. Try as she might, there just didn't seem to be real a place for her in this household. Eventually, she couldn't even find the energy to knit. Was there only a monotonous series of empty days from now on, desperately trying to keep out of other people's way till her time was out? Perhaps she could just fall accidentally over a cliff? Or perhaps some poor family would lose a mother and require her help.

She shivered. The devil was tempting her with black thoughts she should not have. Did he think the preacher's house was a good place to find a backslider? She shivered again, in an effort to throw him off.

"What's wrong, Babs? Are you not feeling well? You're not knitting. Are you not feeling well?"

Her sister-in-law could think of no other reason for a woman to sit motionless round the fire of an evening. Her sight might be failing, but she knew instinctively whether another woman in the room was knitting or not. Old Fair Isle women always had busy hands, even with arthritis or rheumatism. Winter was one of the best times to lay down the supply of knitting for selling or bartering, so knitting at the fireside was the Eleventh Commandment: 'Thou shalt knit,' the good Lord would have said if he had thought of it. So Barbara shook herself again, took up her wires and tried to talk as if all was normal.

"Och, I'm just wondering what the future holds for an old wifie like me. There doesn't seem much at all, now that I've reached the age I have."

"Barbara! What are you speaking of?" Her brother looked at her askance. A Methodist preacher could not countenance such a thought. The Lord had a purpose for all of his subjects, including Barbara Wilson. Questioning God's plan was little short of heresy in Stewart's eyes.

"Remember the Good Book, woman – 'For know the plans I have for you, plans to prosper you and not to harm you, plans to give you hope and a future.' Jeremiah 29 – think of the Good Book if you feel any doubt. It's all there. God has a purpose for us all, even you. He says you have both hope and a future. Your job is to believe it."

Barbara sighed. "That's as may be, Stewart, but it's not how I feel at the moment. In fact I'm not feeling any purpose for me at all. I'm feeling my age and it's not pleasant. An old spinster of sixty-four is just another mouth to feed in a house like this, so that I feel in the way rather than being useful. I can't help it if I don't understand God's plans. He hasn't seen fit to reveal them to me. If He has a plan for Barbara Wilson at Springfield, I'd be grateful if He would let me know in a more obvious way than He's doing at the moment!"

Although her brother opened his mouth to reply, his wife got in first to avoid another biblical quotation. Fair Isle Methodists were awfully fond of biblical quotations and Hannah did not feel they met every need, particularly when aimed at the female sex. Although she couldn't explain this to Stewart, she knew it to be true.

"How do think we feel, Babs? Don't you think we feel in the way here sometimes?" Hannah was less judgemental because she understood. As the preacher, Stewart still had a job to do, but sometimes Hannah too felt redundant in her own home, with a new generation growing up in it. "I'm older than you are and Stewart's seventy-one now. You just have to expect a bit less as the years go by and find your place as you can. Anyway, it's the weather that's getting to us all. January is always a hard month. When the spring comes round you'll be as good as new, you'll see. It's the dark days that finish it as far as I'm concerned, that and the endless moaning of the wind. Have a cup of tea and get on with your knitting. There's a wee one that will go cold if you don't finish that bittie on your wires. I've got my eye on that for Jeannie Eunson, so you get it done. That's your purpose for this evening, at least."

Barbara resumed her knitting, if for no other reason than to calm Hannah, who was now looking upset. Also, she was not anxious to be the focus of one of her brother's sermons, which was what would happen if she continued to complain. But still she felt frustrated, for when she thought about it, she seemed to have achieved so little in her life. Hannah, at least, had her family. What did Barbara have to show for her sixty-four years, but a puckle of knitting? It didn't seem quite enough.

⁓ ⁓

The following morning at Taft, her namesake was still dispirited. She had been overjoyed when Thomas was born alive, after what had happened to the previous two, but nevertheless she felt overwhelmed by him. Perhaps it was her age, she mused, as she struggled through tasks that she would once have taken minutes to complete. He was three and a half months old now, but she still felt totally exhausted, particularly since he still seemed intent on demanding to be fed every couple of minutes. Barbara couldn't understand it. Forty-five was hardly old at all, the age in fact that her mother-in-law was when she had James. And Jeannie had just lost her husband. She had managed. In her heart Barbara knew that they were on the cusp of spring and that things would improve once the days got slightly longer, but the long grind from February and into March lay ahead. The gales would continue and long, dreich days would accompany them. However hard she tried to fight it, depression pressed upon her soul.

It was at times like this that she missed Jeannie. Of course young Hannah was a great help now that she was fourteen, and all the others were well past the difficult baby stage and able to do things for themselves. Really, she had nothing to complain about. If only she didn't feel quite so tired.

Today it was raining again. The wet got to her soul, just as it soaked through clothes every time anyone went outside, making for wet feet, wet children, wet clothes and wet animals. However hard she tried, the floor was always muddy and the warmth from the peat fire never seemed enough to dry anything. Clothing hung from strings all around the room, clothes that she despaired of drying before midsummer. With no school for the children, when the weather was bad they all had to be inside. John was trying to give them some lessons at home in the evenings but, if the truth be told, he was not the best of teachers, with little patience for youngsters who did not pick up things as quickly as he thought they should.

So as the children squabbled, Barbara felt the need for a little breathing space and decided on a whim to send them all over to Springfield to give herself a bit of a rest. On top of the tiredness, she now had a terrible headache and she just wanted a bit of peace. Women in Fair Isle seldom had the house to themselves, but for the moment this was what she wanted more than anything else. Perhaps she could even have a lie down, an unthinkable idea in the middle of the day! She would still tend to the baby, but not to the rest of them, not today.

After a fair bit of grumbling and some worry from Hannah about the exceptional request for them all to leave, finally they trailed out the door. Barbara watched as they trooped over to Springfield, slightly guilty for dumping her children on her family, but they would understand, surely, that so soon after the baby sometimes she needed to rest. She hoped they would respect her wish to be alone and not send someone over here to check up on her. Barbara smiled to herself and wondered just how long it would be before she heard the latch lift and her mother's soft voice call her name. Well, she supposed she would be just the same when her own were grown up. You always kept an eye on your children, whatever age they were.

Sheep Rock, where men climbed up from the sea to access the flock.

Rocks in South Harbour challenged the unwary in difficult weather.

Men in yoals set off from South Harbour for a day's fishing.

The Fair Isle fleet from a distance, early in 1897.

Noosts provided a safe haven for yoals.

Fishermen bait one of the tubs of lines they will take on a day's fishing.

The decaying fish store stands beside the fish drying beach at South Harbour. Taft is the white croft in the centre of the skyline and Quoy is between chapel and church.

Robbie Irvine, a cousin of John Wilson of Taft, did not build a new croft. Without attention, old crofts quickly became cold, damp and uncomfortable.

Delling at Springfield with Shetland spades. Laborious work before the oxen.

Men, women and oxen worked together to drag harrows over difficult soil. The crub protected young cabbages.

Haymaking required a calm, dry day. Oxen made all such tasks easier.

Lowry Irvine at Quoy is scything, assisted by John Irvine, his nephew.

In 1851 Willa Mather was orphaned. Her new family moved to Kirkwall and here she sits in her mother's Fair Isle chair, with her daughter Mary Leonard carding wool.

≈ 141 ≈

In 1882 John Wilson of Taft meets his daughter Johanna in Boddam in
Dunrossness. With her husband William Wilson, she has just left Fair Isle.

Thomas Irvine and Jane (Wilson) with their daughters Barbara and Isabella in Edinburgh in 1902.

Fishermen: Springfield Stewart Wilson (brother of Barbara, Polly and Thomas), 3rd from right.

Thomas stirred and girned in the small wooden cradle that was set close to her. She would let him work up a bit more of a noise before she stirred. Yes, that was it. The full-blown cry was coming. It didn't take him long at all. Oh, she wouldn't let him wait any longer. The poor bairn. It wasn't his fault that his mother was feeling poorly. Barbara leant over the crib and both felt and saw the bright, sharp light in her head for a moment, before she fell on the ground beside her child. For an instant she struggled to fight, to get up, to say something, but it was all over before she could speak a word. She lay there on the cold, earth floor, a pile of inanimate clothing wrapped around a slack body whose eyes now stared unseeingly up at the roof, her mouth swinging open in a ghastly grimace. Death had only taken an instant to make his ugly move.

The baby began to howl even louder, but to his surprise nobody came. Babies never usually got to scream for long in a crowded croft house, for there was always someone to pick them up. But not here and certainly not today. As the morning gloom began to lighten, the peat fire in Taft began to fail. Very gradually, the temperature dropped as the child continued to scream. A house that was normally a vibrant, crowded family home was in a moment changed to a cold, dark morgue.

Over at Springfield, Hannah Wilson was indeed upset about her daughter, knowing that if the girl simply needed some peace and quiet for a change, she was hardly going to help by chapping at her door, but worrying that there might be a problem other than Hannah's reported 'tiredness'. Goodness knows, a baby could keep you up some nights. She would just be tired, surely.

The two lots of grandchildren played well together and young Hannah was helping Polly make a meal for them all. It was all under control, but... "I'll just take a turn over there and see if she needs anything. I'll not stay if I'm not needed." Barbara was on her feet, wrapping a warm shawl round her thin shoulders.

Her sister-in-law's unexpected arrival had been a bit unsettling for Hannah, if the truth were known, in the main because Barbara herself was unsettled, but she was a willing pair of hands to help with the chores and above all else, sensitive. She could see without asking that Hannah was perturbed this morning. And it wouldn't be so bad, her going over. It wouldn't seem like interfering if it was her aunt. If the girl was indeed trying to rest, Barbara could look after the baby for a while, without it seeming like a criticism. There was a different relationship between an aunt and a niece.

"I'll give her a hand if she needs it. If she's under the weather, another pair of hands won't be in the way, as long as they're not her mother's."

Hannah smiled at the similarity of their thoughts.

"I'll take over some of these bannocks in the meantime, to give me a reason to brew some tea. Keep the wee ones here till you hear from me. Yes, and if she's not well, I'll run back and tell you." She anticipated her sister-in-law's planned instructions without hearing them, smiling, for now she felt useful rather than in the way.

"I don't think my mother's ill," Hannah spoke up anxiously. Her mother was not old, but there had been a lot of fuss when this last baby was born, which had made her nervous. She hadn't really thought anything of it when she was told to bring the wee ones over, but now she knew it was out of the ordinary. What if something was wrong and she hadn't noticed? What if there was something she should have done for her mother? Almost an adult, she was much more aware that childbirth could be a difficult time. She knew her mother had lost two babies in recent years and had been aware of the tension surrounding this last one. But she had thought the tension was over. Was there something else she didn't know about?

Her grandmother caught her look and calmed her. "Don't you worry, my pettie. Your mother's fine, she's just tired. You lot would tire an army and she's on her own over there since your other granny went away. Sometimes I think it would have been a lot better if she had stayed here where she's needed, rather than gallivanting all over the world at her age."

"I'm not sure Kirkwall is all that far away," Barbara muttered as she made her way to the door. "That poor woman was just doing what she thought best at the time. You know how she doted on James. And she didn't know she might be needed here. Anyway, like as not the Good Lord knew what he was doing, when you think of poor Aggie and her troubles. It's as well Jeannie was there for Aggie and there's plenty of us here to look after Barbara if she needs help from anyone."

"I know. I'm just worried."

Barbara realised that Hannah must indeed be upset to speak against Jeannie, for they had been the very best of friends. She pulled a blanket tightly round her shoulders, put her head down and made her way through the weather to Taft, so close on a good day, but far enough to be soaked when it was like this.

"Hello there!" She called out loudly as she approached the door, not wanting to take her namesake by surprise. Perhaps she couldn't hear her over the wind. But the barrage of noise from the desperate child was a surprise as she gently pushed the door open. It took a few seconds to get used to the gloom, for by now there were few embers left amongst the fire-stones. Then, what gradually took shape in the shadows roused her old bones to distress.

<hr />

"Oh Barbara, oh pettie, what have you done? Oh dear! Oh no! Can you no wake, love? Don't say you've gone. Oh dear! Barbara!"

As she was speaking she threw herself down on the ground and pulled the girl into her arms, patting her face and trying to hear a breath, even though she knew she had gone. Barbara Wilson had seen a lot of death in her sixty-odd years. She held her niece up, but the mouth was quite slack and ugly, the eyes staring, and there was no hint of breathing. The body had already begun to cool. The lass had gone. And now she had to deal with it. Despite all her life experience, she wished that it had not been she who had discovered this tragedy, one that was about to cause so much grief. As she hugged the girl to her, she thought of how many lives would be devastated. It was so unfair. She patted the dead woman, as if trying to assure her all would be well, but the baby reminded her that there were immediate needs. There was no time to grieve or feel sorry for herself. Thomas needed to be fed and the family needed to be told.

Barbara's hands shook as she gently placed her namesake back on the ground, turning now to the baby whose cries had diminished, probably through exhaustion, but whose immediate feeding problems still existed. She lifted the soaking child from the crib and made him dry, crooning all the while to try to comfort him. Help had to be sought, but she couldn't just leave the body on its own. Apart from the custom that a dead body should never be left alone, what if one of the island children came by with a message? What if young Hannah popped back? There were no locked doors here. Anyone could come in and there were others less well accustomed to death than she. Barbara had to stay with her namesake until someone came to take over the duty of care for the dead. As she paced, she thought that she wanted to get the body off the floor, for it looked so undignified, sprawled out like that. But the baby needed comforting and feeding and he was alive. He was the priority. Her thoughts whirled as her hands continued to shake. Think, she told herself. What to do?

First she put some peat on the fire to get it going again. It would do them all no good to have a frigidly cold room. Then she pulled the body over to the side with one hand, apologising to the girl for moving her, blinded by tears as she pushed and pulled at her clothing, trying at least to make her decent. It seemed suddenly important that the woman should retain her dignity when she was seen. Men never saw bodies that women had not prepared properly if they could help it and even now, Barbara wanted to keep this body sacred. But the baby was screaming again and the noise forced her to think harder. Prioritise. She must prioritise.

Holding the child close, she went outside. In the distance she could see young Andrew Wilson. He would do. She began to holler his name, waving with her free hand, juggling young Thomas with the other. The boy came running as fast as he could, for a message boy always got a reward.

Trying to ignore the baby twisting desperately in his shawl, Barbara spoke as slowly as she could. "Now, you listen to me. This is a very important message. I want you to run as fast as you can to Springfield and ask young Mrs Wilson to come here as fast as she can, not Mrs Hannah Wilson mind. I want to see Mrs Aggie Wilson. And if young Mr Stewart is there, send him too. Then off home with you and tell your mother they need some help at Springfield."

There was no need to say more, for he was off as soon as he saw her face. Whatever it was, he knew it was serious. This was no time to loiter for a reward.

Barbara sighed. If she could protect Hannah from this for just a bit longer, she would. Hannah would break her heart and blame herself for not coming over as soon as the children arrived, as if that would have made any difference. The men would cope better, though her brother would be hard pressed to deal with this, for all his religion. They needed to sort things quickly, tell John, arrange for the children to be told and feed this baby. There was hardly any cow's milk here and Thomas was certainly not used to drinking his dinner from a spoon. The old woman remembered Barbara saying that her cows were almost dry, but she needed to find something for the child and she couldn't leave Barbara alone. Barbara had sat with many a dying soul, but still she was shaking as she worked around the corpse. It wasn't just the baby's noise, it was the terrible tragedy of it all.

There was a little milk in a jug on the larder shelf. She would give it a try, warming it up slightly and sitting with the baby tight in her arms, forcing his face to the bowl to try to make him swallow. However, he was too small to learn when he was as upset as this. Then she tried with a little horn spoon, but still to no avail. Thomas just choked and spluttered all the more, turning his head from side to side in desperation, until they were both wet and distressed in equal measure. The child was inconsolable, wondering why this was not the breast that would pacify him. Where was it? He screamed for it in frustration and hunger.

Barbara felt herself sweating with panic as she failed at every attempt. Finally, all the milk in the house was gone and she doubted if the baby had swallowed any more than a drop or two by accident. And all the while, she felt the eyes of the dead woman watching her, to see what she would do next. Without the child, she could begin to lay her out properly, but there was no way she could put him down and ignore him, for he was alive and had priority over his dead mother.

Poor, poor Barbara. Did He not know they had need of her here? She went to the door to escape the dead woman's eyes, clutching the baby close as she scrutinised the grey landscape, tears of sorrow and frustration coursing down her old, lined face as the rain continued to fall, albeit with less force.

Then she saw them, young Aggie and Stewart and behind them, more slowly of course, her brother and Hannah. Whatever the boy had said, he had got the wind up them all. Well, perhaps it was for the best. They could all see her together and look after her and each other, while she tried to sort something out for the baby. She went inside and waited, pulling a blanket round her shoulders, adding yet more peat to the fire and sitting a kettle on it to warm for tea. Practicalities had to be observed, even in the midst of death.

She met the younger couple at the door and simply said, "I'm so sorry, so terribly, terribly sorry," and stood to one side to let them take it in. The situation was clear, since she had not covered Barbara, only moved her. "She was like this when I came in. She had been gone some time, I think. I'm so sorry. Tell Hannah I'm sorry and Stewart too. I'm off to find some milk for this one. He's starving. I don't want to lose him as well."

"Oh no! Barbara!" The young couple threw themselves to the ground, just as she had done. Then Stewart stumbled to the door in an effort to warn his mother, not that anything he could do or say could protect her from this.

Barbara left her nephew and niece to their tragic business and headed off up the track, holding the baby close to her to protect him from the weather. Tears were streaming down her face, but she had no time to mourn, for she now had an idea of where to find some immediate sustenance for Thomas. She had to see him fed so that he would stop screaming. Once he was fed, she could think. Barbara ran through the mire, the rain and the terrible cold, all the way up to Stoneybrake, breathing hard and loud by the time she got there, for it was a good distance from Taft for an older lady to run in any weather.

She burst in as soon as she got to the door, looking round the room for what she needed, hoping that in her desperation she would not be refused. If she was refused now, she felt she would just collapse. Running round the island was a habit she had long since given up.

Gasping for breath and her knees shaking, she leaned on the rough table, where a meal was in the process of being prepared. "Can you feed this baby, please? I've just found Barbara Wilson at Taft stone dead. I don't know when he last fed, but he's barely got the energy to cry now. Please help him. I'll work something out afterwards, but for now, can you feed him? Please!"

Ellen looked at the older woman and took pity on her immediately. Barbara was one of the respected spinsters on the island, someone who had worked her way through life, not asking anything from anybody. Now she had to ask for something she could not give. Ellen was not particularly close with the Wilsons, but neither would she deny them at such a time.

And the woman knew why she had been asked. God had given her bigger breasts than most. Many of the island women were hard put to feed a baby through the first year, hardly surprising given the amount of work they had to do and the fact that they always ate last and little, but she who had trouble having babies, had no trouble feeding them. No wonder the old lady had chosen her. However willing some of the other mothers might have been, as like as not they would have had nothing to spare.

"Do you tell me that? What a dreadful thing for the family. And such a nice lassie," she said, taking the baby from the old woman as she was talking, realising the need to talk, to give Barbara time to get her breath back again. It was what you did. On an island you helped each other where you could.

"Pour yourself a cup of tea and take your ease. I can only give him one side though. Janet needs to be fed soon." Janet was her five month old child. "What happened to her?" she asked, a question that Barbara was to hear so often in the coming days. "She hadn't been ill, had she? What are they going to do with the baby? I can't be doing this every day. Help yourself to a scone while you wait. You look as if you could do with something."

"I don't know what happened to her. I don't even know what will happen tonight. I just need to get him fed till we have time to think. Poor lassie. She knew she wasn't well, so she sent the children over to Springfield. So she died alone, poor soul. She died alone."

Ellen shook her head as the baby sucked. Imagine. Dying alone and wondering as your last thought if they would find your baby in time. It didn't bear thinking about. In a small community like this, with everyone living cheek by jowl, people seldom died alone.

"Was John home when you left?"

"No. My nephew and Aggie were there and Stewart and Hannah had just arrived. No one else. I'd been there a bittie by myself. I didn't want to leave in case any of her children came in and found her while I was away and all the time the baby was screaming."

"You did right there. That would have been a terrible thing, one of the children finding her on their own."

Barbara shook her head as the tears came back. "This has been the very worst day of my life. I didn't know what to do for the best."

"Well you did the right thing for now. This wee one will have to get used to cow's milk as soon as he can, though he's not chosen the best time of the year to do that."

Barbara knew this. She also knew that not all babies took to cows' milk when they were this young. It even made some of them ill. For all her running around the island, this wee one might still starve before the spring. She looked at him with such deep emotion as he lay in Ellen's arms, replete, sleeping and exhausted, a far cry from the screaming wee monster she had dealt with earlier. Him die? Not if she could help it.

Having rubbed his back to encourage the air from him, the woman rearranged her clothing and handed him back. "That should hold him for a while. But I can't take him on as well. My husband wouldn't let me. Occasionally perhaps, but not often. I have enough for Janet, but at this stage not enough for two on a regular basis. Janet is five months now and the milk might go. I can't take the chance."

"Of course you can't, but I thank you for the moment. I must get back now and see how they all are. They'll have wondered where I ran off to. I just thought you could spare the wee one a little, for the moment."

"It's a pleasure to help you, Mistress Wilson."

Wrapping her shawl tightly round her, Barbara held Thomas close to her own, sadly dry breast.

"Will you manage down on your own?"

"Why would I not? I'm just fine now, or as fine as I can be on a day like today. Thank you for the help and the tea. You've given me a bit of time to think what to do with this wee one. I'm forever in your debt. We all are."

"No. You're not. Barbara was a lovely woman. I'm glad to do this for her, if no one else. Look after the wee one. He's a fine peerie lad."

Barbara made her way home, clutching her small burden and wondering what she would find at Taft. This time, she had neither the need nor urge to hurry, but the wind was up and the light was going so she must make haste if she was to keep them both warm. It would be bad back there, with John and her sister-in-law to deal with, not to mention all the children. Young Mary was only a wee one herself yet. The younger ones would hardly understand. And there was the next feed to find. This respite would not last long.

By the time she arrived back at Taft, all had changed. A good fire warmed the main room and the body lay through in the back of the house. The women, not only her own family but also women from other crofts, were taking it in turns to sit with her, as more and more folk came in to show support, to cry, or to bring a bit of something to eat, so that those mourning at least did not have that job to worry them. The other children were still at Springfield. John and Stewart were out in the barn, cutting and banging, putting together a coffin. They didn't want the children to hear that noise when they came over to say goodbye to their mother.

All the death rituals would be observed and yet nothing would help. Nothing ever helped when it was a young one who died. Just at the end of December it had been young Jerome Williamson. Death always seemed worse at this time of the year.

There was still some milk in the cows at Springfield so, after a bit, Barbara decided to take herself off there to see if she could start Thomas on cow's milk. She had seen it done before, even if not always with great success. Babies did not do well after their mothers died, so that they followed them, as like as not. Well, there were other mothers still nursing on the island. She would ask for help from them till she could get him to sup from a spoon or a cup. Thomas would not die if Barbara could help it.

He did learn to sup, but not readily or easily. Immediately after the funeral Barbara moved into Taft with Thomas. If he was going to die it would be in his home with his family she told them, not that John showed much interest. For the first time he really felt the loss of his family in Kirkwall and the support and advice they might have given. Barbara had been the love of his life. When she agreed to marry him he had been so proud to bring her home. They were the golden couple, and when the children came it seemed as if the Taft Wilsons were bound for success. Then his family left and now his wife was gone. All the dreams of his youth seemed to have crumbled into dust.

John loved Fair Isle. He loved Taft. The man felt Fair Isle to his very core, and even when so many had been set on leaving he had only once doubted that he would stay here till he died. His creed was that if you worked hard and you followed God's word to the letter, He would show you the way. Since he was additionally a Wilson, the man had been arrogant enough to feel sure that some level of prosperity would always be his. Well, his pride had gone before a fall and no mistake. Now, even in prayer he found no solace, and the Good Book was no help either.

In the following months he went through the motions of being a father but, in truth, the man left his children to find their own way. He was unable to relate to anyone, so bound up was he in his grief. At heart, he was angry. What sort of a God would do this to a man who lived his life properly and honoured Him? What sort of reward was this for praising His name and obeying His commandments? John was not sure he had time for such a malicious God.

The combined trauma of losing both his wife and questioning his faith threw the man quite off balance. With no recognition of what happened, he reverted to the single-minded automaton that he was when his father died. Old Stewart tried to tell him that it was not his role to question the Good Lord. After all, he had lost his beloved daughter, but was willing to accept that this was part of the great plan which would be revealed in the fullness of time. Our role was to accept it when God tried our faith. We might not understand, but must hold to the belief that all would be revealed in the hereafter. It was not for us to question the ways of the Lord when he chose to take back one of his own, for whatever their pain, neither doubted that Barbara was safely with the Lord.

Young Stewart was a cousin, a brother-in-law and a close friend, but at ten years younger had always taken the lesser place in the relationship. Now he found it difficult to reach John. Even when he tried to say something to help, it sounded hollow in his own ears, so that he was reduced to religious platitudes, just like his father. However religious you are, there are times when platitudes do not strike the right chord.

The weeks passed, with John remaining distanced from everyone. Finally, Aunt Barbara decided to make her own presence felt so that the family could begin to work as a unit again. It was a different unit of course, but gradually they all learned to adjust. She brought everyone into her struggle to find enough milk for Thomas and then to force him to get it down. Even the boys were made to take a turn at this frustrating task, so that they learned how important the infant was to the family. When you held a baby in your arms and watched his eyes move to follow you, he became very real. It was, she told them, something they could all do for their mother. Rather like his uncle James in Kirkwall, Thomas became a special baby. The first calves would not be born until April and by March the family sometimes despaired, for the child was very stubborn. They begged milk from anyone who might have any to spare and then fought with the baby to make him take every drop of the precious liquid. He got sugared water when all else failed.

Occasionally they asked women who were breast-feeding their own children to give him something, anything. This family, who had so much pride in their own self-sufficiency, humbled themselves (even with those they disliked) without a second thought. Of course they never told John, for men are inclined to let principles go beyond need. Aunt Barbara was utterly focused on keeping the baby out of the churchyard at Kirkigeo, one that was already littered with small, unmarked graves. Barbara's relief when the first cow calved was palpable, and by this time Thomas was confidently drinking from a cup or spoon. The hard struggle to feed him had been a unifying activity that in a small way distanced them from their grief. For everyone, Thomas represented hope against the odds.

For those not involved in the Taft Wilson tragedy, the lack of a school continued to occupy their minds. It was insupportable that an island that had in the past been educationally well-served now lacked this amenity. Even the passing of the 1872 Scottish Education Act failed to provide either school or teacher, at a time when universal educational provision was the law. To add insult to injury, a letter in the Shetland press noted that the islanders now had to pay an education rate, but had no school.

It has to be said that after years of deficiency, ordering universal education in Scotland did not mean that it was immediately accomplished. A government school inspector sent to assess Shetland's needs, reported that Lerwick alone had suitable schools. He estimated that there were 5,649 children who required to be taught in Shetland, but only school places for 1,445. Furthermore, the Education Act created official expectations about what would be taught and how it would be both delivered and assessed. In the past, although it was hoped that reading, some writing and perhaps numeracy would be taught, understanding and learning the catechism and reading the

Bible were the essential goals. Although some teachers had taught more than this there had been no national standards to be met. However, from 1872 there was a specific curriculum and both teachers and children would be externally assessed to see that it was taught. It was now expected that all children would attend school between the ages of five and thirteen, although it was agreed that some children over the age of ten could gain exemptions. It would of course be many years before religious education would fade in importance in Scotland, but the 1872 Act introduced the concept of academic rigour as the central aim.

In Fair Isle, 1872 came and went while the parents continued to complain. Bruce continued to promise that he was working on the problem but still no school appeared, and since the local authority was not yet in a position to fund a school on the island the SSPCK was still involved in any decision concerning a suitable teacher. Sadly, they vetoed both the suggestion of a Mr Telfer and then a combination of two islanders, Andrew and Stewart Wilson (the objection being not that the two men were unable to do the job, but that they were 'American Methodists'). Parents became increasingly frustrated.

It was, in fact, 1875 before William Laurence was appointed by the SSPCK as catechist and teacher. In the 1871 census there is record of an unoccupied 'New Hall', a building that was eventually kitted out as a temporary school. The hall was built by local men at Taft Brae and was rumoured to have come from money gifted to the islanders after the wreck of the *Gazelle*. Although this building did not fulfil the requirements of the 1872 Education Act, it provided Mr Laurence with somewhere to begin his task. Accommodation was provided for the teacher and his family at The Haa, which was refurbished for this purpose. By 1878 the school's management was finally transferred to the local school board.

A government-prescribed school was eventually constructed by local men, assisted by a qualified mason, who supervised the quarrying of stones at Buness. This work was paid for by a government grant and by 1882 the new building was furnished with desks, books, maps and a blackboard, encompassing all the requirements of the 1872 Education Act. There was also a splendid schoolhouse for the teacher and his family.

William Laurence was born in Leith, near Edinburgh, where his father was a bookseller. His father then moved to Dunrossness with his family, but William continued to live in Edinburgh with his grandparents and latterly trained as a teacher. He moved to Shetland to teach when his father died in 1861, so that by 1875 the island benefited from an experienced man, one who understood Shetland life.

The first school register comes from October 1878, when the School Board took over management of the school. There are thirty-four pupils, including twelve boys aged between fourteen and nineteen (all of whom were beyond the new legal age limit) in an effort to compensate for the years they had been denied the opportunity to learn. At this time many children left school before twelve or thirteen, for it was possible to gain exceptions in the early years of the national system.

Laurence's classroom was small and hardly suitable for a wide range of ages and abilities. No doubt, since many of the boys had already been working at sea and on the land, some had no great use for school lessons. It says a lot for parents that they felt it important that the older children should learn to read, write and count before they took up their lives as fishermen. It says a lot for the teacher that he made so much effort, knowing that all of the boys would immediately become fishermen.

The first week in May usually saw the cutting of peat, an event celebrated as the 'lift', where after a hard day's work at the peat beds, families visited one another to socialise, with exhausted men folk not expected to do anything but gossip. They had carried their tuskers (special spades for cutting, or 'casting' the peat) to the peat beds, as well as delling spades which might be needed for coarser patches. The tusker had to be sharp, so that its 12-inch length cut the turfs cleanly into slabs. Moorland to the north of the island at Ward Hill was where much of the peat lay, so for many it meant a walk of some two miles there and back. In good weather it was hard but rewarding and people enjoyed being out in the open air. In bad weather, it was simply backbreaking toil.

Over generations the islanders denuded wide areas of land in this manner, since peat was the only fuel in this treeless place. A good supply of fuel was all that made the island habitable, for fires had to be kept going throughout the year for warmth, light and cooking. From the 1880s, the Crofting Commission would urge better management of peat beds, but by this time most of the damage had been done and in Fair Isle there was much less left to cut.

People from the Springfield and Taft crofts usually walked up to the beds together, and that first year after Barbara's death they were all pleased that the sun shone. Shawls and extra sweaters were soon discarded and, despite the strong sense of mourning that still pervaded all their activities, the young ones began to let the pleasure of the new season take over. They joked about the boys' strength and the girls' inability to lift the turves quickly enough and allowed themselves to enjoy the day.

Young Stewart Wilson had intentionally chosen John as his companion on the walk up and when the young ones began to fool about a bit, he quietened John's irritation at their frivolity. "They're in mourning. They need to remember that."

"Aye. I hardly think they need reminding of that, John. But they're young. It's been a hard time for them. Let them have a bit of fun today. They won't work any the less for enjoying the job. Anyway, our Barbara would not want her children to be wrapped up in mourning forever. I know we're still shocked, but life goes on, man. Let the young ones have a day off."

So John said nothing as he began to work, feeling only emptiness himself and quite unable to understand how anyone else could feel differently. The men started by stripping off the top layer of turf to leave a smooth and level surface, a skilled job for a practised hand. Once they started to dig properly, the peat had to be eased carefully off the tuskers and the women would stand at the bottom of the bank to help with this process, before throwing the peats to the surface, where they were left in rows to dry. The cutting would take a week or so to complete, with women returning two or three weeks later to raise the turves, laying a good sized peat on its end and placing two peats on either side of it, so that it aired properly. In another two or three weeks these turves would be turned and any that were dry would be taken down to the croft, where they would be carefully stacked.

The entire process was weather dependent, so it might be some time before the majority were ready to move. At this time, ponies carried the peat down to the crofts in large rope bags called meshies, which were slung on either side of a wooden saddle. Women and older children led the ponies on the slow walk home, often carrying an additional load in baskets on their own backs. With the peat beds being some distance from the crofts this meant the start of many trips to ensure that current and future supplies of fuel would be certain. Those not yet dry (or perhaps not required immediately) were covered with turf and left in situ, until a run up to the hill for peat was made later in the year.

The spring always meant a general clean of the houses, so Barbara felt this would be a good time to move things around a bit at Taft, to introduce a few small changes that indicated that life was moving on. She opened the kist of Barbara's clothes, persuading Jane and Johanna to work their way through the little their mother had owned, choosing something both for themselves and young Mary that they could wrap up and keep for the future. Any material that was not needed was cut down to use for clothes for the younger ones. Of course there were lots of tears and memories before the heavy lid of the box was once more closed, but Barbara knew that tears were part of the mourning process. John was told that she had given the kist to Johanna and Jane to gather their own bits and pieces towards the day when they would leave home. John didn't care. A kist was just a kist. It didn't matter to him who used it, or what was in it. Barbara was dead.

The bright days of the early summer lightened the souls of the rest of the family. The door to the croft house now stood permanently open during good weather, when chairs and boxes were moved outside to allow people to work in the sunshine. Gradually, every article of clothing and bedding was washed in every respectable house. Beds were relined with seaweed, for it would be a while yet before fresh straw and chaff would be available and some of them could not wait that long. Day after day, the women washed, dried and cleaned. Girls liked these summer washing days, when they piled the heavier things into tubs and stamped on them until all the dirt was forced out. This was one of the easier ways to pass the time and their young feet felt better for the task.

During the first half of 1875 the families at Taft and Springfield worked communally, trying to accept what had happened. Each day had a timetable and everyone had a task, so that there was no opportunity to sit and pine for what was lost. The men immersed themselves in the fishing when they were not needed to help elsewhere. For everyone, exhaustion subdued grief. For Barbara's children, of course, life would never be the same, for this gentle soul had been the cement that held the family together. The younger ones missed her presence most of all, for even before her death their father had been a more severe and remote figure, busy at the fishing, on the farm, or urging them to study scriptures or schoolwork.

John was no different from the majority of Fair Isle men when it came to children. When he was in the house, he was either occupied with a bit of carpentry, rope-making, reading the Bible, or just busy at his books. He was a bookworm, as widely read as was possible in Fair Isle, an activity about which he felt slightly guilty since he had been brought up to abhor time-wasting and there was, in his mind, a suspicion that reading (of a non-religious type) might lead him astray. Guilt was an important part of his religion.

Children were women's business, until the boys were old enough to be the men's responsibility, on the beach and in the boats. Of course the children had to be schooled in religious matters to keep them from the devil's path, but the more strenuously religious fathers could alienate their children. Now, totally cocooned in his sorrow and despair, John Wilson distanced himself from everyone. When they heard about the death of his brother-in-law in Kirkwall, the news only served to underscore the unfairness of the world. Having lost a son and then her husband, he wondered how Aggie would manage. For the first time, he felt glad that his mother was with his sister. He knew he wasn't supposed to question God's ways, but his family were hardworking, God-fearing folk. Why would He punish them like this, taking away husbands and wives before their time?

Aunt Barbara did her best. Her brother had promised her "plans to give you hope and a future," the night before his daughter died. Had this been God's intention for her old age? The idea made her shiver, for no one could deny that she now had both hope and a future, as she struggled to find the right way to bolster small, damaged minds at Taft. And, of course, everyone focused on Thomas and keeping him alive through that first year.

*Chapter 10*

# $\mathcal{P}$retty $\mathcal{P}$olly

Still the tide of emigration continued. Four Eunson families accepted free passage to New Zealand. Newspapers might not have been a regular phenomenon but, after *The Shetland Times* was established in 1872 more arrived on the island and they always advertised opportunities elsewhere, since the New World continued to require immigrants. Most of the letters that came back from those who left were entirely positive. All over Shetland people were leaving for pastures new, so that Fair Isle was simply reflecting a general trend. Sometimes families left in groups. At other times it was single, younger men.

Alexander Wilson of Houlaby (a brother of Stewart Wilson, the preacher) died in 1867. His wife Catherine and her children set about managing without him on the croft until her son, Thomas, decided to seek his fortune in New York. Gradually, the other children followed, and in 1872 Catherine too was persuaded to join them, despite being in her sixties. Only her daughter remained, but then her eldest boy decided to join his American relations. It was unorchestrated and unspectacular, but a constant reminder that the outside world offered an alternative.

Many were satisfied with a less demanding move and Kirkwall continued to act as a magnet. Between 1871 and 1881, Thomas and Jacobina Wilson from Kennaby, Robert and Esther Eunson from Busta, Jeremiah and Andrina Wilson from Shadler, Robert and Agnes Wilson from Barkland, Thomas and Ann Wilson from Shadler, and Andrew and Barbara Wilson from Taing all took their families to Kirkwall. Andrina Williamson and Hannah Wilson joined them with their children, after they were widowed. Kirkwall was flourishing, so it was easy to find jobs, but most importantly it provided a massive support system, which made relocation easier. Other families went to Westray and Stronsay, just as they had done in the past.

Since John Wilson of Taft would never consider emigration, he had to focus on his life on his croft, with no thought of reward or enjoyment now that Barbara was dead. He knew he would survive at Taft, but found it hard to escape his black, widower's thoughts. Up earlier than most and out at every opportunity, he found that in exhaustion he could sleep for a while. Sleep was the only liberation from the nightmare that had resulted from Barbara's death. For him there was no joy, no anticipation, no laughter and no comfort. Men were expected to get on with their lives when their wives died, saddened but coping. God's will be done. John was a strongly passionate man, yet like many of his fellows, one who found any expression of emotion horribly embarrassing, shameful even. Up till now he had been successful in maintaining his quietly superior, controlled demeanour.

His wife had known his true feelings and had liked him all the more for his various weaknesses. No man is perfect, although some do find this a difficult fact to face. Very few people knew that John could not bear to kill his own sheep, having relied on Lowry to undertake the task in his stead. When Lowry left the island he was forced to ask for help from Springfield, after yet another disastrous attempt at throat cutting. He tried so hard to draw the knife over the sheep's throat, but just as when he was a young man, he felt the rush of blood from his head and a terrible dizziness that made him stumble and lose hold on the beast. Barbara's brother was quietly relieved that his friend had some weaknesses.

At Springfield in June 1875, despite their religion, Stewart and Hannah were also struggling. Stewart had been devastated by the loss of his beloved daughter. He would willingly have gone in her place, as he told the Lord each night. The man wrestled with despair and felt guilt that in his heart he did not always rejoice that his daughter had gone to heaven, for his Barbara would surely be in heaven. He prayed for guidance and help, but the terrible sadness remained. Hannah too was desolate. She had already lost two children, the eldest as a teenager, the youngest as a baby, but had hoped to go to her grave without more grief. Barbara had been the perfect daughter, so that Hannah, too, found scant consolation in either her religion or her friends' platitudes.

The old couple were thus not in the least ready to cope when, one evening in June, Barbara came to visit, young Thomas closely wrapped to her bosom as was now the norm. She was her usual outspoken self, wasting no time in pleasantries. "You'll have to keep your Polly over here. She's in the way at Taft. The girls don't like it and I'm not sure I do either."

"What on earth are you talking about? Why shouldn't the girl give a hand where it's needed?" Stewart was truly puzzled by his sister's demand. He had in fact been pleased that Polly had found an outlet for the frustration of being just a spare pair of hands here at Springfield. She was thirty now and had been pining for a husband. Even his wife, who had spoiled her from the moment her twin had died as a baby, had begun to find

Polly a little wearing on the subject. Helping at Taft seemed to take her mind off her own troubles and had given her a purpose. What on earth could be wrong with that?

"The older ones think she's after their father!"

For a few minutes, silence was the only possible reply. Then the two old folk spoke at the same time, tripping over their words in their anxiety to squash the awful idea. "That's a terrible thing to say. She wouldn't. It's not allowed. Don't be stupid. They're just upset. Young ones don't understand these things."

"Aye, well that's what I said at first. Then I watched her carefully over the last few days and I think they're right. She's been smooling around after him from the start. She only arrives when she thinks John will be in and works at being charming all the time, rather than doing anything useful. I don't think he notices, the daft gouk, but the children do. Hannah's fifteen now. She knows about things like that at her age. Young John and Jane agree with her and I must say I do too.

"John's still too wrapped up in himself to notice much of anything, but time will pass and if we leave it, we might all regret it. We know they can't get married. Does she? The church is quite clear about marrying a dead sister's husband. It's not allowed. Tell her, Stewart. And keep her away. There'll be trouble if you don't. It's got to be stopped. The last thing we need is more trouble in that family.

"The children are still trying to come to terms with their mother's loss, but Polly's over there now, grinning like a daftie and interfering, trying to attract his notice. It's not seemly. You've got to stop it, Stewart! It's just not good for the children to have her hanging around all the time. Your Barbara's hardly been dead a moment and if you don't sort it, people will start to talk."

Barbara had always been proud of the family's Methodism, as well as her brother's position in the church, and felt obliged to defend both. It is difficult in the 21st century to understand the extent to which religion controlled life at that time. Although by the middle of the 19th century John Knox's Calvinism had become less severe, it still retained a deal of control and most of its followers felt superior to the host of dissenters. On such a small island, any transgression by one of the Methodists would not go unnoticed, or unmentioned.

Whatever your personal views on religious theory at the time, in 1875 the state had a very firm set of rules for everyone to follow, including a long list of prohibited marriages. This list was intended to protect women and the institution of marriage itself and a marriage between Polly and John would threaten the very fabric of the community. Marriage to your wife's younger sister (even if the wife was dead) was forbidden, to ensure that no man (or woman) was tempted to remove their spouse for what might seem to be a better (or younger) option. With so many people having large families over many years, your last sibling could be twenty-five years younger than you. With family members of such disparate ages living in close proximity, you needed to regulate against temptation. Everyone knew that a man could be tempted by a much younger version of his wife, particularly when wives had been worn down by hard work and endless childbearing. Throughout the land the rules were adhered to, except in the upper echelons of society where people could afford to go abroad and marry all sorts of relatives, in all sorts of countries. Such an option was certainly not open to Scots who lived in isolated rural communities.

When his sister spoke of her suspicions, Stewart Wilson immediately understood the threat, both to the couple and the community. If Barbara was right, he must warn his daughter off so that she could extract herself from a potentially threatening situation, both to herself and her church. He thought it was entirely possible that Barbara was wrong, but it could also be that Polly simply did not understand the rules and had let her feelings run away with her. Girls could be awfully silly sometimes. John was probably not aware of anything at all, given the depth of his grief, although that would not last forever. Polly was bonny, but for some reason she had not attracted followers. However, a union with John was not where she would find salvation and this she must be told, in no uncertain terms.

Polly did not argue with her father that night when she came back from Taft. Neither, however, did she agree with him. "I'm just being a good neighbour," she insisted, looking at him directly and showing no signs of backing down. "You're always telling us we have to help people who are in need. I don't see why I should stop. I'm doing nothing wrong."

This was as near insolence as any young woman could get at that time and in that place, particularly when her father was the Methodist lay preacher. Polly listened to Stewart's sermon about obeying the rules. Such a union would be ungodly, he repeated several times. "It is better to die without children, than to leave ungodly children," he thundered.

Her mother could only weep quietly at all the fuss and whisper softly, "Oh, Polly, please don't let us down."

Polly did not argue. She stood there silently, staring at her father for a bit, before taking herself through to the other room and to bed. Her parents did not understand, she told herself. She was a woman now, not a child. They were too old. Times were changing. John liked her, she was certain. She had done nothing wrong. And Barbara was dead. She would just have to be a little more circumspect about her visits to Taft for she was sure John appreciated her presence there. When a woman is in love, she is blind to the opinion of others and deaf to her own moral watchdog. People have always been able to persuade themselves that their love is different, loftier than mundane social rules and formal regulation.

The next day was a Sunday. Stewart had not slept well. He had tossed and turned all night, wondering if Barbara had been correct in her suspicions, for Polly was certainly up to something. As if they did not have enough sorrow to deal with over Barbara. How dare Polly add to their woes! He had to nip this in the bud before it became a real issue for everyone. Was John even aware of Polly's skittishness? He had seemed as overwhelmed in grief as ever last time they had spoken. But the women at Taft were right in one thing: he was ripe for the picking. Island men usually remarried not too long after their wives died for purely practical reasons, but a suitable time-period was respected and it had only been six months since Barbara died. However, even if John had not yet cottoned on to the fact that Polly had set her hat at him, eventually he would. That morning the old man set off to preach with a heavy heart.

Stewart Wilson was well into his sermon that Sunday when, without warning, he collapsed in the pulpit. Suddenly his long life and ministry in Fair Isle were over. People from both sides of the religious divide came together to acknowledge his service, both to God and to the people of the island. Hannah lived for another year, but without enthusiasm, dying in full faith that she would be reunited with her husband and dead children in the sight of God's grace. Their son, Stewart, picked up the family standard and by common consent became the next lay preacher for Methodism in Fair Isle.

One result of Stewart's death was the cessation of Polly's daily visits to Taft. After the initial mourning period, when even she could not countenance such behaviour, she was sufficiently involved in her mother's care to reduce dramatically her spare time. Stewart's wife Aggie had four wee ones to contend with now, so a bedridden invalid who required special care meant much more work in the house. Polly could not escape the fact that, for the moment, it was entirely inappropriate to spend too much time away from home. It was a long winter for her as it was for everyone else at Springfield, but by the end of April 1876, Hannah, too, was dead and Polly felt free to pick up her quest. She began to make daily visits to Taft, despite the fact that both Barbara's children and her aunt made their feelings quite clear every time she pushed open the door. But harsh looks and barbed comments are easily rebuffed by a woman with a man in her sights. Since her parents were now dead, there was only her older brother to offer advice about how she might live her life and she did not feel fettered by his opinions. It seemed that there was no power that would persuade her that this road she had chosen was unwise.

Thus, as John slowly emerged from the dark cave of grief over that second summer, he regularly found Polly there when he arrived home. She both amused him and fed his ego. Last year he had hardly noticed her, but now even he could not help but observe the pretty young woman who laughed at his jokes, listened admiringly to his pronouncements, marvelled at his carpentry and even sewed him a new waistcoat for Sundays. What man of forty-five would not feel his ego encouraged by the devotion and smiles of a younger woman? By the end of that summer he began to wonder if, for the sake of his children, it might be right to consider taking a new wife. The fact that none of his children liked Polly never entered his head.

So great was the distance between father and offspring that he failed to recognise any of the small arrows of displeasure they fired at their aunt, who resolutely ignored them as, painstakingly, she ingratiated herself into the family routine. As time passed, John warmed to her more and more. Even when Aunt Barbara took it upon herself to advise him of the fact that people were talking, he refused to warn the girl off. Perhaps he was meant to marry again, he told himself. Surely these silly rules didn't matter here. He still refrained from touching her, but his looks and smiles showed Polly that her presence was appreciated and she was content to let him take the lead.

Only when the harvest was in and the year's work coming to a close did he discuss the matter with Stewart, his friend and now his preacher. Polly was his sister and there was no question that John would do anything wrong, he told Stewart. His intentions were entirely honourable. As for the law, well he had read the Bible from cover to cover and found no reason why they should not marry. If Stewart could show him where in the Bible it said it was forbidden, he would accept it. If not, well that was another thing entirely. Suddenly, it seemed as if the rules of the land did not apply to John Wilson of Taft.

John was a highly honourable man, one who took his beliefs seriously, as he took himself seriously in all he did. He persuaded himself that the Deceased Wife's Sister Act was irrelevant in Fair Isle and that an intelligent man like himself could freely decide what was right and what was wrong. Here, they ignored many rules and regulations from the mainland, so why not this one? Stewart spent hours arguing with him, for by now people were talking and the Wilsons of Springfield were not partial to gossip. It would not do. Polly would be shunned if there was an illegal union. Surely John must understand. After all, when Peter McGregor had taken a wife in an irregular fashion, John had not been backward in expressing his views. And Peter McGregor was not actually breaking the law.

John only became more and more convinced of the legitimacy of his desire. Surely no one would speak against a man who found a new mother for his children. They would wait until next summer, when the minister came for his annual visit. That would seal a respectable time of mourning and make it all right. Self-delusion is always easy for a man consumed with desire, so Polly could now consider herself engaged. His family at Taft were desolate, but John was able to ignore them. As his home became an increasingly unpleasant place to live, the rest of the island settled down to watch the outcome of this unusual play. Aunt Barbara was beside herself.

On 4th September, 1876, John went fishing as usual in the *Eagle*, along with four other boats. The crew of the *Eagle* were his eldest son John, his brother-in-law Stewart from Springfield, and their nephew, young Tom Wilson from Leogh. It had not been a successful morning and the fish were agreed by all to be too ill-willed to be caught. To finish a bad day off, the weather began to turn difficult until finally the dark sky and fresh breeze threatened to build up to something more. John suggested to Stewart that they should give up, motioning to the other boats that they were setting off for home, but in truth the others were not far behind. The strengthening wind allowed good speed, but the sea was developing more power with every minute and John needed all his skill to get back through the rip tide safely.

Then young John, who had been concentrating on the boats coming behind, shouted to his father that he thought one of them had disappeared. The two older men were not worried. In weather like this, with the waves so high, you could easily lose sight of a yoal for a minute or two. Still, they stood to against the shore for a bit, waiting for their neighbours to go past so that they could count them in. The first yoal shot by, then the second, with two men standing, scanning the horizon behind them. Obviously, all was not well. Stewart nodded to John, who took his boat back into the flood tide and began to search for the other craft.

Young John was the first to spot the wreck of the *Hope*, with two shapes clinging to its upturned hull. The *Hope* had been crewed by Robert Wilson of Kennaby, Andrew Wilson of Gaila and Jerome Wilson of Leogh. Young Tom Wilson of Leogh was by now beside himself with terror, desperate to find out if one of the two figures clinging to the wreckage was his father. The sea was extremely difficult, sweeping right over them as they tried to get some response from the prostrate figures that clung to the wreck, everyone crying out to the men, to God, or in the case of young Tom, to his father.

Stewart and John were excellent sailors, but even they had difficulty getting close enough to help without turning themselves over and into the water with their friends. Finally, they managed to throw ropes, but by now only Andrew Wilson had the strength to catch one and even then they almost lost him as they drew him into the boat, semiconscious and numb. Robert Wilson was too exhausted to catch hold, any remaining strength he had being devoted to clinging to the wreck. Eventually they sailed right up to and almost on top of the ruined timbers, until they could clasp the man and haul him on board.

By now the seas were quite dreadful, but still they continued to search for Jerome, knowing that his boy would never rest if he thought that every effort had not been made. With the complexity of Wilson family relationships on the island, Jerome was both John's cousin and Stewart's brother-in-law. Although the pair would have fought as hard as they did to save any of their fellow fishermen, this fight was personal and highly emotive because of young Tom. The men tried to ignore both the helpless youngster and the soaked souls who lay prostrate at their feet, as they searched desperately, for as long as they dared. All the while the loose remains of the broken yoal splintered, banged and crashed against their own fragile craft until finally they knew that there was nothing left to do. The body had been taken by the sea. Jerome Wilson was lost.

They explained to the orphaned boy that they must return, if for no other reason than to save themselves and their two companions who were cold and senseless in the well of the boat. They made Tom nod in agreement, although whether he really understood was debatable. Young Tom was shocked and shaking with fright, even though he tried to hide it, so the journey home was a challenge, taking them once more over the rip tide with only two men and a frightened boy able to manoeuvre. Yet the joy felt by the islanders for the men saved was tempered by the distress felt for the man lost. Jerome left a wife and six children. The incident was reported to the laird and written about in the newspapers in Lerwick, with some emphasis on the bravery of the *Eagle's* crew. This unlooked-for boost to his character made it more difficult to criticise John for a while.

When his liking for Polly had been universally recognised, the island divided into two camps – those who criticised John for entertaining the idea of an illegal union and those who felt that a man should be able to find happiness where he could. Over the winter there would be no visiting minister, and with no minister John could do nothing to validate any relationship. Whatever else, he was not a man who would consider a union unblessed by God. No one could deny that John had principles. The question was, were they the right principles?

In October 1876, the three-masted sailing ship *Wilhelmina* found herself caught in thick fog and gales and was wrecked when her master miscalculated the distance he was from the island. The crew took refuge in rigging, where they spent the night with waves crashing over their heads. Eventually, the mate tried to reach the shore but drowned in the attempt. Finally, the rest of the crew managed to save themselves but were then trapped in a deep, steep geo, before a fisherman spotted them and organised their rescue. The weather did not abate so the crew could not leave the island for another eight days, but local men salvaged some of the cargo which was eventually loaded onto the Grutness boat, the *Star of the West*, owned by John Bruce.

Unfortunately, the *Star of the West* itself then floundered in North Haven, losing its £300 cargo as well as a horse belonging to the master and two sheep that were being sent to market. This crew managed to come ashore, but there was still the crew of the *Wilhelmina* to be taken back to Lerwick. The *Erin* had to make the journey, a more substantial boat that had been given to Fair Isle men to enable them to get to the mainland over the winter. It was thus no longer available for this purpose.

That was not the end of the run of bad luck for merchant shipping in sea area, Fair Isle. On 6th December, 1876, the *Carl Constantine* was lost, together with her cargo of coal. With her two huge masts broken like matchsticks, she was in a sinking condition by the time she made land. The ship's carpenter and the master were lost but the rest of the crew landed on a small ledge to which they clung for dear life. Again, this crew's fate was noticed and men on shore once more attempted a rescue, this time in the face of truly dreadful conditions. A yoal was carried from South Harbour to Hestigeo on the west of the island, no mean feat in such foul weather. After a wicked struggle the *Constantine's* crew was finally hauled on board. A combination of brute strength, incredible skill and innate bravery enabled a successful rescue. Thomas Wilson of Leogh was the skipper of the yoal. He led William Wilson, Stewart Wilson, Thomas Wilson, Laurence Irvine, George Stout and Alexander Eunson. This particular act of valour was eventually recognised by the German government.

The rescued sailors appreciated the courage of their rescuers. Dreadful weather continued to batter the island for days so that, even although fires were lit to attract passing steamers, ships were unable to come close enough to be boarded. During their stay on the island the visitors observed the wreckage of two further vessels battering the shoreline, only to see the detritus carried away on the next tide, underlining their own good fortune.

In due course, the men boarded the steamer *St Clair* on its way to Lerwick. It was a stormy day and the transfer from yoal to steamer was fraught with danger in quite dreadful seas. It was a tribute to sailors in both yoals and steamers that seldom did an accident occur during such an operation. It has to be said, however, that many of those transferred swore on their lives never to undertake this particular activity again. For females enveloped in long skirts and embarrassment, or men unused to the sea, it could be a truly terrifying experience.

There was at that time a German Consulate in Lerwick, where the crew of the *Carl Constantine* were given shelter until a boat could be found to take them home. Its staff listened to the men's plea for a lighthouse that would warn other mariners of this awe-inspiring island. Representation was once more duly made to the British government and once more duly ignored. The issue of ships wrecking themselves on Fair Isle would continue to occupy the island's new teacher for some time to come, for one of Mr Laurence's responsibilities was to be the official Receiver of Wrecks. He wrote to the Prime Minister to try to obtain his support, but to no avail. No one seemed willing to come up with adequate funding.

To round off 1876, on the 14th December the *Hertigen* struck Sheep Rock and went to pieces with the loss of her entire crew. A good amount of her cargo of wood came ashore for local men to salvage, while a chest filled with the mate's personal belongings travelled all the way over to Dunrossness. The men were glad of all the wood and worked hard at storing it safely away for future use, but they were fully aware of the price that the crew paid for their haul.

On the 23rd December a letter to *The Shetland Times* noted that the people of Fair Isle still had only the medieval practice of lighting a bonfire as a beacon when there was a disaster: *'It seems strange that a man trap like Fair Isle has no lighthouse or lifesaving apparatus.'* It was not that the outside world was unaware of the acts of bravery demanded of the fishermen. It seemed only that no one cared.

All this excitement put gossip about Polly and John into abeyance for a bit, but by the following spring John officially announced to friends and family that they would marry in the summer. His dearest friend Stewart spent hours at Taft, struggling to make him understand that this would not be countenanced by the minister when he visited, that the scandal and tittle-tattle would do no good for Methodism and that everyone, including his children, would suffer as a consequence.

But John had made up his mind and men like John always know beyond doubt when they are right. He challenged any man to show him that this union was forbidden by God. Islanders responded that it was not legal and that was that. Philosophical discussion was neither their interest, nor their forte, and they were quite content to accept the rules of the church and the law of the land. Surely, with all his book learning, even John Wilson had to admit to the law. Some people wondered if the man had gone mad, for love and madness are not that far apart. It was oft repeated that John Wilson had been one of those who had seen fit to criticise Peter McGregor. It seemed that the man wanted one rule for himself and a different one for others.

Polly could not be persuaded that there was a problem. In fact, for a young woman who had been ignored for much of her life, she now took a perverse delight in finding herself the centre of attention. John was her heroic figure, and if he said they could marry, there was no problem. Polly was illiterate, which was not unusual for women of her age, so she did not involve herself in any theoretical arguments. She was raised to be guided by men's superiority in such matters. They would be married in the summer and she would not lose sleep over the matter meantime, even if others did. Polly started to sew a trousseau.

At Taft, her presence was totally disagreeable to all except John. His children loathed the fact that they were now the centre of attention for all the wrong reasons and it didn't help that, in the main, those who disagreed strongly with John's views were afraid to voice them to him. Their offspring showed no such reticence with the Taft children, however, who were left in no doubt that when Polly came to Taft it would become a house of ill-repute and all who lived in it would be tarred by that brush. None of them really knew what a house of ill-repute was, but it sounded pretty awful.

Where fathers rule their homes with a God-given certainty, there is often a failure to comprehend issues other than their own, so John had no idea that his older children were the constant target of smutty remarks or that Aunt Barbara was forever having to deal with ill-concealed critical barbs, for which she at least was more than equal. The Springfield family was also under pressure. As the families waited for the minister's annual visit, tension mounted.

The Reverend William Brand of Dunrossness, in whose parish the island lay, duly arrived in Fair Isle in June 1877. He was adamant. Briefed immediately by leading members of his Church of Scotland flock, he had his opposition prepared long before John came to see him. The Reverend Brand generally had no doubt about what was wrong and what was right. The law was very clear on the matter, he told John, and he was surprised that such a 'religious' man could even suggest marrying his dead wife's young sister. Did he not realise that a man who married his sister-in-law was guilty, in the eyes of the law, of incest? There was no way that a respectable minister could be expected to become involved in such a distasteful union.

If truth be told, the Reverend Brand was not particularly sympathetic to members of the Methodist persuasion in the first place, so that when John argued with him the man of God dismissed the rude fisherman with condescending ease, reiterating that the law of the land existed in Fair Isle as much as it did anywhere else. He had to be quite abrupt in the end, but he was adamant. The good man went on to marry several other couples and so offended John that he refused to have young Thomas baptised. Aunt Barbara was by now doubly furious. Any slight to her charge hurt her deeply, for surely Thomas deserved baptism as much as any other Christian soul, whatever his father's difficulties. Taft was not a pleasant place to be throughout the minister's visit.

It hardly helped that John's uncle, the factor, chose this ministerial visit to remarry. Sixty-year-old Jerome Wilson's wife had died the previous year and he had chosen a 26-year-old replacement, so there was bound to be a bit of cheerful gossip from someone. What made the 5th June, 1877, all the more remarkable was that the factor's 24-year-old daughter Agnes was marrying her cousin on that day. She wore a particularly pretty and detailed dress and this couple (together with their two witnesses) caught the steamer to Lerwick after the ceremony, where the union was recorded by a photographer – an unusual thrill for a newly married bride on the island. John Wilson of Taft thought it particularly hard that his uncle could remarry while he could not, and made everyone quite clear about his views. Since all of those involved were Methodists, the Church of Scotland congregation had a field day.

All this fuss ensured that Polly was neither more welcome at Taft nor the marriage deemed more acceptable throughout the general community. The couple were the subject of open gossip in every croft house and everyone had an opinion, few of them charitable. John's children were black ashamed and increasingly angry as the affair rolled on, although still no one dared to voice an opinion at home. To be publicly at odds with such an important person as the minister was a terrible disgrace. Ministers were held in great respect, even awe at that time. There were a few (men in the main) who supported John's cause. Some unwisely voiced their opinions to their wives, who in the main supported the Reverend Brand. It was all extremely upsetting.

In July there was another focus for people's attention, when the steam ship *Duncan*, bound for Archangel, struck the south end of the island in a thick fog before becoming a total wreck. Only one crew member, Alexander Paterson, was lost. This new ship was built in 1874 and it carried a single passenger, the Reverend James Watt, who when he had recovered from his experience agreed to preach on the island. He declined, however, to marry John and Polly, when John took the opportunity to request that his union be blessed. Even this unbidden stranger, with no knowledge of the affair, was steadfast in the church's rules.

John was furious. The master of the *Duncan* was equally disturbed by his trip to Fair Isle, since he lost his master's certificate for six months when the inquiry into the wreck was conducted in Dundee. The inquiry did, however, suggest to the government that a lighthouse and a fog-horn should be erected in Fair Isle, as soon as possible.

John now decided that the fishing could do without him for a week. He would take Polly to Kirkwall, to be married there. No doubt his mother, brothers and sisters would support him. The pair were taken out to catch the steamer, full of hope and enthusiasm. No one had imagined that things would take this turn and the prattle spread like wildfire. At Taft, the children were bereft. In all probability, in the heady metropolis of Kirkwall the pair would find someone to marry them and Polly would return as a wife. At Springfield, Stewart could only pray that Kirkwall might offer some sort of deliverance for them all, for the current situation was unsustainable. Who would have thought that his family would have become embroiled in such a scandal? What would his father have said?

Gossips could not resist visiting Taft while the pair were absent in the hope of some petty detail, although most quickly left with a flea in their ear if Barbara was at home. There were those who felt sorry for the children, but there were others who relished the sight of the Taft Wilsons at odds with the world. It is a terrible thing to bask in the public mess made by your parents at a time when you are trying to forge your own way in the world. From the eldest to the youngest they were all party to the fall-out. Aunt Barbara, who believed that activity was the only answer to their woes, drove them to the croft and beach work. They waited for the sight of the returning steamer with dread and wound one another up constantly. "I'm leaving," the older ones assured each other, and at this the younger ones cried even more.

To everyone's surprise, the couple returned one week later, still single. Ministers in Kirkwall had been quite as determined to resist John's pleas as their Dunrossness colleague. It was both church law and the law of the land, John was told, and laws did not have a pick and choose option for those who did not like them. John could, if he wished, enter into an irregular marriage, which would go some way to protecting the children of such a union, but with his strong religious beliefs John could not stomach this. After the McGregor debacle, neither he nor anyone else in Fair Isle would consider it to be a real marriage for a moment – not after all this fuss. To make matters worse, the couple's Kirkwall families had been less than enthusiastic. It was their reaction that made John review his position.

Despite his frustration, John prepared himself to let Polly go. She might have to move somewhere else. Perhaps he ought to have left her with their families in Kirkwall, where no one knew her history? When the yoal brought them into Kirkigeo, he intimated to both Polly and Stewart that it would probably be best if she stayed at Springfield and did not come around Taft again, until he had considered what should happen next. In truth, the struggle seemed to be over.

Back at home Polly wept and wept, both at the hopelessness of her marriage and the humiliation that must now be endured, for even Polly knew that this situation would not speedily be forgotten. The trip to Kirkwall was to have been the pinnacle of her new life, meeting John's family and then returning home in splendour, with the bit of paper to prove her status as a wife. To make things worse, no one at Springfield afforded her much sympathy, considering the infamy that her behaviour had brought both to them and their chapel. Her brother wondered if Polly should visit relatives somewhere else, now, before the winter weather held her hostage. In the silence of his own mind, he wondered if she could emigrate to Canada, or America even, to join family there. Such a change would enable her to start a new life and the rest of them to put the last few months behind them. His wife agreed, but when he broached the topic with his sister, she cried even more.

John's children rejoiced secretly, not daring to risk their father's wrath, but grinning to one another furiously and gesticulating manically when they were out of his sight. Their prayers had been answered. They were spared the fate that was Polly. John became depressed, but Aunt Barbara had no sympathy for him. Barbara had seen it before on the island. Crowded homes that added new wives to families with existing children so often engendered unrelenting disagreement. With everyone living so close to the poverty line tension was never far away in families that were not united, and when they came, new children only added to the problem.

It was now August and, unexpectedly, the island received an intimation that John Bruce had been instructed by the Board of Trade to give a reward to those who had saved men during the wrecks of the previous year. He arrived with a party of friends to announce that John and Stewart Wilson were to receive gold medals for their gallantry, while the two Wilson boys were each to receive ten shillings for the part they played in saving the two men from certain death. Furthermore, Thomas Wilson of Leogh was to be awarded a gold watch from the German government for his bravery in saving the crew of the *Carl Constantine* and each member of his crew was awarded £3 by the Board of Trade. This was a time for universal celebration and the island set about preparing a meal at the school hall.

On hearing of his intended trip, three visitors (two United Free Presbyterian clergymen from mainland Scotland and an Edinburgh lawyer) decided at the last moment to join Bruce. At the height of the Victorian absorption with all things Scottish, Fair Isle had become a place of almost mystical fame, somewhere people from the south wanted to add to their travel itinerary, simply because so few folk were given the opportunity. John Bruce was always pleased to show off this part of his estate, so it was a very jovial and enthusiastic party that arrived for the awards ceremony.

Speeches were made and many good things were said about bravery and fortitude. Afterwards, all sat down for tea, the best the ladies of the island could produce. Then John spotted his opportunity. He took the two ministers aside and passionately made his case, with all his finely honed use of language and religious argument spilling out of him like a stream in spate. The lawyer, who knew himself to be a worldly soul, was drawn into the discussion. Finally, after hearing the lengths that John had gone to to make a decent woman of Polly, delighted to overrule decisions made by their conservative Church of Scotland colleagues, and with the blessing of the Edinburgh lawyer, the two United Free ministers married the pair on the spot. After all, what was the point of sticking to the letter of the law out here in the middle of the ocean? They had not expected to meet a man so skilled in either language or religious deliberation in such a singular environment and all thought John to be a fine chap. It would be a good tale to tell back home. They rounded off the day by christening young Thomas.

When the group left, well pleased by their contribution to the island's welfare, they little guessed what they left behind. All the Church of Scotland women, and not a few of the men, were outraged at this slight to their ministers, by seceders, people who thought they could do anything they wanted with the law, be it religious or secular. For some, the worst of it was that the ministers were from the Free Church of Scotland. A few local men admired John and his unexpected opportunity to take a younger wife, a fact which only served to irritate their spouses even more. Younger sisters were now looked at differently in many houses. The equilibrium had altered, for if you can break one law, why not more?

At Taft, life would never be the same. Here, only John welcomed his new bride, a fact of which she was well aware, even if her husband remained in doubt or denial about his family's views. The long battle between Barbara's children and their new mother would colour most family experiences and opinions over many years. Much of this was kept from John, but even he finally recognised that things were not as they had been before. His first wife had exerted a happy, measured atmosphere which had permeated both his life and that of his children. Now there was always some form of tension and increasingly the older ones made excuses to be somewhere else. Tempers frayed and squabbles flared up without warning, with Polly regularly appealing to him to mediate. So concentrated had he been on having this new life that he had let his old one run away from him. That was the price he would pay. When men think only of themselves, there is always a price.

In an effort to make life a little easier over that first winter, Aunt Barbara decided to persuade John to let her buy some material for the older girls to work at, once she saw how their interest in fashion was beginning to develop. By 1877, more young girls on the island were aware of style, even if some of them did not have the means to create many pretty things. Led by the factor's family, who had easier access to cash, Sunday best was by now surprisingly up to date. Indeed, that summer the factor's daughter's wedding dress had been the height of fashion. The occasional visiting female also brought stylish trends, while more ideas came from the newspapers, which were bought by people like the factor who wanted to keep abreast of the outside world. Occasionally copies of the *People's Journal* or the *People's Friend* came from relatives in Lerwick or Kirkwall.

For many girls their wedding clothes would be their most important item of dress for many years, for once you had children there was less time for sewing, but even in poor crofts there was often a girl trying to fashion something special over the winter months. It was challenging to cut and sew a new outfit in the crowded, dark confines of any croft's living space and, since every stitch must be sewn by hand, it was a task that took many hours.

Barbara realised that at Taft they needed something other than bile and knitting to occupy their minds throughout that long, dark first winter, although she had to stand up to John when he wondered aloud if focusing excessively on self-adornment might lead his girls astray. Finally, Polly and the three girls were allowed to choose material for a new dress, even although Mary was only eight. Since she had been the most traumatised by her mother's death and the ensuing marriage, Barbara understood that, even if they had to help her, Mary must be included in this project. She would need a lot of assistance and her dress would not be terribly fashionable because of her age, but she would be part of the family project and it would improve her sewing skills.

The buying of the material and the planning of the styles went on for much longer than Aunt Barbara had anticipated. It seemed that the old-fashioned, fully gathered dresses that the women had made for emigration to New Brunswick were no longer in vogue. Today it appeared that folds of material had to be pulled more to the back of the skirt, so that it seemed to trail behind. Waists were becoming narrower and lower than before, there were high-necked bodices, and there must be tiny, detailed ruches or folds to demonstrate the needlewoman's skill.

Barbara, who had sewed herself the same pattern of dress for the last forty years and intended to continue doing so till she died, just nodded and reminded them that, "It has to be decent for Sundays and prayer meetings." When she was a girl, she told them regularly, you were grateful just to have something that covered you properly. She began to wonder if her nephew had been right to consider that so much discussion about the creation of a dress was indeed heretical. But she, who had seen so much change since the 1820s, understood that life in Fair Isle in 1877 was better, and if fancy dresses for Sunday were part of that improvement, Barbara Wilson would go along with it.

Early in 1877 the islanders again petitioned for a post office. The Postmaster General had in the past refused their requests, stating that it would not be profitable. However, Mr Laurence encouraged the islanders to write a communal letter to the Prime Minister, stating that they may be poor but still they were part of the Queen's empire. Lord Beaconsfield wrote across their petition – '*I think these people should get what they ask for'* – and eventually a fortnightly postal delivery was agreed, depending of course on the whim of the weather, for access to the island could never be guaranteed. Several packet boats (small boats that carried mail, cargo and passengers) were lost over the years in the course of this exercise and people still had to endure the frustration of watching their mail pass them by in bad weather.

All these 1877 improvements reduced people's feeling of isolation and enabled them to have a more regular contact with those who had moved away. With the packet boats, the newspapers brought information about fish landings and prices, political and business news, national stories, recipes, advertisements, fiction serials and fashion snippets, all stimulating an interest in the outside world for those who read them. Some islanders began to answer advertisements, particularly for the many health 'cures' which had become a regular feature of newspapers and journals.

Eventually, the Taft Wilson marriage receded as a primary subject of conversation. With all the difficulties of daily life, most of the population had more than a questionable wedding ceremony to take up their time. Despite the flurry of official recognition for the bravery of the men who risked their lives to save others, shipping disasters continued to occur, since nothing had been done to stop them. In September 1877, the *Black Watch*, a three-masted ship on her way to New York, was wrecked in the south-west corner of the isle. A substantial new ship in full sail, she found herself unable to find enough wind to draw away so that she pushed herself gently into the geo to find her grave. Once again local men had appeared and saved all hands, but the vessel was declared a wreck. It was valued at £11,000 and was only half insured, the master himself owning a share and thus making a loss. This time the master retained his ticket, even though the inquiry found that he had not taken sufficient care. Local men stripped the *Black Watch* of its wood, including some beautiful mahogany panelling and doors, much of which found its way into crofts. Some croft houses became as well panelled as many a great house and, famously, the byre at Stoneybrake had finely crafted portholes. Springfield had a chair with the initials BW firmly gouged on its backrest, not for one of the many Barbara Wilsons the family had reared, but as a commemoration of the *Black Watch*.

In December 1877, the mail boat *Golden Fleece* (owned by John Bruce) wrecked itself on the island's rocks. Once more the crew was saved by the bravery of local men. There was still no news of a lighthouse.

Polly was thrilled when she became pregnant, thus cementing her position at Taft. She felt superior to the older Wilson girls and did not worry about their frissons of dislike.

Young John was seventeen, so he presented no threat to her position in the household, although the boy was terribly disturbed by the thought of this woman in his father's bed. His brother Stewart, although just thirteen, was much more irritating for Polly, smirking at her when his father was not looking and always failing to hear when she asked him to do anything. He would claim open-eyed innocence when rebuked for non-compliance by his father, but she would always see him giving his siblings a meaningful look once he was finally forced to do as she asked. He was a constant irritation, but no great problem surely.

Aunt Barbara was quite another matter. She refused to treat Polly any differently from before, even though she was now a married woman who merited respect. It was as if, in Barbara's eyes, she was still a little girl. Barbara would rebuke her when she burned the dinner, or remind her in front of them all when she forgot to order something from the store. She occasionally inspected her knitting, just as she did with all the girls. And she would not let her deal with the cattle. The cattle were women's work and Barbara had taken over from her namesake when she entered the house. She liked the beasts and they responded to her slow, calm words as she milked them or helped them with their calves. It had been one of the unexpected joys of moving to Taft, finally to be the one in charge of the byre. Polly wanted to claim her share of this 'woman's work', but was surprised when she found this request blocked, both by her aunt and husband.

Barbara's cattle flourished. She gave them lots of extra care and attention denied by some of the other women. During the winter, when little milk was given, Barbara would bleed her cows only once. Some of her neighbours did it twice or more, but she felt that the animals too were struggling to get through the cold, dark months and that they would do better in the spring if they were not bled regularly. The blood she took would be boiled and thickened with a little oatmeal, as a treat. If there was milk to be had, this too was mixed in and the result was a pleasure to present to the family during the hard winter.

She loved all the stages in milk production once the cows had calved. "Shuta, shuta," she would call when she went to see her charges (sweet one, sweet one). Barbara's cows would turn with quiet obedience and let down their milk without kicking her. Some of the milk was left to stand in the churn for two days or so, and once thickened it was known as sour milk. With several cows you would have to churn daily and towards the end of the process you threw in heated churning stones to help the mixture separate. In cold weather the churn would be set near the fire, but at other times it had to be kept cool so that the temperature was just right. When butter gathered at the top it was lifted out and washed, to remove any remaining milk, and finally salt was added, both for flavour and as a preservative. When it was done well, it was wonderful.

Since cleanliness is essential for butter making, it is not surprising that butter was sometimes difficult to achieve and thus many superstitions and rhymes grew up around the process, for buttermilk and curdled milk were vital to family life. When boiled, or heated by hot stones, a white cheese-like substance that the islanders called hard milk separated from the rest and was then hung up in a cloth to drip, until it became a soft cheese. The remaining liquid was put into an oak cask and stored for use as a drink in winter, known as bland, which was taken by the men when they went out for the day to fish, or given to calves after they had been given a little of their mother's milk, for calves were not allowed to suck. Sour milk too was useful, often eaten as a pudding. For the person in charge of the cows it was a delight to bring all the different products to the table, a respected task for the woman of the house and not one to be given up lightly.

Polly wanted to be mistress of Taft, but when she suggested to Barbara that it was her right to take over in the dairy, her aunt made it quite clear that only John could move her from this role.

When pushed, John stated firmly that he would not interfere with the status quo. "Your Aunt Barbara's a respected old lady and in this house we owe her a lot. If she had not been here I don't know how we'd have managed in the days after Barbara died, never mind the fact that I don't think Thomas would have survived at all. We in Taft owe a debt to your aunt and if she wants to keep on with the cows and she can manage it, you will let her. There's little enough pleasure for her in life at her age surely. You can't expect this to be as if nothing had gone before."

And that was that. Polly was beginning to learn that the man who had wooed her was not the man to whom she was now married, although Polly would hardly be the only woman to make this particular discovery. John's pursuit of Polly had been as much a reaction to finding himself thwarted, as it was a desire for Polly herself. He was happy to sleep with her, but otherwise his attitude was more that towards a younger sister who needed guidance, rather than the equal that his first wife had been. John and Barbara had grown into their marriage together, while his mother slowly gave up the reins of Taft. Polly must now find her place in the existing household, as and when she could. She might have had more of a chance in taking over had it just been the girls to manage, but Aunt Barbara was not one to be trifled with.

Despite his apparent disinterest in the daily running of the household, John was old enough to realise that his children had to be accorded some understanding, particularly Johanna (as she now wished to be called) who was now almost a grown woman. Polly had to accept that there was a status quo. As John sat them all down in the evening for the nightly Bible reading, with the odd question on the catechism thrown in to keep them on their mettle, Polly gradually realised she was joining an ongoing situation. John was by no means a man to be managed by his second wife. Neither were his children.

Johanna was the one most irritated by her new 'mother' and made up her mind to leave home as soon as she could. Jane talked of leaving too, but young Mary cried and cried when she heard this, forcing Jane to promise to stay at Taft until she too was old enough to leave. As second youngest, Mary felt quite lost in the new household. Thomas had Barbara, but Mary must look to her sisters, for Polly offered her nothing. The thought of being once more abandoned scared her more than she could explain.

Whereas young Thomas Wilson of Leogh had handed his mother the ten shillings that was given to reward him for bravery, John Wilson junior kept his for himself. His much-anticipated day of honour turned to dust when his father unexpectedly found someone to officiate his second marriage. For John, it was as if he was living a nightmare so there would be no chance of him giving his reward to this unwanted, replacement mother. At another time he might have handed it to his father, but not now. His father would never know the extent to which all the name-calling had hurt a son who always felt that he had never quite met his father's expectations.

So instead of funding the family coffers, John gave his ten shillings to Aunt Barbara, to keep for him until he needed it. "I'm leaving," he told her. "I'm going away to sea. There's no place for me here, not now."

"I'll keep it safe till you decide," she promised him, "but you may change your mind. You are your father's eldest child. This could all be yours one day. Don't do anything rash while you're still young. Things might change. We in this house know that things change. Don't give up on it all because of your Aunt Polly."

Meanwhile, other families had more serious issues to deal with, for there were still those struggling with poverty. The *Orkney Herald* reported that during the winter of 1878 four men went around the island begging for food. This, the writer felt, was at odds with John Bruce's claim in 1877 that his factor had orders to supply destitute families with all they required from his store. It seems clear that the Kirkwall families maintained both communication and ill feeling for their erstwhile landlord and that life in Fair Isle remained challenging, at least for some.

In 1878, Andrew Eunson of Busta and his crew went out to barter with the *Caliope*, whose captain (Robert Sinclair) was a Shetlander. The men were welcomed aboard and after an exchange of goods, the captain and his brother set out a meal for them to enjoy. Sinclair also sent back a gift for the island's teacher and twenty shillings for a poor widow the men had told him about. Such unexpected generosity revives your faith in humanity.

# Chapter 11

# Change at Home and Abroad

**M**r Laurence campaigned ceaselessly about the dangers the island presented to sea-going vessels, but his was a small voice in the complex world of lighthouse commissioning. Although he understood that Fair Isle was the only significant lethal impediment in a fifty-mile stretch of ocean, the government failed to take this on board.

Cardwell's Merchant Shipping Act of 1854 was intended to improve national mercantile standards, including the control of lighthouse development all around Britain's coast. In practice, this meant that all initiatives from the Northern Lighthouse Board in Scotland now had to be approved by the Trinity House Board and then passed to the Board of Trade, which controlled the Mercantile Marine fund. The reality was that the Board of Trade decided which new lighthouses would be built and Trinity House was another powerful force with which to be reckoned. These new management stages in the Northern Lighthouse Board's judgements caused endless tension, as an increased number of experts had quite different views in what was now a fast developing field of engineering.

After an initial flurry of work, there was a hiatus in lighthouse building throughout the country, despite the fact that every year the seas became increasingly crowded with bigger, faster and more expensive vessels. A limited pot of money, a wide range of potential sites, increasing alternatives in construction choices and new developments in optics, together meant that there were many potential sources of conflict. Although the Northern Light Commissioners had absolute faith in the remarkable skills and abilities of the Stevenson family, David Stevenson did not always see eye to eye, either with Trinity House or the Board of Trade. When the latter body refused to add him to their established register of staff, the entire body of Northern Lighthouse Commissioners threatened to resign, stating that they needed to call on Stevenson as and when they wished. Thus instead of uniting different groups in the national need for lighthouses, conflict between different factions became a barrier to development. Most importantly, the government did not adequately fund the activity.

When he replaced his brother Alan as the Commissioners' engineer in 1853, David Stevenson recommended the construction of forty-five new lighthouses in Scotland, but by the time he was pressured to prioritise, only eight remained and Fair Isle was not on the list. Then the Crimean war focused attention on the Northern Isles, as it became necessary to prevent the Russian fleet from moving ships from Murmansk and Archangel down to the Mediterranean in support of Russian armies.

A light was demanded at Whalsay (Out Skerries) in 1854 and also a temporary light at Muckle Flugga, the most northerly rock in the country, where a permanent structure was finally built in 1858, costing £32,000. Such an expensive enterprise greatly depleted the Board of Trade's budget and when that year a further light was constructed at Bressay to protect the entrance to Lerwick harbour, there was no money left for further lighthouse building in Shetland.

Throughout the 1860s it was evident that due to a lack of funds the management of Britain's lighthouses was under strain. Fair Isle was only one of many locations where both British ship owners and maritime representatives from other countries pleaded for a light. Although a group of lighthouse engineers travelled to the island in 1877 to consider the need and recommended two lighthouses and a fog signal, funding was not available. However, with at least five large ships lost in 1876 and three in 1877, the Board of Trade felt forced to do something, so in 1878 they presented the islanders with both a small open lifeboat and life-saving equipment, including breeches buoys and cliff ladders. This may have been the first official lifeboat in Shetland, but it was not a lighthouse. Local men were retained with ten shillings on the understanding that they would crew the boat when required, and Mr Laurence was appointed 'volunteer in charge', who undertook the responsibility of training the islanders in the use of all the equipment.

Early in 1879 the islanders received the gift of a packet boat, intended to improve communication and trade with Orkney and Shetland and possibly help with the fishing. The *Deasil* made two trips to Orkney, but the men found her difficult to handle. The boat did not serve their fishing needs because it was tricky to manage around their challenging harbour in heavy seas. It was also arduous for a small crew to drag a heavier boat up to safety on the beach after a trip. No one had overall responsibility for the boat so that, after damage was incurred during a trip to Orkney, she was hauled above the water line and turned over to serve as the boathouse for the lifeboat. The islanders' primary need remained that of having a safe harbour for larger boats, one that would change the type of fishing that they could follow. Without this facility, bigger boats served no real purpose.

In May 1879, the islanders saved both the captain and crew from a German ship, the *Monchgut*. Later, the laird bought the wreck and employed island men to save its cargo of wood and tar, but Laurence Irvine of Houll drowned while working on this project. Bruce had by now learned to include island men in his endeavours with shipwrecks, allowing some to work at the ship while others went fishing so that, taking it in turns, all could benefit from salvage operations.

In August 1879, the *Julia* was wrecked in thick fog, the crew managing to jump to safety before the vessel broke away and sank. They were then stuck on an outcrop for twenty-four hours before the ship's carpenter swam ashore for help. Once the man reached land, the alarm was raised and the crew saved. A great deal of wreckage came on shore over the ensuing weeks, adding to the island's stores of timber.

Mindful of his responsibilities to the cousin he had not been able to save in 1876, John Wilson had encouraged the two older Wilson boys from Leogh to visit Taft for help or advice. He tried to include at least one of them when he went fishing so that they would earn enough to keep their croft going. They had been eighteen and sixteen when their father died, old enough to support the family but young enough to need a bit of help. Despite the fact that he had been willing to include the boys in his crew, John was still taken aback when young William Wilson announced that he wanted to marry Johanna, early in 1879, particularly since Johanna was not yet twenty. She was too young, surely? William himself was now twenty-one and still needed to support his father's family, more so when his younger brother left the island.

John would never fully understand that his eldest daughter had focused on moving from Taft from the day he brought Polly home. The girl had retained a sense of guilt for leaving her mother alone that tragic morning, while the distress caused by the contentious wedding meant that there was never any chance of reconciliation with Polly. Now obsessed by the situation, Johanna wanted out of the house as soon as possible. William was a fine looking boy and an excellent sailor. She would have as good a life with him at Leogh as anywhere else.

Johanna had become a fashion enthusiast over the years and was now an excellent needlewoman, so she set about creating herself a smart trousseau with the help of her two sisters. It was said that she had the slimmest waist on the isle, something she worked at showing off to best advantage in her new creations. At least the wedding brought the family together for a while, with all the requisite sewing and planning, for the contracting dress that she wore on the Sunday before the wedding was one of the most intricate the island would ever see.

Meanwhile, there were other changes afoot in Fair Isle. Thanks to the new fish store and his agricultural improvements, Bruce had seen an increase in the island's productivity. Now he turned his mind to the issue of housing, for the standard of the average croft house was very poor indeed. There was a growing understanding of the connection between disease and poor living conditions, although it would be some time before this information was generally acted upon in Scotland. While not overly involved in the lives of the poor, some lairds finally agreed that families should not be required to share their homes with beasts. Bruce was one of the first of Shetland's landowners to encourage an entire community to better their situation. For a small outlay and his tenants' efforts, masonry walls, wooden floors, chimneys and slate roofs, would vastly improve the islanders' lives. Furthermore, if you removed the cows from close proximity with a family's living quarters, you could also dispense with the malodorous dung heap that stood by the front door.

Better living conditions for the poor in the Highlands and Islands should have been easy to provide by this time, given Scotland's progress in building expertise, but it has to be said that in many areas black houses continued into the 20th century, so Bruce was ahead of his time. He was, however, loath to spend much of his own money on the project, particularly since there was no guarantee of all his tenants remaining.

Also, increasing government intervention was altering the relationship between landlords and tenants, so any investment by a laird had to be considered carefully. As Bruce was to tell the Napier Commission in 1883: *"No landlord can afford to build new houses without getting interest for his money. No tenant, with the earnings of these men, can afford to pay the interest that a really good house costs to build."*

This issue would ensure that many of Scotland's poor, both in town and country, would continue to live in unsanitary hovels for many years to come. Private individuals could only see the point of building new houses if they could then charge higher rents, which generally their tenants could not afford to pay. No one thought that it might be an idea to raise wages to accommodate this concept, any more than they would today.

In a few rural areas, landlords had begun to make improvements, providing plans and some of the materials if the tenants built the homes themselves. This would usually be done with little or no increase in rent, but with some assurance concerning longer leases, so that tenants felt motivated to do the work. It was an added attraction that with slate roofs and solid walls tenants would not now have to examine and repair their homes every year. Of course, the landlord continued to own the properties, which could benefit him in the future if tenants moved. The point of law was that landlords must provide the roofs of these new buildings.

John Arcus, a farmer who had been living in Papa Westray in Orkney, moved into the first modern house to be built in Fair Isle. This used Bruce's architect's plans and construction started in 1879, with completion the following year. Bruce paid for the building and hoped that this example would encourage others to make the effort to raise their standard of living. Arcus was a Dunrossness man who had married a Fair Isle Williamson girl, so Bruce thought the islanders might be pre-disposed to accept his ideas. Arcus had moved from a 12-acre holding on Orkney and one wonders what incentive he was offered. Perhaps a new, sturdily-built house with windows and an extra tiny bedroom was motivation enough.

There were chimneys at the two gable ends, so that fireplaces now channelled smoke skywards. The floor was wooden, rather than dirt. In the fashion of Orkney, where Arcus had been living for many years, this first new croft house was roofed with heavy flagstones. Animals were now housed in outbuildings, separate from the living area. It is fair to say that his wife was proud to show her new home to all the women on the island and these women liked what they saw. There was of course no plumbing included in the plan, but throughout Scotland indoor plumbing was unusual in 1879, particularly in country areas. Indeed, Robert Louis Stevenson's new American wife was surprised, in 1880, to discover that her in-laws' expensive and prestigious home in Edinburgh's New Town still had a privy in the garden, with chamber pots and a washstand jug and ewer set out in the bedrooms. Fair Isle could hardly be accused of being the only place denied such facilities. Indeed, the Royal Commission's Report on Scotland's Housing in 1917 would reveal a horrifying and long-standing chronicle of plumbing misery throughout both town and country.

Sadly, Johnny Arcus did not live to enjoy his new life. By 1881 he was suffering from a serious heart condition from which he died in 1882. When his family moved back to Orkney, the Leslie family from Sculties were happy to take over the croft and by 1881 Bruce had encouraged more tenants to follow the Barkland example, providing architect's plans to enable them to build new homes. He sent a quarryman to help the men to correctly prepare the stone so that local materials could be used to their best advantage. Initially he had hoped for some two-storied houses, but a lack of stone meant that in the main it was wiser to opt for a more limited form of construction, one that imitated Barkland.

Bruce supplied his tenants with slates for the roofs and the Wilsons of Taft and Springfield were said to be accomplished at this task, but most island men were accustomed to building and repair work so that all the houses were sturdily constructed. Red pine was specified for doors and windows and supplied by Bruce from Shetland and before long many crofts were also lined with wood panelling, as supplied by shipwrecked vessels. A few homes were not improved because the people were too old and weak to take on such a large task, but Bruce had no suggestion about how to deal with these families.

The women were thrilled to have a little more space in these smart new houses and for the first time light from sash windows enabled them to see what they were doing throughout much of the day. There were still only two main rooms, but the tiny additional bedroom meant that finally, the head of the house had some privacy. Separation of byre and animals from the living space resulted in a huge improvement in the quality of life, not least because the malodorous pile of muck that had accumulated outside the front door was located elsewhere. The absence of the central hearth with its peat smoke endlessly billowing around, forever lifting and depositing a fine layer of dust on everything it encountered, was much appreciated. To their new environment the women added curtains, rugs and even pictures. Some aspired to clocks and ornaments and new furniture was considered, although this would still be home-made, while others bought new crockery, if only for use on Sundays. Newspapers, magazines and neighbours encouraged some of the women to aspire to a slightly more comfortable home life, one that was no longer only about subsistence.

Fair Isle became an example of what a modern crofting landlord could achieve when he and his tenants set their minds to it. Some islanders used their old houses as barns, adding improved drying kilns for grain on one of the end walls, like huge semi-circular bee skips. Meal grinds better when it is dry and takes much less time to produce fine flour for cooking so that some sort of kiln had always been required, but the ability to dry bere on a bigger scale was beyond price.

Bruce was pleased with the island at this time. He saw his Fair Isle project as a personal success and in September 1882 he was proud to arrive with a group of day visitors on the steamer *Earl of Zetland*, passing the time by showing off all 'his' improvements to his friends. Eighty ladies and gentlemen returned to the mainland, enthused with the clean, organised look of the new buildings, with fenced-off fields that inferred rural modernity. They were all impressed with the way ordinary people could now lead their lives in a civilised manner.

Consequently, John Bruce was furious when he was criticised by the Napier Commission in 1883 for the treatment he meted out to some of his other Dunrossness tenants. When called to give evidence, he stated, "*Many of the tenants of old made their byre the portico to their dwelling house and are loath to alter it,*" adding that, "*the byre keeps the house warm and the fire of the house keeps the cows warm.*"

He went on to admit that in many of these other holdings "*...conditions are very bad. They are in such a state I don't like to see any human being living in some of them. But* *you will find that in many cases the people are perfectly contented. If you were to build new houses, the people would prefer to remain where they were rather than move."*

One has to imagine that by this time he was rattled and thus lacked any sense of what was credible. He went on to say, *"I have attempted a new plan in Fair Isle and if you call there, you will see how it works. The tenants there are all building their own houses and I give each of them a slate roof."*

When questioned further, it became clear that Bruce felt that his Fair Isle tenants were particularly wise and industrious. When criticised for the state of housing on his land in Conningsburgh, he retorted that *"the race (there) is peculiar"*. He explained to the Commission that when he had forwarded some pictures of these Shetlanders to the British Association, it was noted that *"the (Conningsburgh) men had a peculiar appearance; they were dark, short men, evidently a different race from the rest...I was told that it was the Celtic or Irish element that showed in these typical faces."* One gathers that it was not a good time to be either Celtic, or Irish.

It appears that Bruce felt that he could take plaudits for anything he achieved, but lacked responsibility for things that were clearly wrong. Of course the rich had strange views about how the poor 'chose' to live throughout the entire country at this time and Bruce was hardly unique in allowing at least some of his tenants to live in dreadful conditions. But still, there was no excuse for any landlord to expect his people to live in one-roomed huts alongside their animals, even if this was the era of laissez-faire. Although the concept of philanthropy existed in the 1880s, it was hardly universal and many Scottish people were kept in extremely primitive conditions for many years more.

The Napier Commission was the result of agitation in Wester Ross and Lewis during the late 1870s, followed by further dissent in the early 1880s in Skye and the Inverness area. Some of these disturbances resulted in rent strikes, but latterly there had been land raids and disturbances that involved the police and even troops, as people protested against unfair landlords who were often of the absent variety. The result was a Commission (introduced by Gladstone) that looked into both crofters and cottars (those who had a house, but no land). The issues explored were: access to grazing land; security of tenure; and fair rents. Finally, Napier recommended that those with rental values of over £6 a year should be given security of tenure, while those with less than that should be offered supported emigration, since their holdings were probably not viable.

The 1886 Crofters Holding Act guaranteed fair rents, security of tenure and compensation for improvements. Its effects began to be felt as the Commissioners made their way around the country and many benefited from the actions of those in the West of Scotland, who had risen up against their landlords. Sadly, in places like Skye and Lewis (where the agitation had begun) it would take many more years to remove the hardship of black houses.

Although both Bruce senior and junior gave evidence to the Napier Commission, it is doubtful that they persuaded its members that their good work in Fair Isle balanced indiscretions elsewhere. At this time a powerful, public wave of criticism emanated from many of their Shetland tenants, although it is difficult to measure its effect, for truck still existed and the crofter/fisherman was still living under pressure from regulation by his master. However, in Fair Isle, when John Bruce senior died in 1885 it was indeed a different world from the time he purchased the island in 1866. Over these twenty years, the quality of life for many islanders had begun to improve, just as ordinary men had begun to define their rights.

By 1891 there remained on the island only five of the old, single-windowed crofts where the occupants were either too poor, too old or too infirm to build new ones. Because Robbie Irvine of Leogh could not keep his old roof watertight, the damp finally got so bad that the roof began to fall in and as damp affected one of the end walls, the house began to collapse. Finally it became uninhabitable by anyone's standards, so local men got together a building party to rebuild the end wall and repair the roof. The resulting house was smaller, but watertight, and Robbie, the last Irvine to live there, managed to eke out a slightly more comfortable life until his death in 1900.

Whatever other issues had been resolved by 1882, it is clear that forcing everyone to work for the master all of the time continued to be a problem, for a notice appeared in the post office stating: '*Fishermen must attend on receipt of an understood signal and failing this, or leaving before work is finished without leave from the factor, will be charged 2/6 each. The factor cannot allow men themselves to arrange who will go fishing. Sufficient numbers must be there to fish on that day.*' Perhaps it was house building that was keeping men from their duties?

During the early 1880s, ninety to one hundred tons of fish, mainly saithe, were cured annually in Fair Isle. Fifty barrels of oil were also procured, about half of which was best quality. With a reduced population, a moderate income from the fishing, improved agricultural production and more comfortable housing, there seemed to be more hope for the future. Mr Laurence's arrival and the provision of the new school meant that the children's education was assured, although it would still be some time before any Fair Isle child would aspire to secondary school. The men, however, were increasingly aware that the lack of a proper harbour was preventing them from sharing in the fishing bonanza that was occurring elsewhere. More Scottish fishermen could expect to go to sea in 60-foot, decked vessels, with the ability to take on board much larger catches than yoals. They could also fish further afield and for an extended season. Even although it still had a high percentage of older, more traditional vessels, the Shetland herring industry was leaving Fair Isle behind.

Shetland's herring landings were latterly estimated in crans, four basket measures that contained around 1,000 herring. In 1879 Shetland landed 6,800 crans, but by 1881 this had become 46,256 crans, while by 1883 it was 194,000. Even this was not the peak, for in 1885 the total was 243,920 crans! White fish were also caught and processed in increasing quantities. Up to 1,000 British and 450 Dutch boats were reaping profits from this bounty and these profits seeped through to communities where people were involved in processing the fish.

The government continued its efforts to encourage the trade, controlling the standard of fish that was processed by using inspectors so that quality would be guaranteed. A good processing centre could offer employment to thousands during the season – fishermen, gutters, labourers, coopers, and rope makers. Although many of those involved in processing the fish were itinerant workers, some areas also saw local people improving their incomes. The British Fishing Society did everything it could to help by building houses, schools, churches, halls and business accommodation, and encouraging chosen settlements to develop. At Dunrossness, Levenwick flourished, while Grutness also saw a massive turn-around in its fortunes. However, no one saw Fair Isle as a potential processing centre.

Powered boats became more common during the 1880s and by 1892 there were thirty-eight steam trawlers registered in Aberdeen. They were harbingers of a new era, despite rumoured damage to the seabed caused by such indiscriminate fishing. This issue was discussed in high places, but without statistics, no conclusions could be arrived at that would protect either the fish or the small fishing communities that might suffer from this new type of fishing. The 1883 Sea Fisheries Act established a three-mile exclusion zone for foreign vessels and, in 1889, British trawlers were also limited to three miles, but it was difficult either to stop vessels from stealing 'your' fish, or have the offending boats prosecuted. Thus regulation protected local fishermen to some degree, but those who succeeded in the boom years were those who had access to bigger boats and a good harbour.

There was always talk of attracting a firm to set up a fish processing plant in Fair Isle, but never any sign of this happening, for without a safe harbour, alternative locations would always be favoured. An ever-continuing litany of wrecks made it difficult to persuade people that this was a good area for investment. The Fair Isle fleet remained strong, however, and on good days throughout the 1880s, up to two dozen yoals would set off for a day's line fishing, an impressive sight that indicated a vibrant community.

In 1878, a detailed Ordinance Survey of Fair Isle was undertaken by the government. The factor Jerome Wilson and his brother Andrew, joined Mr Laurence in providing the authority for the spelling of island names and denoting their origins. Since local people did not need a map to find their way around the island and few visitors explored its outer reaches, it was difficult for a lot of people to understand why so much effort was put into the exercise. The map would be produced in 1881.

On land, the Wilson factors, long a source of irritation to those who were not Wilsons (and also to some who were), found their power waning. When John of Taft died in 1851 his elder brother Thomas was factor, and when Thomas died in 1865 his position was taken over by his youngest brother, Jerome. Despite having one of the better standards of living on the island, Jerome did not enjoy good health, either because his wife brought tuberculosis with her when they married or because he was predisposed to the illness. Even their relocation from the old schoolhouse to the much superior Melville House did nothing to improve this family's health.

Tuberculosis was a scourge throughout Scotland in the 19th century, attacking rich and poor alike, but focusing on those who endured poor nutrition and close living quarters. It was an angel of death that you prayed would fly past, since prayer seemed to be the only way to ward it off. In communities where all lived similar lives, it favoured some families and ignored others, apparently without reason. Some victims coughed their way through many years of decline, while others died quickly, almost as soon as the disease infected them.

Jerome's wife Jane died in Melville House in 1876, after a "decline of two years". Sadly, although he remarried in 1877, by February 1879 Jerome too was dead, probably from tuberculosis. There can be no doubt that the Wilson factors were able to maintain a slightly higher standard of living than their neighbours, with a regular wage and a guaranteed house providing a level of security that the majority lacked, and as the 1870s progressed, both the role and its remuneration grew. However, since only one of their children could inherit the position, the job did not seem to offer any long-term gain for the family and their other sons became fishermen, while their daughters married fishermen.

Jerome's son Andrew took on the role of factor in 1879. Andrew was just twenty-nine and might have hoped for a long tenure of this position but, sadly, his young wife died just two years later, despite being taken to Lerwick for treatment for her consumption. Perhaps Andrew too was ill by now, for he asked Bruce to allow his younger brother Jerome to be his sub-factor. As well as managing the fish processing operation, there was now the post office and an increasing amount of Victorian official documentation to organise, as well as the shop and the new building project. For a couple of years Andrew struggled on, but it was evident that he was not long for this world. When his 21-year-old brother Jerome caught measles and died in June 1883, it seemed as if the family was cursed.

Andrew himself died that September, leaving four young children to survive with the help of the community. His sister Agnes had no family so she agreed to adopt his two-year-old daughter Margaret. The two older Wilson girls were content to go with Bruce to the mainland, where they worked as servants in his house until they were old enough to set out on their own. Andrew's only boy, his namesake, had contracted measles at the same time as his uncle Jerome and the ensuing ear infection left him profoundly deaf. John Bruce arranged for Andrew to be enrolled at the famous Donaldson's Hospital School in Edinburgh, which offered bursaries for poor and deaf children, and he was sent there. Bruce visited Edinburgh regularly on business matters, where his wealthy father-in-law was no doubt fully cognisant of the opportunities offered by this establishment. Bruce was not a heartless man and no doubt he did what he saw as his best for his employee. The man had himself lost two of his sisters by this time, aged just eighteen and twenty, along with his 24-year-old brother.

By the time the Wilson dynasty of factors died out in the 1880s, the long-term jealousy held against the family began to resolve. Finally no one complained about their power, for despite any advantages in the past it had not protected them from illness and tragedy. All were simply grateful that consumption had not chosen to knock at their door.

William Laurence took on the position of registrar and indeed many other responsibilities, including that of volunteer in charge of lifesaving. Other roles were added to James Anderson's remit. When Laurence died in 1887 it was felt that Bruce required a full-time representative on the island. The growth of the shop and post office, together with increasing rumours that a lighthouse would be built in the very near future, indicated that the position at Melville House was about to expand.

Sadly, the new postmaster/shop manager/registrar/laird's agent (William Manson) found that shortly after he arrived on the island he was required to register in August 1888 that his wife Johannah died from tuberculosis. His 14-year-old son died just a few months later, in all likelihood from intestinal tuberculosis. The position at Melville House merited some respect and allocated a certain standard of living, but just as the factors had found, it did not assure health and happiness.

Although it seemed increasingly likely that a lighthouse would finally be built, this particular saga continued. In 1878 David Stevenson had been asked to quote for two lighthouses in Fair Isle, but once more the Board of Trade could not find the relevant funding. Fishing was a dangerous profession, even for those who had access to new ships and safe harbours. In the summer of 1881, fifty-eight Shetland men from the Gloup area on Yell died in a fierce summer storm. Later that year, 189 fishermen died in a storm that raged around the east coast of Scotland. From the small fishing village of Eyemouth alone there were 129 deaths, and another fifteen from Newhaven on the outskirts of Edinburgh. In 1883 the infamous English trawling fleet disaster killed 255 men. As the litany of fishing losses went on, the cost of lives and ever-more-expensive boats continued to deter careless speculation. If a man was going to spend a considerable amount of his own money on a new boat, he wanted to be sure of recouping his investment by keeping it somewhere safe. Fair Isle's harbour situation kept it out of that equation.

With regard to the shipwreck of ever more expensive merchant and Royal Navy ships, a Fair Isle lighthouse remained centre stage. Despite the willingness of locals to risk their lives to save ships and passengers, the preferred option was that shipwrecks be avoided. Eventually an idea was suggested by Trinity House and agreed by the Board of Trade early in 1884. An experimental rocket station would be set up on the island, to warn passing boats of their proximity to the dangerous isle. One understands that neither the Northern Lighthouse Board nor the Stevensons were in anyway impressed by this suggestion, but discussions and preparations went ahead. An area was chosen well inland, along the line of the dyke that separated the arable and grazing areas, and an inspector of works from Edinburgh came to oversee the construction of an explosive store and launch area. To reduce the running costs of the system, it was stipulated that two unmarried men should be employed to fire the rockets, since they could live in basic, temporary accommodation until some decision was made about the long-term feasibility of the project.

In June 1885, the *London Gazette* announced to mariners that there would be a trial of the fog signal in Fair Isle, where a rocket would be fired every ten minutes when this was deemed necessary. Smaller 4oz charges would be used during fog in calm weather, while during heavy snow showers or stormy, foggy conditions, a 12oz charge would be used. Mariners were also warned that this was an experimental scheme and they could not necessarily depend on hearing the warnings.

The following year, in March 1886, the Board of Trade asked the Northern Lighthouse Board to make an assessment of the value of the experiment in consultation with those who sailed their steamers regularly between Orkney and Shetland. Captains Masson, Angus, Linklater and Nisbet all responded that they did not find the system either reliable or useful. Their continued preference was for a lighthouse. In June 1886 the experiment was abandoned as being not fit for purpose.

David Stevenson had been asked to provide a detailed estimate of the cost of erecting a temporary light on Malcolm's Head, prior to the rocket experiment. His initial estimate was approximately £5,000, which the Board found excessive, but after the rocket experiment he was required to prepare a new, lower estimate. One begins to sense some irritation from the amount of time and effort all these temporary measures were taking and we note that a slimmed-down estimate was prepared and sent to the Board on 25th December, 1886. The new total was £2,513, in part because this scheme would use the empty dwellings that had been used by the rocket station, which had not been available when the first estimate was given. This proposal was not sanctioned by the Board of Trade either.

Fair Isle was not the only location in Scotland waiting for a lighthouse and throughout the 1880s only four new lighthouses were built, in contrast to the twenty-eight that had been completed between 1850 and 1880. Despite ever-increasing traffic in the area, from fishing boats, cargo vessels and emigrant ships, not to mention the Royal Navy, a combination of funding problems and politics meant that plans for the majority of new lighthouses were mothballed.

For the men of Fair Isle, during the years that led up to 1890 their minds were focused on a way to join the herring fishing bonanza and, indeed, to acquire a better harbour. While the women's knitting and the sale of the occasional animal contributed to the community's ability to support itself, they could not be responsible for its long-term survival. It did not help that during the 1880s the value of lamb and beef was either static, or falling, as refrigeration began to allow cheap imports from New Zealand and North America to flood the market and lower prices. Now, at a time of great need, some of their alternative assets were also losing their value.

# Chapter 12

# Jane

Early in 1886, Shetland found fame in a most unusual manner. Betty Mouat of Scatness (near Sumburgh) was a frail spinster who lived quietly on her brother's croft. Unexpectedly, this good woman decided that since she had been unwell for some time she would visit a doctor in Lerwick. Consulting a doctor was an unusual activity for most rural Shetlanders, particularly women who were neither married nor rich. Most poor people never saw a doctor throughout their entire lives. However, Betty felt sure that she would benefit, so she dug out her meagre savings and packed some of the winter's knitting to take with her to sell. Her family wished her well, although they were of the opinion that acceptance of God's will was a more normal reaction to illness in a sixty-year-old woman, rather than a trip to Lerwick.

Betty made her way to Grutness, where she arranged passage on the *Columbine* along with its crew of three and a cargo of hams, herring, potatoes and various articles of metalwork. The sailors stowed Betty safely in the cabin, with due care for her disability, and set about raising sail for Lerwick. She must have been excited and perhaps a little worried about making such a journey on her own in January, even if it would only take a few hours to complete. Whatever the medical outcome, with friends and relatives in Lerwick this small adventure would take her mind off her woes and enliven the dull winter months.

What should have been a simple voyage turned badly wrong before the ship even left harbour. The *Columbine* found itself enveloped by a sudden violent gust that caught the rigging and dislodged the sail, throwing the skipper overboard. In a panic, the mate and deckhand took to the ship's small boat to try to save their captain, but by the time they realised that the poor man had probably drowned, the *Columbine* was well beyond their reach and setting off in a strong sea, for who knew where. They made every effort to reach her, but the weather was such that only with difficulty did they make it safely back to shore. They sent a message to John Bruce (whose ship this was) saying that in all likelihood, the *Columbine*, its captain and solitary passenger were lost.

Bruce was not so ready to give up his craft, offering money to anyone who would launch a boat to find it, but although some were tempted, the seas were such that no one would take the risk. A message was sent to Lerwick for the steamers that plied the islands to keep a lookout for the craft, but they saw nothing. When the weather finally subsided, some boats did indeed make a search, but no trace was found. Betty Mouat's family mourned her loss, reflecting that seeking good health in Lerwick was a very dangerous ploy indeed.

Yet unbeknown to them all, the *Columbine* and its sole passenger survived. Betty had taken with her a small supply of milk and biscuits and, by rationing, she managed to give herself the strength to hold on to ropes in the cabin, which prevented her from being injured over several days of bad weather. Later, she would tell people that she cried out to God and prayed, and in truth He must have heard her prayers for she travelled safely through days of turbulence. Finally, the *Columbine* was washed ashore in Norway, nine long days later. Local men were astonished when they found the ship and its female cargo. It did not take long for the news to arrive back in Britain, where the newspapers loved the story. It was indeed a miracle, an intimation of the power of prayer at a time when ministers liked to encourage congregations about the success of this activity.

The first available ship from Norway took the good lady to Edinburgh's port of Leith, where she was met and feted, both by émigré Shetlanders and by the press. There was so much sympathy for her ghastly journey that a subscription was raised to reward her for her courage. Queen Victoria gave £20! The Norwegian men who rescued her were rewarded both by silver medals and a small cash reward from the British government, while John Bruce contributed £30 for Betty and £20 for the lost skipper's family. William McGonigall set her story down in verse.

Betty returned to Shetland a few weeks later, acclaimed as a heroine (and a much wealthier woman). In the most remote of the islands her name became synonymous with bravery and stoicism. Teachers and ministers reminded their flocks of the power of prayer. As to the nature of her doctor's visit, it can only be noted that whatever had been worrying Betty when she set off for Lerwick, she lived for another thirty-two years.

Shortly after this excitement, a letter was received by Mr Laurence telling him of the proposal that Fair Isle girls were to be included in an International Exhibition of Industry, Science and Art. It would be held in Edinburgh for six months during that summer and young ladies from Fair Isle and Shetland were to represent their islands at this event, which would provide a marketing possibility for their knitting. Girls would be sent for about six to eight weeks at a time, to enable several individuals to have the chance to travel. They would demonstrate knitting, as well as carding, dyeing and spinning.

In 1851, the Prince of Wales had organised a Great Exhibition in London to showcase the excellence of British industry. Other exhibitions followed and now, in 1886, Edinburgh was to follow suit. However, although Mr Laurence read out all that he had been sent describing the event, it was impossible to communicate its scope to the people who would represent Fair Isle. It was difficult enough to convey what it would be like to live in a large city, far less to impart the idea of an event, the like of which he himself had never witnessed. The physical size and scope of the exhibition buildings was extraordinary. There would be a working confectionery, a candle factory, a bakery, silk spinning, glassblowing, envelope making, an aerated water factory and an example of every field of industry that the country could boast. Art and antiques would be exhibited and sold. The Prince of Wales and the Prime Minister would attend. Mr Laurence might explain that there would be 3,200 electric lamps illuminated every evening, but what did that mean to people who had never seen anything more technical than a candle and sometimes few enough of these? An electric railway was equally arcane. All the girls could do was to prepare lots and lots of knitting. There was some discussion about who should be chosen, and not everyone wanted to go, for the trip seemed remarkably challenging, if not alarming.

Jane Wilson of Taft was thrilled to be chosen to represent the island at the exhibition. She was twenty-two years old and Barbara's right hand woman in the croft, for it was still Barbara to whom she answered rather than her stepmother. Her sister Hannah left Fair Isle in 1882 when William decided to find work on larger ships in bigger ports. Hannah was a great loss to Jane, who was tempted to follow her to the mainland where girls could readily find jobs 'in service'. But Jane had promised young Mary that she would not leave yet, since Taft was still a home with issues and factions. Despite the passage of the years and the arrival of more children, Polly was still a problem for the girls, who were with her all day. Everyone had worked out a way of surviving, but without Aunt Barbara, who was now in her mid-seventies, there might have been open warfare. Mary was not quite able to stand up for herself and, at seventeen, she would not be allowed to leave with Jane, for John was careful about his daughters.

Jane was pretty, strong minded and a hard worker. She used her father as her measure for a husband, however, and found it hard to match him when she looked for an island spouse. Illogically, the family still blamed Polly for all that had occurred, their father retaining much of their high regard. Many family situations defy logic. Since Jane had decided that she would only leave Taft for a croft where she would be mistress, this rather reduced her prospects, since most crofts had mistresses already living in them. She was not afraid of hard work, but jumping from the kettle into the fire was not her idea of freedom. Life at Taft had developed a rhythm, one with which she could live, but it was still a croft with issues.

Jane worked hard to prepare for the exhibition and for once they all worked together. John was moved to agree that material could be purchased to create some new clothes. He was, in fact, jealous that one of his children should be given such an experience. Although he occasionally went to the Shetland mainland, or Kirkwall, that could hardly be compared to a visit to Edinburgh. To see the exhibition would be incredible, but Fair Isle men had money to earn and children to raise, particularly when they decided to marry for a second time so, reluctantly, John had accepted that travel would never be part of his life. Jane would have to be his substitute.

The Sheriff of Orkney and Shetland, George Thoms, organised the girls' role in the exhibition. He sent instructions from his Edinburgh base in Charlotte Square explaining what the girls should take with them, advising all to have at least two changes of clothes, a travelling dress, another for wearing at the exhibition and an extra blouse and skirt, so that no small accident might leave the girls looking less than perfect. The exhibition dress should be in the form of a Shetland costume, for which sample drawings were provided, which was a relief since no one knew what a Shetland dress looked like. There were to be hats, smart shoes, respectable stockings and underwear. Brushes and combs must also be spared, from households in which it was often the norm that one set might be shared by all.

The girls were instructed to arrive with a stock of knitting, even though they would be knitting during all the time they were in the exhibition. Never did so many fingers flash over so many detailed garments, to ensure that the island's good name would not be sullied. The opportunity for a new market for their goods, not to mention higher prices, stimulated everyone and all the knitting was inspected by a group of older ladies before being packed. Every croft was entitled to send some garments, although of course the emissaries could pack extra samples in their own luggage. They had been instructed to include modern items that were in keeping with the ideals of the event, as well as traditional fare. It was suggested that they knit jerseys suitable for lawn tennis and also fancy knickerbocker hose. These instructions were exotic and much discussed, but the girls were young, imaginative and hardworking and could adapt to anything they were asked to produce. Knitting was the least of their problems.

Tickets were provided from Lerwick, where the Fair Isle group met the Shetland trio for the journey on the steamer to Leith. They set off in high delight, but the weather was decidedly inclement and it has to be said that by the time they reached the harbour at Edinburgh's port of Leith all were frail of spirit. Yet, the last hour of the voyage revived them and as Leith hove into view almost all felt well enough to tidy hair and smooth skirts in preparation for their baptism into city life.

When the boat finally docked, the girls were quite overwhelmed. There was so much noise, so many people, and so many things they had never seen before that all were terrified that their baggage might be lost in the melee. Leith was far bigger and busier than any of them had imagined, with tall buildings, enormous ships and a seemingly endless tide of humanity that pushed and shouted. Workers shoved and carried vast loads of trunks and boxes, expertly weaving in and out of piles of cargo. Terror at losing their belongings gradually matched a fear of losing their companions.

Luckily they were soon joined by Mrs Muir, who had been hired as matron of the flat in which they were to live in Edinburgh. Once reunited with their luggage, she escorted her bemused group (with the help of two porters) through the crowds and noise to a waiting cart, which the girls thought would be their transport into town. Mrs Muir laughed, explaining that they were to travel with their hand-baggage in a horse-drawn bus, while the carter would take the boxes separately to the lodgings. She assured them that their belongings would be safe, but it was a great act of faith to hand their precious baggage over to someone none of them knew, in a city their parents had warned them would be filled with thieves and vagabonds. What if the man stole the knitting? The carter caught Mrs Muir's eye and looked heavenwards when he heard them discussing this thought, but for the rest of the day every new experience was equally exciting and disturbing. The flat itself was overwhelming in its size and splendour.

When they were taken to the exhibition it reduced them to silence, for it was a wonder of the age. A vast edifice had been erected on the Meadows, an expansive grassed park area surrounded by high flats. In addition to row upon row of exhibition buildings, there was at one end a grand hall with a lofty glass dome that covered ten thousand seats.

The grand opening was on 6th May, 1886, by no less a person than Prince Albert, who was handed a golden key to open the doors. There were speeches, heralds with trumpets and the ascent of a huge air balloon, followed by a procession and choirs singing the *Hallelujah Chorus*, with the great and the good from around the land all dressed in regal finery. Anyone who had any sort of position in the country had a place at the exhibition. It was all so grand that the girls felt they were living a dream. Military bands played every day at the bandstand and the electric railway was a wonder to behold, while every night at nine, just as they had been promised, there was an instantaneous illumination of 3,200 electric bulbs powered by nine engines.

The Shetland girls were located in the Women's Industry Section. At stall 1913 they sat and knitted, all dressed in their 'native costumes' and wondering at the people who passed, who wondered at the girls and their spectacular knitting. They sat on rough wooden seats just as they did at home, surrounded by wool in all its different stages of production. They took it in turns to knit, card and spin, answering questions with increasing confidence as the days went by, quickly learning to erase island words that might not be understood by southerners. Betty Mouat came to join them, since her fame was still sufficient to draw people to their stand. This was a well-executed piece of marketing by Sheriff Thoms, who was familiar with the power of celebrity.

Their area was marked by huge whales' jawbones, festooned with lacy shawls and cotton fishing nets. Everyone was allowed short periods away from the stall so that they could see the rest of the exhibition. Never did anyone get bored, for there was always something different to tell, from the fact that it cost one shilling to hire a bath chair to the fact that the toilets flushed water, even out here in the middle of a field. Best of all, they had to work hard to replace the stock that they were selling. The idea of going home with a pile of cash made fingers fly. Smiling increased sales they discovered. They all smiled.

Sunday was their day off, for Calvin's Scotland expected everyone to be involved in religious services. After church, the Shetland diaspora came to see them and ask about relatives, even those who had been away from the island for years. Homesickness, they discovered, was an ever-nagging toothache for emigrants, particularly the women. It also appeared that the longer you were away, the more idealised were your memories, although few expressed a wish to return. Jane's most regular visitor was cousin Barbara from Kirkwall, who was in service in Edinburgh.

The three Fair Islanders stuck firmly together when they went out. On the few occasions they ventured into the town centre, they were as surprised at the human sights as they were at the buildings, shops and monuments. To them it was as interesting to see rag and bone men, hurdy-gurdy men playing music machines, tradesmen and hawkers, as it was to look at grand folk.

All too soon it was time to go home. Breaking her journey, Jane spent a week with Johanna in Lerwick and the pair giggled as if they were teenagers, so that William found himself bewildered that his mature, responsible wife could so easily revert to her younger self. Jane had enough cash to have a photograph taken in a studio in the town, to remind themselves of the occasion. It broke her heart to leave Johanna, even though she knew there was more family waiting at home. Johanna seemed more worldly in Lerwick, dealing with tradesmen with aplomb and generally running a very smooth home, not that it was in any way grand. Her taste in clothes was the height of fashion, however, and she still had the slimmest waist, even though she now had children. In Lerwick there were plenty of poorer folk and ordinary working men, while others seemed to wear their good clothes every day. In Fair Isle, Sunday best was a simple truth. Jane returned to the island with a different perspective.

Fair Isle welcomed its travellers with enthusiasm, so that for a while they were the centre of attention with all their tales and mementoes. The girls lived for the rest of that year on their stories and each brought home a small nest egg, together with money for all who had sent knitting with them. For a year or so, orders would arrive from people in the south although, in time, such interest gradually began to peter out. Despite all the cost and effort of getting the girls there, no one helped them to use these contacts to establish a market that would grow. Here, John Bruce could have helped, but since he saw no personal advancement from this ploy, he failed to act.

As for the girls, finally people got bored with their tales. By the following spring, for most of them it was just a memory. John Wilson was one of the few who did not bore with the stories his daughter told, taking himself everlastingly to Edinburgh in his imagination, quite paining Jane at times with his endless questions. Polly quickly got sick of them talking about something in which she had no interest, snapping at Jane when yet again the subject arose. It was time Jane found a man and got married, she suggested more than once. Trips to the south were fine, but they were not real life.

In May 1886 one of the new floating shops, the 'Summer Cloud', visited Fair Isle, offering people a much wider range of produce than their own shop, which was at times short of supplies. Although there had been a shop at Melville House from early in the 1870s, it was always expensive and never offered the islanders much choice.

A rather less welcome visitor in 1886 was HMS *Firm*, which launched a new campaign against smuggling. Its aim was to arrest any ship undertaking illegal trade and take their captains to court. Before too long it came upon the *Martha*, close by Fair Isle, surrounded by a number of local boats. The yoals immediately showed off their owners' celebrated rowing expertise, crews making a particularly speedy bee-line for the shore, beaching and disappearing inland before they could be implicated. The *Martha* was not so lucky, being towed back to Lerwick where its contraband was confiscated and its captain arrested. This was only one of a number of ships plying their trade around the islands and although this one flew the North German flag, at least one other was from Shetland. Smuggling was not an activity that the government found easy to police in remote northern waters and no one really knew how much of it went on, only that it did. The men who bought alcohol and tobacco did not feel they were doing anything particularly wrong. It was part of a fisherman's culture, in a place where the law of the land continued to feel somewhat irrelevant.

~———~

Religion was for most islanders still a pivotal part of their existence, around which the week was organised. Sunday was a very special day and these observances required an edifice that reflected this importance. The Church of Scotland had been in the same place near Kirkigeo for some time, probably rebuilt over the years as condition required, although an earlier building had existed near Shirva. Now, the church was structurally unsound and almost impossible to use, so there were appeals made for a new building. There was, however, no immediate response from those in the church hierarchy who must provide the funding.

When the Methodists broke away from the official church in the 1830s, they had at first no official place to join together in worship and had to make do for many years with meeting in one another's homes. These early Methodists were particularly devout and met not only on Sundays but also at other times in the week, to support one another on their path to God. Early in the 1860s this congregation had banded together to build a small chapel close to Taft, using island stone that men, women and children carried on their backs. Like all early Fair Isle buildings, over time it suffered from dampness, due to ill-hewn stone and a permanently wet, turf roof, so that it gradually became less habitable. The Wesleyans still met in one another's homes on a regular basis, but they too began to plead with their leaders for help in building a new chapel.

In 1884 the chairman of the Methodist Circuit reported that the condition of the chapel on the island was 'wretched' and quite beyond repair. In 1885, £200 was made available for a new building, resulting in the arrival of Mr Alex Irvine of Dunrossness to help local men with the construction. He used the existing stone, supplemented by additional material sent from Montrose. Even then, £200 was not a large sum of money, but the dedication of the congregation ensured that a building was created that would be wind and weatherproof for many years to come, although the porch and bell tower would have to wait. Even when the chapel was completed, the Methodists continued to hold enthusiastic meetings in one another's homes, in addition to Sunday services. Class leaders like John Wilson of Taft met with groups of up to twelve adults to discuss the Bible, examine souls and encourage people in their faith. Stewart Wilson was as respected as his father had been as lay preacher and class leaders reported back to him, so that he could support families where he deemed necessary. The state of one's soul was of vital importance to many Christians at this time, but small communities tended to be particularly devout. The nightly reading of the Bible was not undertaken summarily. In religious homes throughout the island, the Bible was a guiding force and questioning accompanied this activity to ensure understanding.

John was also a Sunday school teacher, whose job it was to ensure that a new generation of Methodists would follow the correct path to God. Sundays were totally turned over to religious study, while fast days, nightly Bible readings, and constant theological discussion ensured that religion was seldom far from the minds of the faithful. Once his marriage was legally affirmed, John returned to his devotional life, with no realisation that others might have developed some doubts as to the manner in which he had got his own way. Some members of the official church would never overlook the effort he had made to thwart their ministers.

All the people of Fair Isle came together to welcome the *Earl of Zetland* steamer on 19th August, 1886, many of whose passengers had come to celebrate the opening of the new Wesleyan Chapel. The most eminent of these was the Reverend William Moister from Yorkshire, one of the Methodists' most respected missionaries. Even at seventy-eight, he was more than pleased to make this considerable journey, accompanied by the Reverend Priestley, Superintendent of the Shetland Methodist District. The *Earl of Zetland* had loaded passengers in Lerwick, including a journalist, but it also collected parties both at Sandwick and Grutness (including John Bruce) so that the total number of visitors amounted to one hundred and eleven. Some visitors were more than happy just to wander round the island, enabling the remainder to concentrate on the inaugural service at the chapel, along with many islanders.

This event was a triumph for the Methodists, who basked in such official recognition of their faith. It also underscored the prospect of a long-term future, both for the island and its people. It was noted in *The Shetland Times* that Fair Isle was much improved from twelve years previously, with impressive new houses and tidy fencing imparting a strong feeling of prosperity. No longer was it an outpost of civilisation, with a wild, rough-looking populace that lived in hovels, as had been reported as recently as the 1860s. Now, these were civilised, hardworking people, who lived respectably. Of course, such enthusiasm for the new chapel meant that the Church of Scotland congregation felt increasingly ill-served by their own dilapidated building and fuelled their arguments for a rebuilding programme.

By the following spring, Jane Wilson had an admirer. The combined attributes of fame and a small nest egg probably enhanced the qualities of all the girls who had been away. Willie Stout of Stoneybrake was a lively young man who lived in a challenging croft to the north of the island. His one claim to fame thus far, was that he had survived a dreadful overnight storm with his father. The pair had been fishing when the weather suddenly turned against them and although they desperately tried to make it back to South Harbour, the storm gathered force until they could see nothing but rain and deep dark waves that threatened to submerge their yoal. George Stout senior was determined to save both his son and his boat and in the end he stopped trying to find land and concentrated on working with every wave, baling out when necessary. Since it never got totally dark, the pair could see what they were doing if not always where they were going. When Willie looked as if he was going to fall asleep, his father shouted at him, for the boy had the tiller while his father steadfastly rowed and baled throughout the night. Few men on earth had the stamina and power of Fair Isle fishermen, so that once the storm abated, George senior was able to work out where they were and take his yoal safely home. By the time they came into view of Kirkigeo, there were already boats out looking for them. Whatever else Willie could offer Jane, he had seamanship and an unfaltering determination to improve himself.

In Taft, there was some doubt about this young man who presented himself at the door with increasing regularity to take Jane for a walk of an occasional evening and on Sunday afternoons.

Polly was in her element. "I hope you'll be comfortable up there at Stoneybrake with all those Stouts. Not as comfortable as here maybe, but it's about time you found out what life is really like, my lady. You can take all your fancy ways to Stoneybrake and see where that gets you. He's got an older brother, you know. Even Stoneybrake won't be yours. Now you'll have to learn what it's like to play second fiddle and you'll have to go to the Church of Scotland. Well, we'll all miss you here, you and all your red-headed bairns. It's red-haired children for you in the Stout family."

In her own silly way, Polly had managed to home in on weaknesses in Willie Stout's suit, for Jane had all the prejudices of a Fair Isle Wilson bred into her blood. First of all, Willie was a Stout and not a Wilson. Furthermore, he lived at Stoneybrake and had not obviously got the greatest of futures, since he was one of five brothers in a croft that could not support five families, never mind the old parents. Since Jane would not consider starting her married life in Taft with Polly, they would have to live somewhere else. Then there was his religion. Could she abandon what she had been taught to believe was the true path to God? Other people did, but it was still a big step to take, for Jane was a firm Methodist. Also, when you started to socialise with your husband's family and friends you hardly saw your own, even on a Sunday. Did she love Willie enough for this? Did she, in fact, love Willie at all, or was she just looking for a way out of Taft and freedom from Polly? She had always been the one to boast of having the darkest black hair and yet it was likely her children could have red hair. Did she want red-haired children?

Ridiculously, she allowed this question to niggle at her mind as she considered her future. She spoke of it to Aunt Barbara, who was still lively at seventy-six, although taking life just a little more easily as she approached another decade. She was certainly willing to advise the young, which was as well since the children in the main avoided discussion with their father, lest he preach at them, and Polly's opinion on any subject was always dismissed out of hand. With Johanna away, it had to be Barbara who set Jane thinking.

"Now, let me think. You are wondering if you want to marry a man who will bring you red-haired bairns. In my opinion, Jane Wilson, you need to ask yourself a bit more than that. Do you want to marry the man in the first place? Do you feel he can support you? Good gracious, girl, do you love him? For if you are not sure of any of these things at the start, your life will not get any better once you're wed. Are you sure you want to marry anyone, my girl? There's no shame in being an old maid. You take it from one who knows. I've watched plenty marry in haste and repent at leisure. Red hair indeed! Don't use that as an excuse. You've never settled since you spent all that time in Edinburgh last year. Don't jump into marriage unless you're sure of it. You've seen here how a poor marriage works out. Go off into service if you don't want to stay, but don't marry anyone unless you're sure. Apart from anything else, it's not fair to the man."

Barbara's words were just what Jane needed. Willie was hurrying her to marry him and although she had at first been pleased by all the attention, did she want that? Being a wife was what all the girls lived for, but if she had learned anything these last twenty-four years, it was that if you jumped out of the frying pan and into the fire, you had to live with the consequences.

Polly had produced four children to add to John's original six, but she brought him little real satisfaction. She was not Barbara, rather a silly, illiterate woman who busied herself with local gossip rather than any worthwhile activity. Although she professed religion, she had no interest in the finer points. She had of course mastered all the womanly skills from childhood, but she had no real depth of character and saw his first family as clutter to be squabbled out of his home and, worst of all, she wasn't bright enough to do it with subtlety. Sometimes he felt that it was only her resolute campaign against them that kept them all here. Perhaps this was the curse that accompanied his insistence that he could take the law into his own hands. Perhaps Polly was his punishment, poor soul, for she was nothing more or less now than when he married her. The mistake had been all his.

The following Sunday, when Willie took Jane home to visit his parents, she looked around Stoneybrake and decided she didn't want to live there. And she didn't want red-haired children. Or she didn't want them now. And she didn't want Willie, not really. Willie was a fine young man, a hard worker who would make someone a good husband, but probably not herself and certainly not now. The day after this visit she wrote to her cousin Barbara in Edinburgh and asked her if it would be difficult to find a place in service, for she intended to leave Fair Isle. Barbara replied at the end of September, sending her fare from her future employer, a spinster lady who lived with her sister. Spinsters, Barbara wrote, had a lot to recommend them. All Jane had to do was to catch the steamer and come to Edinburgh.

And tell Willie. And tell Mary. And tell her father. And tell Aunt Barbara, who was old. And leave Taft. For a couple of days she said nothing to anyone, for this sudden response seemed too much, too soon. Abruptly, it was all arranged, almost without her involvement. She had not told Willie that she had no intention to marry him, avoiding the man for the last two weeks. It was as if there was a barrier stopping her from speaking of her betrayal, for betrayal she knew it was, both of Willie and his hopes. However, she had been offered a chance to escape and she must take it. On the third night of worrying, she asked her father to come for a walk, to tell him that she was leaving. She knew he would be upset, and she dreaded telling Mary, who would now feel abandoned. And then there was Aunt Barbara.

John had been preparing to give her matrimonial advice on the walk, but emigration was a different matter and he was shocked by the turn of events. Johanna had moved on to South Shields and now Jane was going away too. His children were leaving, just as his siblings had done. But the girl was taking a chance and perhaps for her this was right, for this was a different world to the one he had known as a youngster. Willie Stout had seemed a fair choice, even if he was a Stout, but now Jane had changed her mind. Although he would be loath to lose her, Edinburgh sounded a grand city and his niece was already there to help the girl. While John had to admit that life was changing all the time, progress in Fair Isle was still slow. Despite writing that they felt homesick for the island, most of those who left never felt the need to come back. Like all the local fishermen, John could see the value of saithe declining, while there seemed to be no more likelihood of a harbour than there had ever been. Perhaps a marriage in Fair Isle was not in Jane's best interest.

"Have you told Willie?"

"No, Faither."

"Well, the boy has to be told. He'll say you've just been leading him on otherwise. He's not going to be happy about this, whatever happens. What with this being the Stouts, they'll all be unhappy."

"But I wasn't leading him on. I just realised too late that I don't love him enough, that's all. I didn't know that at first."

Jane was both upset and guilty, for she had just started to go out with Willie because that was what you did when a nice boy showed interest. He was a nice boy, and fun to be with during the limited time they had spent together. But she didn't want to marry him. That knowledge didn't make it any easier to tell him, however. She sent Thomas up to Stoneybrake with a message that she wanted to speak with Willie and was ready to go out as soon as he arrived at Taft. The poor young man was totally unaware of the thunderbolt about to strike him as they walked down to the graveyard. The news struck him like a blow. How could she do this to him? He was crushed.

"Were you just leading me on for a laugh? Did I do something wrong? Are we not good enough for you?" All the questions that ran through his head, he immediately voiced.

"No. I thought I wanted to marry you, but I don't. It's not about you. It's about me. I'm not ready to get married yet. That's all."

"That's all! You lead me up the path so that I make a complete fool of myself in front of everyone and then change your mind for no reason. I don't think so. There has to be a reason. Is your father against us?"

"No. My father has nothing to do with this at all. It's my decision. I just don't want to get married yet."

"Then why did you encourage me?"

"Because I thought I wanted it. I'm sorry. I'm so sorry. I didn't plan it. I just don't want to marry you, at any rate not at the moment."

Willie turned away in disgust and distress. He had been happy. Jane was to be the light of his life. Now he would be the laughing stock of the island, a lovesick swain. Whatever happened elsewhere, women here didn't abandon men they were walking out with. Only men did that and even then it wasn't really considered acceptable to lead a girl on. What were women coming to? From the height of joy and anticipation, his life was suddenly turned on its head. What a laugh they would all have at his expense. He walked home to Stoneybrake and went straight to bed. No one said anything. Everyone looked at each other in open-eyed question, but knew enough to say nothing. Young lovers and their tiffs were best left to sort themselves out.

Later that night, just as the rest of the Stouts were going to bed, there was a knock on the door but no one entered, which in itself was unusual. George went to open it.

John Wilson of Taft stood there in the twilight. "Could I have a word out here, George?"

"Aye."

These men were of similar ages, John just a few years older. They had similar lives, with similar problems. Most of George's family, uncles, cousins and all his brothers and sisters went to Canada in 1862. The rest of his uncles had gone to Stronsay. The man knew about fishing and crofting and loss.

"I'm sorry to have to come up to see you, George."

"Aye."

"It's about Willie and Jane."

"Well." Suspecting that this would not be good news, George was loath to commit himself.

"Jane told him tonight that she was backing off their friendship. It was nothing to do with me and nothing really to do with Willie. She says she's just not ready to settle yet. We're sorry for any upset."

"Aye, well the lad seemed upset enough when he came in tonight, but he'll get over it. Plenty more fish in the sea."

"Yes, but Jane forgot to tell him something, and she wanted him to know from us, not from anyone else. She was upset when she told him."

"Aye." Irritated that his son had been spurned, George was not inclined to make this easier for a man who liked to see himself with the upper hand.

"Well, the thing is, she doesn't want to stay here with all the upset this might cause so she's off to Edinburgh to work in service. So you can tell Willie she won't be around very soon. She's sorry, George. The young ones live different lives nowadays, you know. It's a different world."

"Aye, well I'll tell him. Good night to you."

The meeting ended on a frosty but not unpleasant note, although Jane's foray into love had done nothing to cement any bonds between Wilsons and Stouts.

John sighed as he walked back down to Taft. "Well, Barbara. I don't know if it would have been any different if you'd been here. The young ones all have their own ideas today. It's not as simple as it was when we were young."

Over the years he still talked to Barbara about their children. Once he recognised that there would be no point in speaking with Polly, he had to talk to someone. He believed his first wife heard. Tonight, sighing, he went back into the barn to work on strengthening the kist that would take Jane's belongings to Edinburgh. For all he knew, this could be the last help he was to her. She was leaving, perhaps forever. Nothing was as it had been. Nothing was as he had expected all these years ago when he had been a young man, courting Barbara. He well remembered the thrill and excitement. Young Willie Stout would get over it. There were lots of young things ready to marry a strong young man. His pride would be dented, but he would survive.

When she was ready to go, John rowed his daughter to the steamer with a heavy heart. This was the second child he had rowed off the island. He seldom saw Johanna now. And he felt that John was thinking of leaving too. He had never imagined that his eldest son would abandon his inheritance. Would this be the way from now? Would they all leave? To think he had still imagined that all his children would settle on the island, even after his own mother led his brothers and sisters away. He helped his daughter up onto the steamer and watched as the crew manhandled her box onto the deck, without anything but cheerful farewells, even though by now she was crying, as they all did at this point. His own eyes filled as the steamer made way and he turned to row steadily back to shore, thankful that Stewart was with him. Stewart seemed set to stay and constantly came up with new ideas about fishing and crofting, which his father did not always appreciate. Perhaps he needed to change his attitude to the boy. If he wanted his children to stay, they needed to feel they had a future here. The island was proving just too easy to leave.

Jane too was reflecting on the future and what it might bring. Although convinced that she had been right to stop the marriage plans, that didn't make the future any easier to contemplate. Despite her confidence in the planning stages of her journey, there was nothing now but sorrow. Aunt Barbara was an old woman. Who knew if Barbara would be there when she returned? This was quite a different farewell from the exhibition trip. This time she might not return. Jane couldn't imagine that.

Of course, young Willie Stout did get over it, but not immediately. He was upset at losing Jane and humiliated at being discarded, for he was a young man in his prime. He refused to talk about it to anyone at home and hit out when any of his friends pulled his leg. It was a long winter for his family and in the spring, as soon as he could catch a boat to Lerwick, he made his way there and then on to South Shields, to join the increasing numbers of Shetland men who found work in the merchant navy. Travel and adventure soon broadened his mind and overcame his disappointment. He would return when he was ready, when he felt able to start again with a clean slate.

When William Laurence came to the island as a schoolteacher and catechist it would have been hard to prophesy the influence he would have. One of the first contributions he had made was to try to make up for the lack of education in the past by including older boys in day classes, and offering classes in the winter evenings to older lads like the Irvines at Quoy who had missed out on education. That family had not the time to waste on school learning as they struggled to earn enough to stay on their land. William Laurence offered the Irvines, and others like them, a second chance.

Even after the 1872 Education Act it had taken some time for education to reach all of those encompassed by the legislation, with Anderson, who eventually took on the role of school attendance officer, chivvying families to send children on a regular basis. It took everyone time to accept that school was now heavily regimented including, initially, Mr Laurence himself. In 1879 he was late in restarting the school after his annual summer trip to the Shetland mainland and was surprised to discover, at the end of the academic year, that the school was penalised for a lack of openings. He tried to explain that sometimes his return to the island after a holiday could be held up by bad weather. It was also necessary to close the school when a wreck occurred, since he was in charge of the lifeboat and the children liked to watch the proceedings. The arrival of the fortnightly mail boat also saw school cancelled, for no child would think of missing that excitement. Visitors and bartering trips were equally celebrated. Bouts of illness could require general closure for weeks, given the mothers' attitude to infection control, and of course the spring planting required every hand to be put to the land. Then there was the harvest. Mr Laurence patiently explained that in Fair Isle there were many reasons for a school to be closed.

But the education department responded that Mr Laurence was far short of the official requirement, by eight weeks! With no one to monitor the days, they had simply slipped away. Bruce and the local school board came to their teacher's defence so that the money was eventually paid, but both Laurence and the parents had learned that consistent attendance was a necessity in this new world of regulated learning. The school now opened regularly and most children attended until they were thirteen, although it was still possible, even until 1908, for children over the age of ten to gain exemption from education in Scotland, providing they had achieved a grade five level or could prove an over-riding need at home.

Laurence's steady hand bridged the gap between the previous informal, church-led education and the greater academic rigour that was required after the Education Act. He also supported the islanders in a myriad of other useful ways – writing official letters on their behalf, trying to improve their local services and conditions, providing accommodation and support for visitors and introducing a small library. He became a Justice of the Peace. His efforts to obtain a lighthouse were universally admired and he led the men in their life-saving activities when this was required.

In 1887 the teacher developed a small infection in one of his fingers, at first nothing of note. Then the poison spread. Despite the efforts of the women, this simple septic finger became a serious ailment and finally Laurence became quite unwell. His fingers were soaked in hot seawater, then wrapped in cold seaweed to draw the poison, all to no avail. Finally, on 4th September, 1887, he was taken to seek professional help in Lerwick, but once there it became clear that the infection had overtaken his system's ability to fight. Two fingers were immediately amputated but the poison quickly overwhelmed his body and he died shortly afterwards. William Laurence was a huge loss to the island, a man who was truly devoted to people's welfare on so many different levels.

His passing once more left the school without a teacher, but in 1887 a system was in place that would provide a temporary replacement. Miss Duncan was the first schoolmistress the children had experienced and it took everyone a little time to adapt to the idea. In December she returned to Shetland and, in February 1888, William Brown came to take over most of the roles that Laurence had embraced, his permanency encouraging everyone to think that life might get back to normal. But these were difficult footsteps in which to tread and William Brown was a very different kind of man from William Laurence. Brown was a strict man who had very definite views about the Presbyterian religion, about which he left no one in doubt. Gradually the school settled down to the new regime, although there were times when William Laurence was remembered fondly, by both children and parents.

～･～

Meanwhile, Jane was not the only one to leave Taft. Worn down by Polly's constant criticism and his father's continuing disappointment, young John Wilson finally decided to move. He was twenty-six and wanted to explore new opportunities that might release him from the pressures his father exerted. Like most Fair Isle men he was a competent sailor, so he decided to join Johanna and William in South Shields where William assured him there were lots of opportunities for ambitious young men. His father bid him farewell with a deep sadness, for although he did not fully understand the reason, he knew that somehow he had let the boy down.

Polly had hoped to wear all the older boys down, in the belief that if they left, her sons would inherit the croft. John was in his late fifties and still very hale and hearty, so given the longevity of the Wilsons, time was on her side. When young John left and everyone else mourned his loss, she simply ticked this son off her list, for leaving the island generally meant forever. Indeed, Jane was one of the few young people who wrote home regularly, her father above all others relishing her epistles.

Stewart and Thomas presented Polly with more of a problem, particularly Stewart, who was quite a different kettle of fish from his brother. As a young man of twenty-two, he was a fully-fledged fisherman and quite the lad for the ladies, not that he was ready to settle down just yet. He enjoyed life and simply ignored Polly, renovating the old croft house/barn and moving in there with Thomas, the pair only taking their meals at Taft. This meant that the two could come and go as they pleased and, more importantly, stay out of Polly's hair and away from her tongue. Perhaps his father had criticised Stewart less, since he had not seen him as the potential new head of the family, but whatever the reason, the boy flourished. And of course no one was allowed to say anything against Thomas in Barbara's hearing, so he continued to live a fairly charmed life.

Jane wrote home every Sunday, saying that she had come to a good home and the labour here was less demanding than on a croft, simply because so much of it was inside work. The kitchen had a big stove and the two young women who served their mistress slept in a bed recess there. At least they were always warm. Food was never an issue, and Jane had been provided with a uniform so that she was always smart when she answered the door. The fact that there was a sink with a tap in the kitchen, one that drained to the outside, was wonderful, and there was an inside flushing toilet and a bath. Meals were varied and tasty and on Sundays there was time off. The wage was slight, but like all the Shetland girls who came to town, Jane soon found a small shop that would buy her knitting, so she managed well on her income. Knitting was still as much a part of all the girls' lives as breathing.

Although she assured the family that she was enjoying herself, Jane made it quite clear that Edinburgh was not utopia. Sometimes the two servants would quarrel, but they still had to work together and you couldn't escape each other in the confines of a small flat, not to mention a shared bed. Sometimes their mistress asked too much from them, especially when she entertained. And it took a while to comprehend how dirty a city could be, for not only did every home have several chimneys, not far enough from the flat, tall factory chimneys bellowed out dark, poisonous fumes throughout the day and night. It was convenient for Edinburgh's wealthy to have several train lines running through the city, but coal-fired railway engines added to the miasma. Throughout the winter, heavy, suffocating fogs sometimes made it almost impossible either to see or breathe outside, and it was surprising how much of this type of dirt adhered to your clothing. Although there were all the grand sights, sickly, barefoot children, gaunt, begging women and drunken, dishevelled men all had their place here too. When you felt lonely, for all emigrants have lonely days, you longed for Fair Isle, with all the well-kent faces, the wonderful panoramas and the sweet, fresh air.

Her father had said, "Keep your fare home by your side and you'll never go wrong. Work as hard as you can for your mistress, but remember, you can always walk away from it if they don't treat you well. Find a chapel and make friends there and you'll always have someone to turn to."

Saving money was easy for Jane, for frugality was bred into her bones and, now that she was well fed and did not wear out her own clothes during the day, she gradually built up a small nest egg, both from her wages and the selling of woollen garments. What this would be used for she did not know, but the ability to save pleased her greatly. Looking at the post office savings book, where the clerk recorded all the small sums she deposited, provided both enjoyment and security.

In Fair Isle too it had become possible to save at the post office. After the exhibition, women increasingly sold their knitted goods to merchants further afield than Shetland, but there was an issue about payment, which also affected those wishing to buy merchandise from the mainland. The problem was that everyone knew it was dangerous to send cash in the mail, but a money order office was not at first included in the island's post office responsibilities and there was, of course, no bank. This was an issue for anyone who bought or sold goods, or received gifts from emigrant families. Any money orders that were sent had to be privately exchanged into cash, often with the imposition of a hefty premium. Stamps were sometimes used as a method of payment, but they also attracted a fee when they were exchanged for cash or goods. Once more it was Sheriff Thoms who furthered the islanders' attempts to market their goods and buy things more cheaply. He persuaded the GPO to grant the island a money order office, along with a savings bank. Only his reminder that there would soon be lighthouses on the island and his provision of a £7 annual guarantee enabled these services to go ahead.

Tuberculosis continued its arbitrary attack on the local population, taking young and old, seemingly at random. Young Thomas Eunson was sent by his family to Lerwick for treatment, but he died there, aged twenty-three, in March 1888. Increasingly, people would travel to Lerwick for medical attention but there were many ailments for which Lerwick had no cure.

June 1888 saw two more young men leave, Charles Leslie and another Thomas Eunson. Charles moved at first to Lerwick with Edith Eunson, where the pair married. From there the couple took the boat to Kirkwall where they were welcomed by erstwhile friends and family, raising a family of four in that town until 1900, when they joined the Edinburgh diaspora.

By now there was a sufficiently strong network of relatives and friends scattered around the world to offer a range of destinations that provided support. Emigration was unspectacular, but constant, for although life was improving, Fair Isle remained a very small island. Young people did not fear the idea and were encouraged by word sent home by friends and relatives. Often it was their children's lives that parents hoped to improve for, despite all the improvements, the only trade Fair Isle offered was that of a fisherman, with a product that a diminishing number of people seemed to want to eat.

Of course there was no guarantee of a better life elsewhere. Women often found themselves in overcrowded tenement buildings, with husbands who struggled without formal qualifications to find a well-paid job. In towns you lived much closer to people you didn't know, and their bad habits, their noise and their attitudes could make your life difficult. But with apprenticeships available in a host of trades many of these emigrants' boys could progress to more comfortable lives, since a time-served man always had a higher wage.

Life was not better for everyone. Thomas Eunson, who left Fair Isle on the same day as Charles Leslie in 1888, did not find a better life. He was motivated to leave when his daughter Catherine died in 1887, cause unknown, although most likely tuberculosis. Perhaps he hoped that the rest of his family might be spared in a different environment, for his wife and several children had persistent coughs. Thomas chose Leith as his destination and, once he was settled, he sent the fare north for the rest of his family to join him. Sadly, his eldest daughter Jacobina was ill by the time she arrived and all too soon she found herself in Edinburgh's Royal Infirmary, where she died that September from tuberculosis.

After this bad start to their new lives there was a short hiatus during which the family appeared to prosper and the older children found jobs. The winter of 1888 engendered false hopes, however, for early in 1889, nine-year-old Robert succumbed, followed shortly afterwards by his mother Laurina and then, over a few months, young Margaret, Helen, and Thomas. A combination of measles and tuberculosis took them all. Not much more than a year from leaving Fair Isle, Thomas and his son William were alone in Edinburgh. In all probability the family brought the disease with them, but a room and a kitchen in Leith was never going to be an environment in which to combat tuberculosis. Leith was a busy, crowded port area, filled with manufacturing enterprises of all kinds – engineering, breweries, mills, cement factories and lead works. It was hardly a place to treat a serious illness and even the rich, who travelled at this time to the south of France, stood little chance once this terrible disease took hold.

Thomas Eunson did have one child left, however, and William created hope for the future when he married another Fair Isle Barbara Wilson in 1892 and brought her to Leith to live with his father. William and Barbara had six children, four girls and two boys. Sadly, one daughter died during childbirth, while one of their two boys drowned and the other succumbed to septicaemia, all during the decade after Thomas died. At least Thomas was spared the continued suffering of his son. During the years prior to modern medicine, luck played a big part in your ability to survive.

# Chapter 13

# Quoy Tammy

The Crofters Holding Act of 1886 finally gave crofters in Scotland security of tenure and established the Crofters Commission to oversee their rights. It had been a long struggle, but this august group slowly made its way all around the Highlands and Islands, looking at the different types of tenancies that existed in different areas and advising on the resolution of disputes between crofters and landlords.

It would be fair to say that John Bruce had little sympathy for the Crofter's Act. '*The fixing of rents by the Commissioner is downright plunder and I will resist it to the very uttermost. As for the fixing of tenure, the crofters are quite unfit for it. They need to be ruled.*'

After the Commission's visit, Bruce's Sumburgh estate rents were reduced by up to 40 per cent and rent arrears were also drastically diminished. Furthermore, in Shetland, the Commission found John Bruce responsible for forty-five families who were still living in dreadful, one-roomed accommodation. He was severely criticised.

In September 1888, men from Sandwick in Shetland drove ashore at Hoswick beach 340 pilot whales, which they set about butchering and selling. John Bruce owned Hoswick beach and claimed his part of the proceeds of this venture, just as all lairds had done in the past when whales landed on 'their' coastline. But now that the Crofting Commission had removed the fear of publicly disagreeing with landlords, the men who had done the work on the whales questioned Bruce's right to the money, since he had not contributed any effort. The local shopkeeper, Sinclair Duncan, and the Free Church minister, George Clark, supported their claim, even when they were taken to court by the furious landowner.

The publicity this case invoked encouraged ordinary Shetlanders (both local and far removed) to fund the case and, in July 1889, Sheriff Mackenzie in Lerwick found in favour of the men. It is almost impossible to contemplate Bruce's anger at this loss of what he considered to be his God-given right. He decided to take the case to the Court of Session in Edinburgh, while supporters continued to fund the fishermen, often with just a few pence. In June 1890, three of the four judges in Edinburgh found in favour of the fishermen, stating that they found Bruce's case 'not just or reasonable'. Ordinary Shetlanders had proved that the law was also for them and that the unacceptable serfdom of the past might now be questioned. The court case took up a good deal of the fishermen's profits, but a principle now existed that would protect them all in the future.

When the Commission visited Shetland in 1888, many Fair Islanders decided to write to complain about the leases they were given after building their new homes. It was, however, 1892 before the Commission found the time to travel to Fair Isle and, just prior to the visit, more crofters took the opportunity to return their leases to John Bruce stating that they were no longer under an obligation to live by such unfair documentation. Bruce was by now well aware that the Commission had reduced rents elsewhere and that the islanders hoped for similar reductions. The 1892 Fair Isle meetings were described in *The Scotsman* newspaper to have been 'lively'. Several people took the opportunity to level accusations at Bruce, with all the pent up frustration of people who had suffered many years of dictatorship.

Knowing that he was going to be reported in the newspapers probably had an effect on what the master did next, for he did not want a repetition of the Truck System Enquiry when he found himself reported in the national press in a decidedly negative manner. In truth, whatever his tenants thought, he saw himself as a protector of Fair Isle, rather than its tyrant. Thus, on day two of the Fair Isle Enquiry, just when everyone felt inspired to heap even more vitriol on his character, Bruce took the wind from his tenants' sails. He stated that he would cancel any lease to which any tenant had objections. New, longer leases would be issued, recognising improvements, but control would be maintained on the division of the common land, the cutting of peat and the digging of ditches. From this time, all the common land would be nominally divided into thirty shares and shared amongst the crofters.

The Commission recommended that a committee of islanders should dictate the new regulations governing the grazing land, and Bruce agreed. Intriguingly, the Sheriff stated that he had not in fact found much wrong with Fair Isle's existing leases, and certainly not enough to confirm many of the tenants' outspoken claims from the day before, but still the tenants felt they had won a battle. Although the Commission did not alter a great deal on the island, people still felt empowered by this new umbrella group.

Sadly, the islanders who had attacked Bruce openly at these meetings did not understand the extent to which their actions affected him. Bruce felt that he had tried to improve Fair Isle and the lives of the people who lived there, and was offended by all the vitriol. He was fifty-five years of age and, although he was a rich, successful man, his 21-year marriage had produced no children, so there was no John Bruce dynasty upon which to build. To some extent it must have been a disappointed man who was considering the future of the island and its ongoing economic difficulties.

For Bruce, Fair Isle's real problem was that by this time he was no longer making any great profit from the fishermen. Dried saithe had continued to lose its popularity as a food of choice for the poor, so that if the island was to survive, the people would need help from someone who cared for their situation. By publicly deriding him they would not succeed in encouraging their laird's advocacy. Furthermore, due to all the ongoing emigration, the number of crofters paying rent had continued to drop so that by this time the island was hardly a great investment, by anyone's measure. Landlords now had to cope with greater taxation on both a local and national basis, so that they were less inclined to invest in unprofitable holdings. Although Bruce had diversified and successfully invested in the herring fishing, Fair Isle's fishing was no longer a valuable part of his portfolio. As with many other similar small communities, it was difficult to see a way forward. The new laws may have given ordinary men powers beyond their imagination, but these powers did not necessarily make any location commercially viable.

On a more positive note, however, by the summer of 1889, David Alan and Charles Stevenson were finally preparing plans for two new lighthouses in Fair Isle. After so many years of indecision, people were thrilled and wondered what sort of a difference such a large building project would mean. There was great excitement when the Trinity House yacht, *Galatea*, anchored offshore and unloaded a variety of dignitaries, including a deputation from the Trinity House Elder Brethren, the President of the Board of Trade, the Deputy Master of Trinity House (with his engineer) and David Alan Stevenson.

In addition to the lights there would be two fog signals. The two towers were to be situated at Skadan, at the south of the island, and Skroo in the north, while accommodation would also be built for keepers and their families. A telegraph system would both link the two lighthouses and the island to the mainland. Landing places for building materials and the long-term delivery of supplies would be constructed both at North Haven and South Harbour. An improved road would be built, to connect the two lighthouses. David Stevenson estimated that the cost would be £28,335, including the building of roads and landing places. He allocated £4,657 for the lighting apparatus, machinery and lamps; the fog signal engine apparatus would cost £3,500; while £500 would be paid to John Bruce for the building land, quarry rights and water rights. Bruce gained not only a reasonable sum of money from the project, but also the knowledge that his land would be improved by the new infrastructure.

Just when life seemed to be progressing well, in 1890 John Wilson of Taft began to suffer from double vision and headaches. None of the local remedies would clear his ailment, so he took the opportunity late in the year to make a visit to his Kirkwall family, to consult a doctor there. The doctor reported that he could find nothing wrong and suggested that John did less reading in the dark light of a croft. But the double vision was irritating, especially for someone in charge of a boat. It made him feel dizzy sometimes, and he was more worried than he told his family, but if a doctor could find nothing wrong, perhaps it would pass. While he was in Kirkwall, his sister Jane went out every morning to gather water from a local spring that was said to have special healing properties for eyes. To pacify her, as much as anything else, her brother agreed to this treatment.

John was never the same after he returned home, although for some months he had both good and bad days. However, when he announced that Stewart would be in charge of the boat in future, he indicated to everyone that there was something seriously wrong. Some days he was fine, but at other times he simply sat by the fire, the activity of an old man rather than someone who had just turned sixty. In the Wilson family, sixty was no age at all. Polly began to panic. Aunt Barbara was filled with sadness when she realised that she might outlive her nephew and wondered if Taft was simply cursed. The days passed and although some were good and raised their confidence, others were quite awful and dashed all hope.

Finally, Mary wrote to Jane in Edinburgh early in the spring of 1891, to say that things were now much worse than they had thought. '*We are all very worried about father. He gets these terrible headaches all the time now and has become quite different, quiet and unhappy. He stays in bed on the bad days. Aunt Barbara is trying everything she can think of, but nothing seems to help. He's really ill, Jane.*'

The morning she got the letter, Jane gave notice to her employers and asked that she be allowed to leave the following weekend. The two ladies were quite distressed, since their maid would give no return date. "We can't retain your position for you if you are to be away for any length of time. A week or two we would understand, but longer would be a problem. You have to give us a return date now. It's not convenient, you rushing off like this."

"I'm sorry, ma'am, I can't tell you anything. My father's ill and might be for some time. I must be there with him. My brothers and sisters will need me if he is ill. And I have to see him. I can't stay here if there's something I can do at home to help, and I can't give you any idea of when I will return. I'm very sorry."

She could not bring herself to say the words she was avoiding and they were all thinking: "My father might die."

There followed an exciting flurry of preparation, for in truth Jane was pleased to be going home, even if it was for the wrong reason. Her stomach had lurched as soon as she read Mary's words and her mind frantically tried to absorb the idea that her father was seriously ill. Black thoughts hovered during everything she did, even as she tried to concentrate on her preparations. She dragged out the kist that had been stored away in the flat's small lumber-room, and started to think about what she could take home. Jane had been in Edinburgh for three years and had enjoyed most of it, but she missed her island, with its different tempo, sounds and smells, and found herself intensely excited about this unexpected homecoming, even while saddened by the reason. Most emigrants carry a burden of homesickness somewhere in their hearts and, like all the rest, Jane forgot about the cold and damp, having to pee in the byre, the boring, repetitive diet and the constant worry about managing to survive.

She remembered the soothing joy of a summer's evening, silly puffins pecking and tumbling over each other at the cliff edge, the sea in all its power and glory, the soothing atmosphere of the small chapel, the familiar patchwork of crofts, the carpets of wild flowers, the smell of fresh hay, and her family, in all its extended beauty and horror. When you are brought up with family round every corner it is hard to adjust to an endless stream of city strangers.

Jane had squirreled away some of her wages regularly and although she intended to keep part of her savings, she wanted to take things home to her siblings, things from the big city. Cousin Barbara and she went shopping, buying dried fruit, dress lengths of material, bars of perfumed soap, packets of suet and jellies, a range of sweets, some small tins of fruit, sugar lumps and cans of condensed milk. For Aunt Barbara she bought some chocolate. For her father, there had to be a book, even if she had to read it to him herself. The book took ages to choose, for she wanted something new, one that he had not read before. Finally she chose *The White Company* by Arthur Conan Doyle. It would make a fine contrast to the Good Book, which would no doubt be his favoured alternative. When her mistress heard that her father liked to read, she donated *The Adventures of Sherlock Holmes*, a frivolous, unwanted present she did not wish to have any longer on her shelves. Just at the last minute Jane bought some fresh fruit that she hoped would travel well in her hand luggage. There were a few small toys and games for Polly's children and she forced herself to buy a small scarf for Polly, for appearances if nothing else. Cousin Barbara donated a small fruitcake, for which Jane suspected her employers had unwittingly supplied the ingredients.

Most of her friends were servants and when they heard that her family were readers, they collected their employers' cast-off magazines, the *People's Journal* and the *People's Friend*, as well as fancier productions, like the *Scottish Geographical Magazine*.

Additional dried fruit came as well, in tiny packets that had clearly been purloined from employers (despite her friends' denials), so that there was enough for two rich cakes, for Fair Isle still lacked ovens to produce such delicacies. Jane thanked everyone, knowing that homesick acquaintances were more than happy to contribute to a journey they might never make. As the smoky train to Aberdeen drew out of the Waverley Station, she wondered if she would return to Edinburgh, trying to burn final images into her brain lest this was the last time she would see them. Perhaps she would try somewhere else next time. Or perhaps she might stay a while in Fair Isle.

The journey home was long and hard, for there were no good thoughts once she was in transit. Mary would never have written if it were not important and as soon as she set eyes on John, standing at Kirkigeo while Stewart and Thomas rowed her towards him, she could see that she had been right to come. The man who stood waiting for her was wearing clothes that were now too big for him, with a sunken, grey face, his lifelong weathered tan fading now that he spent so much time indoors. But his dark eyes sparkled. He was glad to see her home and she knew she had been right to come.

Although no one said so, they all knew he was dying. Mary was anxious, while Polly was shocked into silence much of the time, as she realised that her husband might leave her. Aunt Barbara was frail, but what else would she be at seventy-nine years of age? Nothing shocked her of course, for although she had not thought her nephew would go first, Barbara had long ago come to terms with God's mysterious ways. Brothers, sisters, nephews and nieces had all gone ahead and she accepted that God's will be done, whatever she thought of His choices. Polly, who loved her husband as much as she had ever done, understood that now her life at Taft was threatened, for her husband's personality had been all that stood between her and his first family.

Her own children were not aware of the route their father was following, only that something was not right. They were too young to fully comprehend a slow death, since in the main, life went on around them as it always did in a farming household that had to be mindful of the seasons. So they still went to school, while the first family went about the fishing and croft work. Only their father had changed his routine. Stewart, Jane, Mary and Thomas shared their distress, but not in front of the young ones, all working hard to maintain a pretence of normality.

The one good thing was that Jane arrived home in the middle of April, just as the croft was in the midst of the new work cycle, so she could slip right back into the old life without thought or discussion. The days were not yet warm, but they were longer and much more fresh than in the city and she relished the sweet, clean smells. Peat smoke might hang in the air if it was still, but there was none of the dreadful smog that you got in Edinburgh, the thick, dark murk of coal fires and factory effluvium that on bad days threatened to suffocate. There was no mistress either, telling you what you had to do next. At Taft she worked to her own hand, the family respecting her independence and grateful for her help. She relished the closeness of the community too, after walking amongst strangers for so many years. Even if some of them had a good gossip about her behind her back, they all appreciated her efforts to be with her family at this time. She had not known the extent to which she had missed the place.

Her father accepted his lot. His faith was secure and he knew that his God was calling him, even if he felt disappointed not to be allowed his three score years and ten. No one diagnosed what ailed him, but there was a sense of frailty in his body that everyone could read, a lassitude that was so very different from his vibrant former self. The man had not thought to see this daughter again and was thrilled with her presence, for she was above all a distraction, with all her talk of Edinburgh and what went on there. Hours would pass as he listened and asked questions, until finally his eyes grew heavy and he dozed. When he grew tired, it was easier for him if she read from the books, newspapers and magazines she had brought home. At other times he preferred the words of the Good Book.

Jane found herself scouring the periodicals in the evenings, searching for articles that would interest him, anything that would start a conversation and take up his attention for a while. Displacement activity is vital when the elephant in the room is death. Increasingly, John would drop off while she was speaking and then Jane worried that she was tiring him.

"Should I stop talking so much, Barbara? Am I wearing him out?" she asked her aunt.

Always, Barbara would respond, "No, you just keep on with what you're doing. It takes his mind off things, helps him pass the time. Otherwise he'll sit and worry about Polly and the children. You give him other things to think about and he's always been interested in everything. Your trip to Edinburgh has been a godsend and no mistake."

So they talked of clothes, of traffic, of houses, of museums, of anything Jane could think that might interest him. She helped him to picture Edinburgh's great parks, the newly opened Braid Hills Reserve, the Portrait Gallery and the Carnegie library that stretched from way beneath George IV Bridge to way above it. She talked of the castle and the new Forth Railway Bridge, in all its cantilevered glory, and described the circus, the theatre, girls on bicycles, folk skating on frozen ponds and grand funerals led by huge plumed horses. Then there were the wonders of the museum, the executions in the jail, people walking in Princes Street gardens on a Sunday afternoon, the grand Methodist chapel in Nicolson Square and the Royal Botanical Gardens, with hothouses full of exotic plants from all over the world. It was very different from life in Fair Isle and John liked to hear about it all.

There were sufficient tales to see him to the state where he no longer knew much of what went on around him. Life continued in the croft of course and people dropped in to pass the time and ask if they could help, or brought a little something they had cooked, while the little ones began to understand that their father was really ill. For the last couple of days they were taken over to Springfield to be minded, so that the house would be totally quiet. Polly was now inconsolable and could not bear to sit with him for long periods of time, but Jane and Barbara sat quietly, night and day, watching him slip slowly from this world to the next. The brightness of the June day that he went seemed a paradox.

"Aye, I saw him into the world and it's only fitting I see him out," Barbara said when the final breathe was quietly taken. "He was some man, your father. Away and get that daft lassie in to say goodbye to her man now. I've no doubt she'll carry on a bit, but you have to be sorry for her, with the four peerie ones to mind and not a lot of folk with any time for her."

After Polly, there was Stewart and Mary and young Thomas, who at sixteen was almost a man. Jane made her way over to Springfield with the news and asked for their help telling James, Andrew, Barbara and Aggie that their father had died. James was almost thirteen, but young Aggie was just five years old. No one had thought that John would fail to make old bones. There was a lesson there for them all. Live for the day, they told each other. As was the norm, the funeral was quickly organised, for there was only the registrar to notify and the grave to dig, though there was a host of letters to write, for they must tell the diaspora, including Johanna and John.

The funeral was large, for despite Polly and all the fuss of the second marriage, John had been well respected. The women wept and prepared a meal for afterwards. As Jane served tea in her old home she found that her Edinburgh life had receded and all the old familiar faces from her past seemed more real than that other life. The grief and tiredness from John's illness left her exhausted and she was unwilling to rush back to the town and its demands. It seemed necessary to stay a while, to reassess her life and touch her roots. There was still a place for her here at Taft, so she would take time to consider what to do next. The island was much the same as it had always been, but it was also different, for the lighthouse building with its influx of newcomers had caused a great deal of change. On some days, when she watched the masons toiling away, she found it difficult to relate either to this life or to her previous one. The very fabric of the island was changing, and when the work was completed new people would live beside these lighthouses, altering the balance of the community.

Willie Stout had returned from his travels and was now married with a child and living with his family at Stoneybrake. This fact interested Jane, but caused her no regret.

Life in Edinburgh had broadened her mind and exposed her to all sorts of new ideas and experiences that she did not regret for a moment. She was, for now, comfortable in her old skin and held her head up high when she passed folk who gossiped about her, mainly Church of Scotland ladies, for naturally they mostly sided with Willie and felt that she had discarded him unkindly. Maggie, his new wife, eyed her with ill-concealed dislike when they met but never said a word, which was odd since her own family were Wilsons. So be it. Willie himself was polite enough when she congratulated him on his first child and, if Maggie wanted to hold a grudge, she could do it all on her own. Gossip was always rife on a small island and, given what Jane had endured after her mother died, she was now a dab hand at ignoring anyone who tried to prick her self-confidence.

It was Polly who made Jane's decision to stay longer. Just a couple of days after the funeral, she had to put her oar into the temporary calm that followed all the emotion. It was as if the woman could not help herself. "Well, you'll be off back to Edinburgh I suppose, now you've played the heroine here. Aye, well, we'll all be glad to see the back of you, coming home here and trying to impress us with all the things they have in the town. As soon as you want, you get yourself back to it."

"Why should I?"

"Because there's no place for you here, that's why."

"This is my home, Polly, and the way things are for you I'd remind you to think on that. I'll stay here till I'm good and ready to leave. Just you remember that I was in Taft long before you came here to live. Or I could go and live at Springfield. I'm sure they'd have me there. But I'd tell everyone you'd made me leave my home. I don't think that would be quite the thing."

Polly's only response was to cry. She cried a lot of the time now. Life had not turned out as she had planned. Now she had to live with her hated stepchildren, since she must rely on the two older boys to earn money from the fishing. And Stewart, not her own eldest son, would inherit the house. To make things worse, the quiet respect that she had enjoyed from her neighbours as John's wife was now receding. Little did she know that there were those already whispering that she had never really been married to John and that her children were all bastards. Although there would be respect during the mourning period, Polly's unfortunate attitude and loose tongue had blighted her relationship with more than her stepchildren. With John gone, she would have to work hard to maintain her position. Awareness of this fact would have helped her cause.

As summer came and went, they all fitted back into the routine laid down by the seasons and history. They would be very busy until winter, so that no one was required to think too much, just to tick off task after task until each day was ended and the sleep of the exhausted returned you to oblivion. Before they all knew, it was autumn, time to lift the bere, the corn and the remaining vegetables. If you worked steadily, each task ordered itself without too much thought, but still there would be times when John's absence was conspicuous and people must try to hide their feelings.

Gradually, everyone evolved into their new position in the family, with 25-year-old Stewart taking John's place at the head of the table, reading the Bible, in charge of the yoal and allocating the work in the fields. Old Barbara quietly got on with all her tasks too, using Mary and Jane when she had the need, but resolutely providing a daily example of how life must go on and paying particular attention to the younger children. Everyone settled into the new regime except for Polly. As winter approached, her sense of loss and unfairness threatened to overwhelm her. Her four youngsters increasingly became dejected, desolate little souls, having lost not only their father but to some extent their mother too, for Polly's mourning quite enveloped her. In one sweep, her role had changed from being the wife of a respected member of the community to something very different indeed. She wore her mourning as a badge of honour, perhaps in the hope that it would maintain her status, and became increasingly religious, quoting the scriptures like a new convert, reminding everyone of the fearful power of God. At Taft they said nothing, watching and waiting to see how it would all unfold. No one was in a hurry to make any changes.

Thomas was still too young to leave and Barbara too old, while Stewart was in no rush to assert his position as head of house, which would be the most likely long-term outcome of his father's death, since John showed no desire to return to claim his place and Polly's children were still too young. Mary and Jane were happy to take on their share of the work, Mary relishing the return of a sister who sewed, knitted and giggled with her as if she had never been away.

But would Polly want to stay in Taft under the current circumstances? Stewart had never bothered over much about the woman, having years since decided that it was best just to ignore her. Now, with his father gone, he began to wonder how life would go on at Taft, particularly if he decided to marry. It would be a hard thing for any girl to come here to live with Polly in residence. For now, since there was no particular girl, he would just try to come to terms with the status quo.

One ongoing distraction in all their lives remained the building of the two lighthouses. The task had begun in August 1890, with as much as possible of the required materials being landed before the winter. The access road between the two stations, and the foundations for all the buildings at the south, were completed by December. At first there was a deal of difficulty in persuading labourers to go to Fair Isle, so local men undertook most of the initial work and glad they were to earn the extra cash. Road building and foundations were tasks they could manage easily, but it was made quite clear to Stevenson that this situation would come to an end when the new fishing season began, as the great majority of Bruce's tenants were still required to fish. From the start of 1891, labourers must come from elsewhere and they would additionally require skilled masons to fashion the stone.

So, gradually, the influx of temporary newcomers arrived: quarrymen, masons, labourers, a plasterer, carpenter, clerk-timekeeper and an Inspector of Public Works. A range of officials visited from the Northern Lighthouse Board and the designer himself also made regular trips. A blacksmith came to settle on the island, with a smithy set up at South Harbour, someone whose skills the islanders were delighted to realise for their own purposes when he had spare time. Some of these new people brought either family or housekeepers and rented empty houses from Bruce. It was the most important input of new blood that the island had ever known. By the time William Manson undertook the 1891 census, there were twenty-four incomers working full-time on the project, with a further five island men classifying themselves as full-time 'labourers'. Manson himself had to employ a clerk and a grocer to help him to run the shop and post office, as he was distracted by so much extra paperwork.

George Birse was the smith whose job it was to undertake all the welding and ironwork. He came from Angus with his wife and four children, settling at Field. Birse was an easy-going man who accommodated islanders' demands when he could, but made it clear that his full-time job was to supply the two lighthouses and this would leave only a small parcel of time for their projects.

Pund and Field were rented to the Lighthouse Board for £12 per annum by Anderson, accommodating the smith and foreman mason. Other buildings were utilised to house individuals like the Inspector of Public Works, while two bothies provided shelter for another sixteen workers, in what would seem to have been extremely basic quarters even by Fair Isle standards. The two lighthouses, their associated stores and accommodation premises, as well as the new road between the north and south, were all completed in record time. Everything required for the project had to be brought from elsewhere, so provisioning the building and the workers was a major undertaking, given the potential for setbacks due to bad weather, not that this particular challenge phased the Northern Lighthouse Board.

Improved roads during the 1880s had already encouraged some individuals to purchase oxen and wheels, for which carts were quickly fashioned from the island's stores of timber. The usefulness of these beasts both in carrying loads and pulling ploughs was inestimable. Now they were occasionally hired out to supplement the work of the contractor's carter, so that with the income from roadwork and other labouring tasks there was at last some extra money to spend in many homes. Anderson also gained by providing grazing for the carter's horses, additionally charging for oats and hay. Of course, ponies were still used for small loads, and by older people like the Leogh Irvines, who could not afford an ox. It would be 1912 before the number of Shetland ponies would dwindle to no more than a dozen or so. By this time mechanisation in Scotland's mines had largely removed the need these small animals. Oxen, however, would be a mainstay in Fair Isle until the Second World War.

The introduction of lighthouse contractors' wives and families meant, that for a short time, a group of women from the outside world came to mingle with the locals, bringing with them new habits, ideas and fashions. Several children were temporarily added to the school roll, introducing new ideas to the younger generation. All these people brought interest, information and gossip, as well as a small flow of cash, as milk, meat, fish, vegetables and birds' eggs were all occasionally sold to them. There was a sense of purpose in the early 1890s, which infused everyone with a feeling of confidence for the future. However, although the 1891 census numbers were similar to those of 1881, this hid the fact that thirty-four of the people were temporary residents. Despite a high birth rate, emigration was clearly continuing.

It was difficult to think of such problems during the period of lighthouse construction, for the island buzzed with activity. A group of skilled masons came from Aberdeen, where the men were famed for this type of work, and the islanders were fascinated by their accents and dialect and somewhat bemused to find that their own speech caused equal difficulty for their visitors. Once the initial wariness was overcome, the residents became used to the newcomers, stopping to chat on the road, in the shop and at church.

At Quoy, Tom Irvine was one of those whose life would change markedly with the lighthouses. He largely abandoned the fishing (with the laird's permission) and worked almost full-time as labourer to the blacksmith, learning the trade without the benefit of an apprenticeship. It helped that, like most local men, he had powerful arms and shoulders and was known to be a hard worker. With the purchase of a new yoal in his sights, Tom gave good value for his pay. His two brothers continued to fish for Bruce, while he worked to buy the extras that had previously been outwith their grasp. When the boys were young they had struggled to survive and for a while people had wondered if they would join the continuing band of emigrants. But Lowry had been adamant that they would turn their luck around and had led his brothers to keep the croft afloat. The Irvines had been poor in an island where no one was rich, but now Quoy was on an even keel and indeed flourishing in the new 'cash rich' environment that resulted from Tom's job. Not a penny of his earnings was wasted, as it was all deposited in the bank.

Fair Isle South lighthouse, or 'Skadan', was built very close to South Harbour, while Fair Isle North, or 'Skroo', was located on a rocky promontory at the extreme north-east end of the island. For the Stevensons, this project did not present the challenges faced by many rock stations although, as ever, the weather called the tune when it came to delivering men and materials. The taller of the two buildings, South Light, is eighty-six feet high, while North Light is only forty-seven feet high, relying on the elevation of the land on which it is built to give it height. The South Light was first exhibited early in January 1892, incorporating the redundant light from the Isle of May lighthouse and later that year a fog signal was added. North Light was powered by a new design of paraffin lamp, the Stevensons' first hyper radiant (large) lens, one that could be seen from twenty-two miles away, hopefully giving passing ships fair warning of the island's treacherous shoreline. This was first lit in November 1892. Work continued around the lighthouses for another six months or so, but eventually all the workers went home, leaving the keepers and their families as welcome additions to the social scene.

David Stevenson was proud of this Fair Isle venture, pointing out that these two lighthouses took little more than two years to complete. He commented that: *'Considering the magnitude of the works, the remoteness of the locality and the difficulty of landing materials and machinery, the various contractors deserve credit for the manner in which the works have been executed. I am able to state that the estimate will not be exceeded.'*

The estimated cost of the project had been £28,335. Such was the quality of major public works in 1892 that no one thought it unusual that two lighthouses could be completed up to standard, on time and within budget.

Accommodation blocks were constructed alongside each lighthouse, along with engine and storage blocks, while South Light had additional buildings to accommodate visiting lighthouse staff. Fortuitously, they were completed in time to billet the Crofting Commission when it visited in 1892. Keepers had to be self-sufficient in food and fuel for months at a time, but the Lighthouse Board was well accustomed to provisioning staff in locations far more challenging than Fair Isle. A substantial stone pier was built at the south of the island (along with a large store) and there was a further pier at North Haven. More importantly, the Commissioners installed small cranes, which quickly became indispensable to local men when faced with heavy, bulky loads that must be lifted up from small boats. These cranes were to be the source of many future arguments, for no one ever owned up when anything went wrong and they were damaged and it was always the Lighthouse Board that had to pay for repairs.

The lighthouses changed the island forever, bringing regular visitors in addition to the six keepers and their families. Furthermore, some of the local men were trained and retained as temporary keepers, to cover illness or holiday periods. Occasionally, local women would be asked to act as housekeepers, while there was sometimes paid work to be had unloading and transporting supplies, with a regular contract being awarded to three crofts. There was also a small market for milk and fish.

Lighthouse construction only masked the ongoing economic issues that plagued Fair Isle, however, and now that there was a reduction in the number of wrecks, there was a corresponding reduction in bounty from the sea and salvage work. Saithe fishing continued to provide a less reliable return than ten years previously. With fewer people to support there was no longer a desperate shortage of housing or land, but there was no answer to the ongoing problem of paying for a family's needs. More regular visitors and increased contact with the outside world brought with them the temptation of a better life elsewhere. Increasingly, girls decided to go into service on the mainland, while some of the boys chose to find work on bigger boats that paid cash at the end of a voyage. Most of them intended to come home with their earnings, but sometimes they found life elsewhere more attractive. At least the school's future was secured by the influx of the lighthouse children, but still no one was tempted to apply for a bursary to take their education further. Only the chief lighthouse keeper's children aspired to secondary and higher education.

By the time the two lights were lit, there were changes afoot at Taft. The tension between Polly and the first family had continued to smoulder relentlessly, as Polly seemed unable to find a place for herself in the new hierarchy and, indeed, became increasingly morose in her religious obsession. The interminable bickering and tension developed further over the winter months when people were pushed together in the confines of the house. John's strong presence had quashed much of the hostility his wife engendered, so that his death, as well as causing sadness, caused more bitterness than anyone would have imagined. It was Aunt Barbara who finally took it upon herself to find a solution. She slowly made her way to Springfield one Sunday afternoon to ask her nephew Stewart for help. For the sake of John's four younger children, some sort of civilised solution had to be found and as her preacher and nephew, he should be able to suggest something.

"Do you think she could come here for a bit?" Barbara suggested, once she had outlined the problem to her nephew. "Polly just seems to say the wrong thing every blessed day and the atmosphere over there is awful. It's not good for the young ones. They've just lost their father and they don't need all this fighting. Stewart's doing his best to hold his temper, but I'm not sure she won't push him too far. I think she needs to move to another croft to avoid trouble."

Stewart's look of alarm was quickly repressed. He was a good man, a man of God, but adding Polly to his household would simply be moving the problem elsewhere... here! He was aware of the increased gossip about Polly, for her inability to keep quiet encouraged unkindness that a different personality would not have attracted. He knew there was more murmuring about her not having been properly married. Bringing his sister and her four children into his home might be a saintly thing to do, but his wife Aggie was as like to be irritated by Polly as anyone else, a fact that would only result in more upset for John's younger children, not to mention himself.

"I'm not sure Aggie would like that," was his only comment, "but I'll talk to her, to see if she has any suggestions. We must see that Polly is looked after. Stewart's not arguing to put her out, I take it? As John's widow, it's still her home."

"Of course not. He would never do that, even if he could. But there's a terrible atmosphere all the time and you'll have heard all the gossip about the marriage starting up again. We have to think of what's best for the four children. Perhaps she could go to Kirkwall for a bit? Tom and Andrew are there and they are her brothers after all, so they might help, and there's John's sisters and brother. It might be better her starting up again somewhere new. The wee ones have nothing to gain from staying here, since Taft will never be theirs, so they might as well make a new beginning where there is family to support them and a better chance in life."

Stewart looked at his aunt, astonished. She had all this worked out before she came, he was sure. For an old woman, she still had plenty of guile. But perhaps she was right. Without John's protection Polly was vulnerable, and the children too. He owed it to John to see that his second family was taken care of and if that could be accomplished without disturbing his own family life, all the better. Polly was his sister after all. He set about writing letters to his two brothers in Kirkwall to see if they would help. If Polly could survive until James and Andrew were a bit older, she might just manage to make a new life for herself. Perhaps he could contribute too. There was never much spare cash, but for a couple of years he was willing to make sacrifices. Aggie would certainly agree, if one of the alternatives was that Polly might come to live here with them.

His brothers agreed to support their sister for the sake of her children, for Tom and Andrew were good Christian men. Tom and Jane would arrange for her to rent a room in the stair where they lived and Andrew would help her with settling in and see that she always had something to eat, at least until the boys were earning. Young James could start to look for a job as soon as they arrived.

When Stewart approached Polly he was careful to suggest that the idea had come from his brothers in Kirkwall. It would be a new life he told her, with opportunities for the children, for Kirkwall was booming. She would have her own home and not be beholden to John's first family. She would have to work, but she worked here. A new start was perhaps what she wanted.

To everyone's surprise, Polly leapt at the idea. She always knew that her children were superior and now they would have the opportunity to blossom in the metropolis that was Kirkwall. Anyway, Polly was increasingly aware that she had become isolated in Fair Isle. Without John, she had lost her position in the island's pecking order and would eternally be at the mercy of Stewart if she stayed at Taft. Kirkwall would be a chance to start again without the first family, so Polly would go. All were pleased that the matter was being resolved without more ill feeling.

Naturally, Polly managed to upset people during the process of leaving. She insisted on taking as much as possible from Taft. She would use some of the money she had been left by John to pay for the process of moving, but she would take all the household goods she could to Kirkwall, to help her to settle there. As John's wife, even if she would not keep the croft, she surely inherited the furniture. It did not occur to her that leaving John's family without the bits and pieces he had carefully carved by his own hand over many years might be insensitive. After all, some of it had been there long before she came.

Polly did not know about negotiation. As she daily added to the inventory, shock and irritation grew in equal measure.

"You can't take the kitchen chairs. Where will we sit?"

"That wee chest has always stood there!"

"That was my mother's knitting chair!"

"My father made that stool for me when I was a boy!"

"You're never taking the spoons!"

Each day there was something more, so that Taft seethed with irritation. The short period of delight that had ensued when Polly's removal was announced was now replaced by friction over goods and chattels. Polly made it quite clear that she understood that, as John's widow, her husband's belongings were rightfully hers. All of them.

"I swear she won't be happy unless we're all sitting on the floor, barefoot and begging," Jane said to Stewart. "But I don't care what she takes as long as she leaves my mother's knitting chair. It's not hers. I remember my mother putting her wool in these drawers as if it were yesterday."

"And I remember my father making these kitchen chairs when we moved in here. They belong here."

To make things worse, the laird was now refusing to acknowledge Stewart as the new tenant, since his brother John should rightfully take over. John had not initially responded to a letter asking him to rescind any claim, so that just as Polly was marking all she would take, Stewart became increasingly nervous about his right to the croft. Even with the Crofting Commission to support you, who knew what the laird might come up with next? Tension and Taft now seemed to be synonymous.

Once more Aunt Barbara had to sort everyone out. She gathered them all together, having organised that Polly and her children would visit Springfield. "Look, she's going. Let her take all she will and concentrate on the fact that she's leaving. And think about the young ones. They have lost their father and now their home. Have you thought that the furniture might help them feel at home in Kirkwall, where they know no one? Have you thought what all this means for the two peerie girls? They're still very young. Could we all just concentrate on making this easier for them? After all, furniture is just bits of wood. When you're my age you'll understand that. You get to keep the memories. The knitting chair and all the rest are staying in the family. Your mother was Polly's sister, after all. Let the young ones have the bits and pieces. Even if she takes the lot, Stewart will give you a hand to make some new things. Could we at least send her off in a reasonable way? The whole island's laughing at us fighting about furniture."

"They'll laugh a lot more when they have to sit on the floor when they visit!" said Thomas. "But you're right. If this is the price we have to pay for getting rid of her, it's worth it. And Aggie and Barbara don't know what's happening, poor wee souls. Let her take what she wants. Anyway, she can't take it all into a single room in Kirkwall. It'll not fit."

Which was exactly right. As Polly began to pack all the clothes and household linen that she felt was hers by right, she found that the kists began to fill much too quickly. Sadly, she decided to abandon some of her original plans for denuding the house of its contents, but she would take the knitting chair, which had been her sister Barbara's, her spinning wheel, the two kitchen chairs and two small stools. Even then, when she started to pack all the kitchen equipment, suddenly it seemed an awful lot and gradually she decided to let more things stay. Her desire for the belongings had been fuelled by the first family's desire to keep them. Now they didn't seem to care, she saw things in a new light. As the date for her leaving approached, she came closer to a more reasonable total, discarding more and more as "not being worth the bother". Of course Taft would have gaps, but surely gaps would be easily enough filled. The most important gap would be their half-brothers and sisters, for these children were now part of Taft and it seemed strange to think that they were all to disappear from their lives. As Aunt Barbara began to mourn their coming loss, everyone made a special effort to make the departure easy for the young and the very old.

This time when the steamer bore another family away from the island there were mixed feelings. Unlike the young folk, Aunt Barbara knew that there was little chance to see any of the children again and she, who had helped bring each of them into the world, mourned their loss. Her role in recent years had been to act as a buffer between Polly and the rest. What role would she have now? Polly's disappearance was a godsend to the first family, but it marked a watershed for Aunt Barbara. They all went home to a Taft strangely empty of people and furniture. It would be some time before it felt like home again.

Emigration continued. There was more talk of everyone leaving as a group, to set up a new life in somewhere easier, but always there was a cohort that swore that they would stay here till their dying day. It was hard to decide on the right course of action.

At least Jane Wilson of Taft appeared to be impressed by the island's ongoing ability to support itself, when to everyone's surprise she took an interest in Tom Irvine of Quoy. It was hardly a sudden decision, for Jane had learned from her father about the problems that an impetuous marriage could bring and, to be honest, at first she had not considered Tom seriously. The Quoy croft had certainly improved over the years and the Irvines were no longer the poverty-stricken clan they had been when their father died. Tom had grown up well, with Lowry's lead. Anderson, hardly an over-sensitive man, had learned to admire Lowry's perseverance and directed odd jobs in his direction throughout his lifetime, knowing they would be thoroughly done. Lowry was thought of as being idiosyncratic, but a hard worker and his reliability enabled the croft to stay in the family's hands.

John, the second Irvine boy, was asthmatic. Isabella was not known as the best of managers, but the good woman had spent many a night sitting up with him, listening to her son heave for each breath and wondering if he would make it through the night. There was no treatment for asthma at that time, although Isabella did her best, trying to see that he got a good share of what little they had to make him strong. She experimented with all the old wives' cures, like strong tea and sips of brandy. Someone read in the newspaper that smoking would help, but even to a simple woman from Fair Isle this seemed to be a ridiculous idea. Like Polly, Isabella had discovered too late the drawback of marrying an older man, but back then, when John had shown an interest in her, single men with the likelihood of their own croft were thin on the ground.

As time passed, Lowry and Tom pulled the family away from the threat of eviction. The harder they worked, the more respect they gained, and although John was often ill in the winter he worked when he could. Bina, their sister, was a pretty young thing, but she took her mother's lead when it came to housework, so that the house never quite amounted to what it might, even when it was rebuilt. Whatever the state of the house, the rent was always paid, and even before the lighthouse building began they had their sights on the purchase of a yoal.

Lowry became an avid reader, fond of the teacher's small lending library which had been augmented by books sent from Lerwick after Sir Thomas Bressay agreed to land two large boxes of donated texts onto the isle. At that time few homes could boast more than copies of the Good Book and a couple of additional inspirational tombs like *Pilgrim's Progress*, so the library was a godsend for readers. There were of course those who felt that reading other than the Good Book was a questionable pursuit, but real harm was difficult to measure, particularly when the activity was wholeheartedly supported by the teacher.

Over the 1880s, oxen began to make an appearance in Fair Isle. They had long been a feature of life on the Shetland Isles, but it took Bruce's road improvements to encourage their use on the island. Once one family saw that the arduous work of delling could be replaced, others quickly followed, and the Irvine boys began to save as soon as they could, Tom finally buying a plough in 1888, paying one pound, nineteen shillings and sixpence, a serious investment indeed. The ox, plough and cart had changed families' lives beyond measure, reducing the immense effort of delling, which was now used mainly in awkward, less-accessible areas.

The next Irvine project was a family yoal. Saving was not an issue for a family that was not accustomed to wasting money on fripperies. With no children to support, as they approached 1890 Quoy had become relatively prosperous. Yet, despite the improvement in status, when Tom decided to make a play for Jane he was not sure how to get started. He was thirty, but overwhelmed by smart women like Jane and unsure if she would consider looking at one of the Quoy boys. It didn't help that his family were members of the Church of Scotland, so that social meetings were limited. Tom's initial problem was getting started.

His prospects altered on so many levels when Anderson advised George Birse (the lighthouse blacksmith) to take the man on as his assistant. Apart from providing additional earnings, the smith was a married man who was happy to encourage his apprentice to start courting. For a while progress was painfully slow, and at first the blacksmith had to encourage him every week. "Well then, Tom, how's the wynching going?" was his constant refrain on a Monday morning. "Did you ask her out for a walk this Sunday?"

Regularly he found that the man had not. Weather, work and religion combined against him. Fair Isle weather was not always suitable for a languid romantic stroll and work left only a small window of opportunity for young people to socialise. Religious observance took up even more time, particularly at Taft, since Sunday was not the only day this family met with other Methodists. But love will find a way and eventually, like so many other young lovers over the religious divide, Tom developed the knack of bumping into Jane when he could, until no one was in any doubt about his intentions.

Jane was amused by Tom's perseverance. She gave him no real encouragement but the man just kept turning up and was quietly pleasing in his determination. And the Irvines were relatives, even if they were Church of Scotland. Her grandmother had been a Quoy Irvine after all.

Finally, Tom summoned up the courage to ask her to walk with him to the Saturday night soiree at the old schoolhouse, a real public statement of intent.

"Do you think I should go with him?" she asked Aunt Barbara.

"If you feel you'd like to, I see no reason why not. The good Lord knows how hard that lot have worked to pull themselves up over the last few years, so I imagine you could do worse than Tom Irvine. Be careful though. He's C of S and after Willie Stout they'll all be watching you."

So Jane considered and saw no reason why Tom should not accompany her to the Saturday evening entertainment. It's not as if they would be alone, and if she found she didn't enjoy his company she could simply avoid him in the future. Anyway, it might even be fun.

At the height of the lighthouse construction, regular events had been organised in the village hall on a Saturday evening, in part because the labourers were lodging in particularly primitive conditions and needed somewhere to go at the end of their week, somewhere that was not the church. Not all came from religious backgrounds and, lacking a public house, they needed some diversion at the weekends. In the main, those who attended the soirees were the incomers and local single youngsters, although some of the young married folk sometimes came too, for innocent fun is tempting. Songs and 'penny readings' were the primary amusement and George Birse was particularly fond of maudlin ballads from his native Forfarshire, while the labourers from Aberdeen had their songs too, so they all entertained the locals with no thought of any possible repercussions. The islanders responded by sharing some of their own traditional songs. Now who could object to young people spending a few hours singing and listening to stories?

At that time however, singing, other than for religious purposes, was suspect, particularly in a communal situation that was not either the church or chapel, where content and purpose were specifically aimed at praising God. In 1890, an island mother might sing to her children and there were a few songs handed down by the old folk to be crooned round the peat fire, but the idea of a group of young folk meeting to sing non-religious songs about who knew what was highly suspect. The Church of Scotland in particular was always suspicious of any frivolity that might set young people on the road to damnation. This institution might have been losing some of its power in the burgeoning towns but in the countryside, where religion still gave a strong sense of identity, this was not the case. Scottish religion was centred round a disciplined congregation and it was the dedicated work of all church leaders to ensure that their people did not fall by the wayside, where they could be tempted by the devil. In the 1890s, the devil was still a very real threat and mothers continued to scare their children with the burning fire, even for minor sins. The burning fire was no metaphor either. Damnation, for most folk, was quite real.

The God of Calvin particularly frowned on anything that might lead to sex before marriage, something that threatened the very structure of society. Any frivolity of dress, undue levity, dancing, drink and a hundred other small, perceived vices made Calvin's God an easy one to offend. Singing was right up there with the rest of the forbidden fruit and listening to ungodly stories was also highly suspect. It has to be said that, in Fair Isle, sex prior to marriage was not uncommon long before some of the locals started to listen to ballads from the mainland!

William Brown, who was by now Fair Isle's 'teacher and missionary', saw himself as being nominated by the church to ensure that morality on the island did not slip, at least not while he was in charge. When the influx of single men came to work on the lighthouse, this put Brown and many of the other elders in the community on their guard. With the workers came the father of the foreman mason, a spirit merchant, which must have caused some upset on this otherwise nominally 'dry' island. Although the fishermen liked to barter for the demon drink, liquor was in the main kept hidden, both from the women and the church, and for most it was seldom taken to excess. But the incoming workers' jobs involved long hours and hard manual labour, in sometimes appalling weather, and they must have found their Spartan bothy less than comfortable, even by the standards of the time. It is little wonder that the spirit merchant would have found ready customers for any wares he chose to sell.

Saturday nights in the very recent past had universally been spent making preparation for the Sabbath, with families devoting the time to praying and reading the Bible with relatives, the men arguing over niceties of scriptural detail. As this habit had waned slightly over the decades, Saturday night had become, for some, more of a relaxation, a time where people visited one another and gossiped or discussed local news. Increasingly, some of the faithful preferred to keep religion for the Sabbath.

Not only was there singing at these Saturday events, there were also readings. 'Penny dreadfuls', as they have come to be known, were inexpensive, often slightly 'sensational' novels, produced in great numbers for the newly-literate working poor that resulted from the Education Acts of the 1870s. Although some of their topics involved violent adventure or crime, by today's standards they were hardly shocking. Most of the tales read out at the penny readings in the village hall in Fair Isle were simply exciting adventure stories. For William Brown, however, the combination of suspect literature and the singing of bothy ballads (about who knew what) was a threat to the morals of the island's young people. To be honest, singing anything other than the metrical psalms was heresy to him. The Methodists might enjoy a good hymn tune, but William Brown knew that the devil used music as an instrument to tempt his flock.

So he railed about the dangers of the Saturday night readings two weeks running from the pulpit and told his congregation that he had written to Bruce about the misuse of public property, so that very soon 'all smiles ceased' and the entertainments were terminated. Of course, the Methodists could hardly allow their young to continue to attend suspicious events. For the workmen, ballad singing still went on in the bothy, but in that environment and without the local young people it lacked the fun of the events at the old school.

Brown's interference was difficult for many of the younger folk to forgive, for they were doing nothing wrong, simply attempting to move with the times. Brown and his supporters had inferred they were doing something immoral and this upset them. Young people knew that things were changing, for they had read of change. Older people felt that things might be changing elsewhere, but knew that they should always remain the same in Fair Isle. It was ever thus. Yet Brown's interference did not manage to stop all the relationships: James Clouston, one of the masons, married Agnes Wilson of Leogh in the spring of 1892.

By this time Tom Irvine had thoroughly engaged the interest of Jane, although she made one condition before she would agree to the relationship. Nicknames were common in Fair Isle, with Mary becoming Polly, Jeremiah – Jerry, and Isabella – Bella. To avoid confusion, namesakes were differentiated by adding the name of the croft to which they were connected. Tom was thus known to many of his fellows as Quoy Tammy. Jane had never liked Tammy as a name. Indeed her own father had forbidden his son to answer to this title. Tom would henceforth be her suitors' name, at home and abroad, if he was to remain her suitor. Lowry laughed as if he would have a fit when Tom shamefacedly explained he would prefer in future to be called by his new name, but he agreed when he saw how important it was for his brother. George Birse led the way at work and firmly corrected anyone who tried to forget. The smith was a big strong man whose opinion was hard to ignore and soon most folk embraced the change.

Tom wasn't really worried by all the jocularity, for the man was in love. He talked endlessly to Jane of his plans for the croft and the future and persuaded her that he had a strategy for overcoming at least some of the island's problems. The last ten years had seen a steady improvement in his situation and Tom saw no reason why this trend should not continue. He still had money in the post office, and Quoy needed a young family to give it a future.

Then Tom's best laid plans encountered a hurdle. He invited Jane to Quoy for Sunday afternoon tea. They both knew that this was to be his precursor to asking for her hand, but suddenly the plan stalled. Tom's mother was very frail and really quite ill, so that the house was even more unkempt than ever. Despite its physical proximity, Quoy was a far cry from Taft. Different homes use different yardsticks to measure their lives and Jane understood that this was hardly the time to suggest any big changes at Quoy, for a sick, old lady could not be expected to change her life for an incomer. Equally, Jane could not move into Quoy in its current state. She told Tom that it would be inappropriate for her to consider moving into Quoy while Isabella was so ill, but they could begin to talk about a marriage. There was no rush, she told Tom. They should wait until the time was right. Since they were both hardly in the first flush of youth Tom was rather more anxious to move things along, but Jane insisted she needed time to gather a trousseau. Tom, who had never heard of such a thing, could only agree.

In the meantime the island had a new church building to celebrate. The Church of Scotland had become virtually a ruin. The schoolteacher took responsibility for leading Sunday worship when there was no minister and his congregation's enthusiasm had for some years been tempered by the number of leaks in the roof and the quality of the wind whistling round their heads and feet. By the late 1880s it was structurally unsound and, although there had been much talk of a replacement, it was 1891 before a formal appeal for funds to replace it was placed in *The Shetland Times*, stating that: '*It is at least half a century since a new church was required.*'

Its proximity to the small graveyard was its only redeeming feature. The new Methodist Chapel had provided the impetus for a similar (or superior) Church of Scotland edifice and encouraged the collection of funds from Shetland's great and good. All around Scotland at that time, competitive church building was common.

When the lighthouses were completed there was some good stone left and it was only natural that this should be used for the islanders' benefit. The new church was to be situated further north and much of the additional building stone that was required was sent from Shetland, dumped in the sea during high tide in Leestit geo and carted to the building site by local men at low tide. The cost was between seven and eight hundred pounds and late in 1892 this building was completed, with an inaugural service that included allocated places for everyone on the island, including the lighthouse men.

All contributed to the building one way or another. George Birse, who had remained on the island to complete further work on the lighthouse buildings after the second light was lit, worked with Tom to erect a bell on the small church tower, a task that they both found unexpectedly difficult. The Strong family, who had hoped to buy the island in 1866, still retained an interest in its wellbeing and donated the pulpit, Bible and Psalter. Tom was so involved in the building process that he was appointed church officer, a public position that gave him a little more status and confidence. This set the seal on the Irvines of Quoy officially becoming a respectable family, one that you could think of marrying into. When George Birse finally abandoned the small forge down by the lighthouse, it seemed natural that Tom would continue with his work as a smith, albeit on an irregular basis. He bought some of the blacksmith's tools and equipment and accepted work from both his neighbours and the lighthouse, as and when it was offered.

Isabella died in May 1892. There was first the funeral and then a period of mourning to be observed before any marriage could be arranged. It was well into the autumn when Jane and Tom agreed that the following spring would be the date of their union. That would allow Jane time to prepare both her own trousseau and Quoy. Tom was far too thrilled at the thought of marriage to worry about any changes to his living accommodation. In fact, now that he was to be married, Tom would agree to anything Jane suggested. Anyway, he had no idea what she meant by changes. Surely there was not much that anyone needed to do at Quoy? They had built it as well as any of the other houses, just ten years ago.

"How do you think I should go about it?" Jane asked Aunt Barbara, who was utterly thrilled, having not thought she would live long enough to witness the remaining girls' marriages. She had become very fond of Jane and Mary, considering them surrogate daughters, and her great wish was to see them both settled. Unlike some of her neighbours, Barbara was quite accepting of the progress that had been made at Quoy. There were those who continued to feel superior to that croft with its rough and ready ways, but Barbara had learned to value substance over style and appreciated the Irvine children's tenacity and energy. She liked Jane's ability to see Tom for what he was, a strong, hard-working man who would make a good husband. No doubt he didn't have the learning that Jane's father had boasted, but where had that got him in the end? No, the Irvines would be just fine, once Jane got her hands on them.

"Go gently with them," she advised. "They're a nice lot at Quoy, but you have to remember that the three boys were left to do their own thing for most of their lives and Isabella was never all that keen on the housekeeping. So it was a very poor house for many a year and by the time they got it turned around, Isabella was past caring about fancy things. The children were just glad when they knew where the rent money was coming from, not to mention the next meal. You never knew poverty like that here, so you mustn't be seen to be criticising how they do things, but more particularly say nothing against Isabella. The poor woman did her best, even if it wasn't what we would have done, and the boys have worked hard to get where they are. Maybe you could start with Bina. Goodness knows she could do with a bit of attention. Once you have Bina on board, they might all be a bit more enthusiastic about your improvements."

Bina was a shy, quiet, wee thing who seldom had much to say when she visited Taft. Being the only girl, there had been no opportunity for fripperies and no discussion of clothes or hairstyles in her home. So Bina's wardrobe could certainly do with some work, for the girl had nothing much to wear and certainly no fashionable Sunday clothes like the Taft Wilson girls. Mary and Jane were already busy with all sorts of sewing for Jane's new life, so they decided to invite Bina round and include her in the task. Bina was thrilled to spend a couple of evenings a week at Taft and excited beyond belief to discover that she was to have an entirely new wardrobe, one that might even be considered fashionable. Her brothers joked about it for a bit, but when they saw how much it meant to her they found some money to let her buy material. New clothes gave her confidence and turned her into a really pretty girl for the first time in her life. Mary spent hours patiently explaining how to add small details to clothes, until they almost seemed too good to wear, even on a Sunday.

With Bina on board, the subject of the house was then tackled, with her support. Although she never spoke of it, Jane saw herself as the new mistress of Quoy. True, it was the Irvine's home and Bina had lived there all her life, but Jane had always been self-assured, even before she went to work in Edinburgh. Her mother, her father and Aunt Barbara had all been positive role models and the struggles with Polly had strengthened her character. However, having learned lessons from her stepmother, she understood the importance of setting about the refurbishment of Quoy sensitively.

First she told Tom that she wanted him to clear out the small room that would be theirs for sleeping, organising him to paint the walls and procuring new bedding that she forbade him to use till they were married. Meanwhile she worked on a rug for the floor. Lowry and John were openly amused by Jane's gentle bullying, ragging their brother endlessly, until she turned her charms on them. That they found less entertaining. Eventually, however, everything in the house was scrubbed, cleaned, or discarded. She did not force them to do it, but neither did she expect to be thwarted. Lowry had to hold his tongue several times and a couple of times he did not, but the process relentlessly ploughed on, quiet, huffy days notwithstanding. Stewart and Thomas had been working on a new dresser as their wedding present for Jane and Tom, a special place where she planned to store the new crockery which had already been bought with some of her savings. Gradually, all the stained, cracked and chipped bits and pieces that the Irvines had become accustomed to over the years were removed.

Walls were painted, new curtains hung and chairs were taken outside to be cleaned and polished, while two new chairs were also constructed. Tom worked at each given task quietly and steadily. Lowry and John sometimes felt the house was no longer their home, but Jane occasionally cooked them a meal that was much better than anything Bina could provide, so they persevered. In truth, Tom was so happy and proud of his intended wife that there was no way they felt that they could spoil his joy.

The more Jane achieved, the more she wanted, however, so that Barbara finally had to rein her in as she made increasingly fanciful plans for 'Castle Quoy', as Lowry was now want to call it. "Be careful not to overreach yourself, lass. You'll make everyone uncomfortable if you do and remember, it's their home too. Don't make the same mistakes as our Polly. Take it carefully, mind."

Jane didn't want to take it carefully, but she reined herself in, lest she cause umbrage. Lessons learned from Polly were entrenched in all the Taft Wilsons.

During the weeks before the wedding, presents began to arrive, both from islanders and from those who had left. The Kirkwall family sent a variety of gifts, as did her brother and sister in South Shields. John sent a set of fancy spoons and Johanna a beautifully ornate American clock that chimed the hours. It would sit beautifully on top of the new dresser, Jane told her new family, who were fascinated. The chimes took a bit of getting used to, but eventually they all stopped reacting to it, both night and day, until the steady tick became a presence that was missed when the clock stopped.

There had been some discussion about whether it should be church or chapel, given Tom's position in the church and Jane's family's strong affiliation with the chapel. In the end Jane decided that Taft would do just fine. She sent to Lerwick for invitations to be printed, which a few of the islanders thought was a tad affected for someone about to move into Quoy. Printed invitations! What next? Tom didn't care in the least where they were married for he had begun to wonder if the day would ever arrive. He was thirty-three and Jane thirty, so they were hardly youngsters blinded by romantic nonsense. When all was completed and the presents added to Quoy it became a different place altogether, so that Lowry told Tom that the next time the laird arrived from Shetland he might be tempted to move in with the Irvines, since Castle Quoy was quite so grand.

On 25th May, 1893, Jane and Tom were married at Taft by a visiting Methodist minister. For some, the Quoy Irvines would always be a bit of a joke, while others focused on the ever-changing circumstances of the Taft Wilsons. Thus the wedding was embraced by many, but not everyone. Aunt Barbara, who had not thought to live to see the event, was utterly joyous, convinced that the girl's parents were looking down on the occasion with equal pleasure.

Committing to the Church of Scotland (with its different customs and habits) was a far bigger challenge for Jane than it would be today and, of course, the Church of Scotland held Maggie Stout. Although Jane marked the Sunday prior to her wedding with the wearing of the traditional contracting dress and the procession into the chapel with her bridesmaid, Tom and his groomsman, after the marriage she would worship with the Irvine family in the church.

~·~

Just as they were all beginning to adjust to the new regime at Quoy, Fate reminded them that she was in charge. There was nothing to warn the men of the approaching storm when they brought the boats out of the water that evening, but while they were asleep, huge waves beat far up onto the beach, throwing some of the yoals out of their noosts. In the morning two were missing. One of them was the *Lily*.

The three men cast about desperately in the immediate locality for their beloved craft. When there was no sign of it they split up and, accompanied by a few willing beach boys, began the long walk round the coast of the entire island, searching in every cave and geo for the yoal or its wreckage. By evening, nothing had been found. Such a loss was an appalling shock and a sombre silence was their only company when finally everyone went to bed that night. The next day they were all up and out at dawn, searching. Sometimes the sea's habit was to return on one of the next tides that which it had taken away to play, although often its play had been so rough that all that reappeared was the shattered remains of a boat. Those who lived on an island strewn with the names of wrecks were never in any doubt about the power of the sea.

It was one of the lighthouse men who brought the news down to Quoy. He had been on his way from North Light to South when he noticed a yoal, washed up well into a geo. He climbed down to pull it further up to safety and rushed to Quoy when he recognised its name. When the family said their evening prayers that night, there was real emotion in the words of thanks said by Tom. Although there were a few knocks and scrapes on the *Lily*, there was nothing that could not be remedied by a few hours work. The croft could continue to earn its living, reminded of how little it took to separate them from disaster. The *Lily* was henceforth hauled up further than any other boat, till it became a joke amongst the other fishermen. But this yoal was the Irvine's pride and joy, too hard won to be treated carelessly. To lose the thing twice would be ridiculous. They all accepted God's warning of His dreadful powers and thanked Him fervently for His reprimand.

It didn't take long for Jane to settle into her new home, and Tom was so proud of his croft, his yoal, and his wife that people just had to smile at his enthusiasm, for there wasn't a bad bone in his body. Most were quite pleased with the upswing in Quoy's change of fortune. To be sure, the croft was Lowry's by right, but Tom was the married man and Jane was certainly the woman of the house. There was always the possibility that Lowry might marry, but he was thirty-five and had not found anyone yet. If he did, things would change, but you could hardly spend your life worrying about things that might or might not happen, when daily life was a constant struggle to survive. Anyway, with folk always leaving for pastures new, there was always the possibility of another croft for the couple, should the need arise.

Quoy was not the only croft to change over these years. Farming improvements and new houses benefited many families, along with the flurry of money that some of the men earned during the lighthouse construction. While it would be ridiculous to compare Jane and Tom's improved standards in Fair Isle with that of John Bruce in Shetland, he too was enriching his lifestyle.

In 1893, Bruce junior bought Lunna House (a mansion situated to the north of Lerwick), which he intended for summer use. On an elevated position on the Lunna peninsula, and served by a pier and harbour, this desirable location had long been a prime site for construction. Successive owners had added to the existing 17th century structure so that now it was a grand, three-storied edifice with several splendid reception rooms, an impressive walled garden and an enclosed park, surrounded by a sophisticated system of roads and paths. It is interesting to note that, for all their complaining when their tenants demanded improvements, Shetland's lairds made sufficient profit from their various trading activities to create imposing homes.

The cost of Lunna House in 1893 was £9,740 – a considerable sum of money for a house in Shetland at the time and a fortune to tenants who struggled to pay £10 (or less) for a year's rent. Not long after he paid this exceptional price, Bruce set about making improvements just as any rich man would do today: changing windows, fireplaces and stairwells, creating a much grander entrance and an ornate vaulted ceiling for the library. Then he added a new wing. John Bruce junior lived at Sand Lodge, Sandwick, after he married, until his father died in 1885.

John Bruce senior had built Sumburgh House as the family home in 1867, shortly after his purchase of Fair Isle. The architect he engaged was one of the most prestigious in Scotland, David Rhind, whose works include the magnificent Daniel Stewart's hospital (now school) in Edinburgh, so that Sumburgh House was a very grand edifice indeed. Bruce junior also made further alterations to this mansion not long after his father died. One might note the contrast between the living conditions of the laird and his tenants, but such disparity in society is still with us today so it is difficult to pass meaningful comment. However, Bruce junior would remain childless, unlike many of his tenants.

In Fair Isle, Jane began to suspect that she might be pregnant and was filled with a combination of pleasure and worry at the prospect. Although at thirty she was more than familiar with the facts of life, expecting your first child can be a little disturbing, particularly with no mother or older sister to guide you through the various stages. Since there was no one at Quoy to offer advice, she reverted to Barbara at Taft, who assured her that she would be there to see this child into the world just as she had been for so many others. There really was nothing to worry about.

That August, when Charlotte Irvine of Lower Stoneybrake developed problems in delivering her first child, the experience disturbed everyone. Despite being in labour for two days, the baby failed to arrive and eventually the young woman was in agony and weakening by the hour. All the childbearing expertise of the island was concentrated on Stoneybrake and every Christian man and woman on the island prayed heartily that the poor girl would be delivered successfully. No one spoke of the 'lack of medical support' that was mentioned on so many death certificates. This was the first child of James and Charlotte and her poor husband became more and more distraught as the hours passed.

Occasionally there was a problem in childbirth, one that endangered a mother or child, and there was always this same sense of helplessness. Thus, when a boat was seen on the horizon at the beginning of the third day, some of the men rowed out to it in desperation to ask if there was anyone on board who might be able to help their neighbour. Doing nothing while a young woman slowly tired and faded away in such a horrible fashion was unthinkable. The *Pandora* was, in fact, a small pleasure vessel which had been hired for a trip to Norway and, with amazing good fortune, it had a surgeon on board, one who had brought equipment with him in case an accident might occur on the voyage. This man was quickly brought to Stoneybrake and the child was finally delivered.

The communal relief was immeasurable and everyone celebrated. The good man himself, used to more refined working conditions, felt this was a most challenging environment in which to make a delivery and doubted that the baby would live. However, the child was duly christened Charles Sturrock Irvine in honour of the doctor. Although the young mother did survive, young Charles Sturrock was brain damaged by his long and difficult delivery. His mother fought to give him a childhood as near normal as possible, but he was always a sad wee soul, unable to take part in island life, a burden at a time when life was already hard enough.

Jane was one of those who lost her first child and her grief at this failure, for that was how she saw it, was terrible. At Quoy no one seemed to be able to help her, and for a while she seemed to withdraw into herself, finding it difficult even to drag herself out of bed far less push everyone around as she had so very recently been accustomed to do. The Irvines, especially Tom, had become quite willing to be jollied along by their new, single-minded taskmaster, but all found this dark, morose character upsetting and increasingly irritating. They too were disappointed and upset. Depression is still difficult either to understand or treat, and living with a sufferer can be hard at the best of times. A long, dark, cold winter in a small croft is not the ideal place to recover from this particular illness.

It was a great relief to some of the islanders when the teacher, Mr Brown, left the island in 1894. This stern Calvinist had irritated more than just the young people when he had stopped their Saturday night entertainments. He had argued with a few of the church's elders, some of the parents and, more importantly, the laird, for he had been thought to be a driving force in the disaffection during the visit by the Crofter's Commission. Throughout 1893 he was at odds with Anderson. He was finally asked by the School Board in Dunrossness to leave Fair Isle in 1894. Initially he declined. It was the talk of the whole area. The Dunrossness School Board raised a legal action, craving the court to evict Mr Brown from both the school and schoolhouse at Fair Isle. Mr Brown insisted that the School Board was not legally constituted and had no power to evict him. The whole matter dominated the island for some months, although finally the teacher/missionary lodged a Minute of Abandonment, indicating that he would not follow his suit.

One positive thing that the children remembered about Mr Brown was his wife's provision at the school of a special Christmas dinner on the 27th of December, since special meals were few and far between in their young lives. No doubt the man had good points, but to live successfully in a small community you need to be part of it. Times were changing and even the missionary could be regarded as being over-judgemental. Mr Donald MacLean, who followed as teacher and catechist, would prove to be quite a different type of man.

When Jane became pregnant for a second time in the summer of 1894, her joy was measured. She feared the disappointment of another failure, for that was how she judged her recent loss. To make things worse, this time she felt so sick that she could not hide it from people, as rushing off to vomit could not but encourage comment. Since everything made her feel ill, she stopped wanting to eat or cook and abandoned food preparation to Bina. Worried by his wife's withdrawn state, Tom finally took himself over to Taft to speak with Barbara. The old lady was failing a bit, but she was one of the few people Jane might allow to help her. Tom explained that he was worried about Jane's sadness, but at Quoy they did not know how to deal with pregnant women. Perhaps Jane was just a bit down, Tom suggested, but perhaps it was something worse. Perhaps she was beginning to lose her mind? He had heard that this could happen.

"Fiddlesticks! There's nothing wrong with her. She's just mourning the loss of her first baby and, despite her body's ideas, she's not ready yet to cope yet with another. If it had been my doing I'd have let her be for a while to let her mourn, but you men are all the same."

Tom looked suitably surprised and guilty. He had not given the idea of long-term mourning for dead babies a thought. It was not the habit of the time. He looked steadfastly at his feet, saying nothing as his tormentor continued.

"Just because she didn't hold that baby doesn't mean she can't mourn it. Mourning takes time to work itself out. The trouble is, if she's expecting again so soon she's not had time to go through the process. Ach, you men don't understand anything that's not a fish or a boat. Send the lassie to me. I've not the strength to walk to Quoy."

Tom at least had the good sense not to tell Jane that he had been talking about her behind her back. He just explained that he had called in at Taft and thought Barbara was looking frail, which she certainly was. Perhaps Jane could call on her? He also had the good sense not to tell Aunt Barbara how bad she looked. Marriage was teaching Tom a bit about the ways of the female gender, even if it was still a very complicated and mysterious issue for him. Saying less rather than more was his normal fall-back position.

Jane, of course, had her shawl round her shoulders and was off immediately she heard of her great aunt's frailty. No one had told her of Barbara being ill, but neither had she dropped into Taft regularly of late to ask, now that everything was such an effort. She felt guilty and worried in equal measure. She found the old lady huddled in a big Fair Isle chair that had found its way over from Springfield, its high rope-woven back padded with a sheepskin. Barbara was swaddled in shawls, even though she was sitting close to the fire. For once, she was not knitting. This in itself was a warning that all was not right. Jane's stomach turned over in fear.

"Well, what's this I hear?" Barbara was never one to use devious means to express herself. "You're expecting again. That's good news, my dear, even if you feel a bit sick. It's my belief that sick mothers make healthy babies. How are you feeling apart from the sickness? Tom says you're a bit down in the mouth."

Almost immediately Jane realised that she had been tricked by her husband, but she was grateful to Tom for coming to Taft, for Barbara did indeed look awful. No one had said anything to her and, not attending the chapel, Jane had not spoken to anyone of late.

She took a deep breath and made an effort to speak cheerfully, not realising that this in itself was a big step forward. Jane had not cared enough to make such an effort for anyone recently. "I'm fine, really. Just a bit down. Yes, and I'm worried I'll lose this one too. But never mind me. You look awful."

"Don't mince your words, will you. Aye, well, I've been a bit tired recently. I'm eighty-three now, so what else can you expect. The good Lord may finally be getting ready to relieve me of the pain in my joints. There's not anything you can do about it, so don't look like that. I'm just at that stage in my life. It's natural. If you come over to see me a bit more I'll feel better. We can cheer one another up. To be truthful, you don't look the best yourself. I don't really know which of us looks worse."

"I've been a bit fed up. Things are not turning out as I planned."

Jane had expected suitable sympathy and understanding as a response. But the old lady laughed. She laughed till tears ran down her face. Her great niece tightened her lips. Jane had not thought her feelings funny in the least. She was mourning a dead baby and feeling sick with another. Surely that merited some sympathy.

Finally, Barbara stopped laughing and took her hand. "Lass, things never turn out as we plan. If I've learned anything in eighty years, I've learned that. I planned to marry and have a family. Your mother planned to bring up her children. Your father never saw that he might leave Polly and her brood to fend for themselves. We just have to deal with what we're given. It's all right to be sad for a bit, but then we just have to get on with it, whatever it is. So, what do you want to do now, talk about dead babies, or the one you're expecting? You choose."

Jane was dumbstruck. No one in Quoy would dare to talk like that to her. "I don't need to talk about either," she retorted, with an edge to her voice.

"But you do, my dear. That's why you're here. You're not talking over the way, so you have to come here. Get going. I've time left yet. I'm not going to die today."

"Don't say that."

"Why not? I'm not going to die today, I think. But we all have to die sometime and I really believe I had the best of life in Fair Isle. It's all changing and what with someone else leaving every other minute, I'm not sure there'll be anyone left at all in a few years. So when the good Lord intends to take me, I'm ready. In the meantime, you can make us a brew of tea and get talking. I believe I'll be spared this afternoon at least. What do you think?"

Jane could not help but smile at the old lady's words as she set about making the tea. Surprisingly, she felt better, despite Barbara's talk of dying. There was something very comforting about her honesty and Jane still felt at home here in Taft, in a way she seldom did elsewhere.

"Take plenty of sugar in the tea. While you can't eat, the sugar will give you energy. Babies take what they need from mothers, I believe. You just look after yourself and eat what and when you can. Leave the cooking to Bina for a while. She's a willing worker, I'll give her that. You just concentrate on feeling better. So let's talk. Now what's it to be, the dead or the living. I don't mind in the least."

Jane giggled. "I think I need some juicy details about the ladies of the chapel. I'll exchange you for some stories about the kirk."

"Excellent. Now did you hear about old Maggie Wilson of..."

And so they sat and gossiped through the afternoon, doing one another good by talking of the new and the old, both good and bad. As she left, Jane promised both herself and her aunt that she would be back regularly. It was coming up for harvest time now, and the weather had improved so that they could get it in without too much trouble. She would be spared to come over to Taft as soon as she explained the reason, and she would let Bina have the running of the kitchen at Quoy.

Gradually, the people at Quoy felt more able to relax and, despite the days when sickness made it hard to get out of bed, Jane's daily visit to Taft quickly became essential, for Barbara was failing fast. Mary tried to cook anything that smelt strongly early in the mornings or later at night, so that by the time Jane appeared the aroma of warm fresh baking of some sort overwhelmed residual odours. The days developed a firm structure that pleased everyone, even though Barbara shrank before their eyes. When neighbours sent small gifts of food to tempt the old lady they were tasted and politely turned aside, for the old woman had lost her appetite. When talking became tiring she asked Jane to read to her, but she only relished her favourite passages from the Bible, as if she was preparing herself for the next world. Surely she would wait to see the baby, Jane prayed, for as the weeks passed and the child made its presence increasingly felt, its mother dared on the good days to believe that this time the baby would live. Even when she heard that Maggie Stout was to be delivered of her third child at the same time as she, the news did not upset her.

They were blessed that year with a deal of fine days for the hairst, so that the grain was in good condition. The hard graft of potato lifting had also been accompanied by fair weather, so that back-breaking task was less daunting. By the time the harsh autumn storms arrived, with howling winds and towering waves beating along the shore, Barbara was ready to die. Jane and Mary cared for their great aunt till the end, listening as she made plans for what she would say to her brother and all the rest when she got to heaven. Her simple faith assured her of God's grace and a reunion with all of the family who had gone before.

One day, however, she sighed. It was not like her to sigh. Right at the end of her life there was an issue. Jane encouraged her to share. "What is it Auntie?"

There was a bit of a silence. "I don't know if I should say."

"Well, if you don't I'll just worry about it, and you know Tom says I've not to worry."

"You're always the smart one, aren't you. I was just wondering."

"Yes?"

"I would like to die at Springfield. I know it's silly but I'd like to be there at the end. Do you think they'd mind over there?"

Of course they did not mind and of course she was made welcome. Thomas carried her over, swathed in blankets and shawls and followed by a trail of folk carrying her few bits and pieces. Soon she was laid down in their best bed, from which she never emerged alive, slipping from life with the grace she had embraced all her days.

It was a lovely funeral and she was buried beside her family. Barbara left behind a legacy of goodness and a sense of right that was difficult to explain. She may not have had her own children, but John's family remembered her with love, along with a host of others on the island, and she was held up as an example of how a good Christian woman should conduct herself. So, although it was November and the days were now quite cold and dark, Jane did not feel cast down. Barbara had lived her life according to God's plan and had died in certainty of a future with Him. It was reassuring to be part of something much bigger than yourself.

Thomas was most affected by the loss of his surrogate mother. Even when it is expected, wished for even, there is still mourning to be endured. A few days after the burial, he came to visit Jane. "I feel badly. I'd wanted a stone for her in the churchyard. She was very special to me."

Barbara had no headstone, although this was not in the least abnormal. Many had other priorities than spending money they could ill afford on a headstone. Jane pointed this out to the boy. They did not have city habits here. Their own parents had no headstones.

"The last person in the world to worry about a stone would be Aunt Barbara. She's engraved in all our minds as one of the best people we ever knew. Why would she need a headstone?"

"She did so much for me. I just don't want folk to forget her."

"Tom, they won't, but why don't you wait a bit and if you ever have the money to spare, buy her one. She'll always be here. There's no need for the present, and it's not as if any of us will forget her in the meantime. Get her a stone later on."

"Will that be all right? I've a bit put by, but I'm saving in case I leave some day, not yet, but perhaps some day. You know how things are here and I'd maybe like to see the world."

Thomas leaving? What would Aunt Barbara have thought of that? And what on earth would Stewart do on his own at Taft if Thomas left? Already, with Barbara away, Stewart, Mary and Thomas were rolling around in the place. Unless one of them got married and had a family it would never get back its old sense of purpose. The house needed a young family to keep it alive.

Thomas could see Jane thinking and knew without being told what she was considering. "Don't worry. I won't go immediately, but I might, eventually. I could never have left as long as she was alive, you see. I'll never forget her."

"None of us will, Thomas. Aunt Barbara was one of a kind. I don't know how we would have coped without her when you were born, and then when Polly came to stay with us she kept us all sane."

And with that they went on to talk about her, keeping her memory alive for as long as they remembered, all without the benefit of a stone, laughing and crying as the old memories came back.

In February 1895, Jane's daughter was safely delivered and, of course, she named her Barbara. Everyone sighed with relief and prayed that this birth would be the first of many. Children were why people married and the possibility of failure had haunted Jane. As a mother, she felt that she had established her position at Quoy.

Never had there been such a beautiful child. Never had there been such a clever child. Certainly, never had there been such a well-dressed child. With five adults and no other youngster for company, from the start Barbara was near to being spoiled. She was the seal of success for Quoy, the promise of a better future. Life was difficult, but it was difficult everywhere surely?

In July 1895, the men of Fair Isle went to the Shetland mainland to vote. The 1884 Act had the specific purpose of enfranchising men in agricultural areas, although it did not manage to deal with this issue entirely, so that only two out of three men qualified. (Of course, this was well before the time when women were considered to be deserving of the vote.) The problem was that, since the Act focused on householders who paid rent, it did not take on board the fact that in Fair Isle (and elsewhere) several men could and would live in one house, but only one of them could be named as the householder. However, MacLean, the new teacher, urged all the men who could vote to do so and suggested that the rest might join them on a voting outing. The steam yacht *Tourmaline* called at the island and took them to Lerwick, their allocated polling station. MacLean himself had then to travel to Whalsay, where he was registered, before rushing back to catch the *Tourmaline* the following day. Everyone thoroughly enjoyed the experience. People felt that, by voting, they had become part of the wider community.

Also in 1895, progress was made in managing the stock of beasts that was kept on the island and a public meeting was held to discuss the numbers of ponies and sheep kept on the hill. It was agreed that different sheep marks should be allocated to different crofts, with the lambs cut on their ears with the agreed mark of a particular croft. This meant that although individuals might be sure of knowing which lambs were theirs, during the lambing period men had to chase around to catch and to cut their new lambs. Eventually this system would be abandoned and in a communal lottery everyone would be allocated a share of the year's lambs on the hill. Fair Isle sheep were never large and certainly not a commercial butcher's first choice for meat, so as new and meatier breeds took over the market on the mainland, the price of island sheep fell, although their fleeces retained a value as long as knitting was highly regarded.

Fair Isle gradually found itself receiving more visitors, since travel to unusual places was becoming fashionable for those with sufficient cash to enable them to enjoy this new concept of leisure time. Unusual Scottish locations were in vogue and, although the concept of a holiday remained alien to the majority, increased ease of communication meant that more people (in the main young men) of the middle classes now aspired to travel. Steamboat companies advertised day and longer trips to the north when they realised that people were willing to pay for such experiences. The summer months saw increasing numbers of visitors coming to Fair Isle, having heard of its frightening cliffs, fascinating birdlife and its fearful history of wrecks. Despite the fact that no one stayed more than a few hours, they brought in a little cash and thus were always welcome. Although knitting was the main island product, the children soon realised that shells, bird's eggs and even feathers might be rewarded with a few coins, if their vendors seemed appealing. Some of the visitors were like those from the *Pandora* – private, very rich families – while others, like the thirty excursionists on the *St Nicholas* from Leith in 1894, were simply people willing to make an arduous journey to see something unusual.

Sadly, Bruce now found himself having to deal with paupers in Fair Isle, a childless widow and an old bachelor who could no longer work. In the past there had almost always been some sort of family to take care of the old and infirm, however tenuous the relationship, but now things were changing so that there had to be an appeal to public funds. Bruce agreed to send small weekly payments to the island from Dunrossness, just enough to enable the paupers to buy a little food. Fish was provided by neighbours, but most families had little else to spare.

Shetland was now the top fishing area in Scotland for both herring and white fish landings, and the bigger harbours were gradually converting their fleets to larger, decked boats. Fair Isle continued its efforts to interest outside bodies in their plea for a harbour and a fish processing plant, but there was never any positive response. Increasing numbers of trawlers came within the three nautical miles that were supposed by law to indicate the islanders' protected fishing zone. Since the trawlers picked up saithe (which they did not want) these would then be lost to local people who were set up to process them. The trawlers covered their registration numbers to avoid detection and, whatever their excuse, they probably contributed to the demise of fishing around the island, forcing the yoals to go ever further afield to locate their low-value catch.

All the families now felt under increased monetary pressure, since everything was becoming more expensive with the passing of the years, while local incomes continued to shrink. Although more goods were available in the outside world, saithe fishing brought in less cash, so that islanders were unable to benefit from progress. In the quiet of the night, people wondered if they had a future. No home was without someone who questioned the wisdom of staying.

Despite their run of improved luck around the time of the lighthouse building and the safe arrival of Barbara, the Irvines at Quoy also pondered their future. To be truthful, it was Jane who pondered most, for Jane was the one who had seen something else and had no fear of moving to find a better life. When questioned, Lowry vowed never to leave and John knew he was tied to Lowry, for his asthma increasingly meant that he was prone to days when he could not work and needed his family's support. Bina could imagine no existence other than Fair Isle and, unless a man proposed marriage, she would stay at Quoy forever.

When Jane occasionally raised the subject with Tom, he would not be moved to discuss it. They would stick it out for the moment he said. They had seen bad times before and for all they knew things might look up soon. For Tom, brought up in absolute poverty, even the increasing strictures of his current life meant an existence much improved on that which he had endured in his youth, when the Irvines had been the poorest of the poor and hunger a constant companion. Quoy was as successful as anywhere else on the island, even if that meant less than it did previously. They were good fishermen and they had the boat, while Tom had his position, both in the community and in the church. There were three men working and only two women and a child to support. They would stick it out to see what the future held. There were many worse off. Jane knew that her place was to agree to her husband's wishes, so she kept her peace.

In June 1896, the Irvine family from Houll left for Lerwick. Barbara had done very well to raise her family when Laurence died in 1879, falling from the boat he was using to remove cargo from the wreck of the *Monchgut*. He had been carried away so quickly by the rip tide that he could not be saved. The ensuing years had been a struggle, her eldest child being only ten at the time. The woman had taken in a series of male lodgers to give her croft a fisherman's input until the children were old enough to cope on their own. Now they were grown and wanted to leave, to find something better. George, her eldest, fancied life in Lerwick where he could work on bigger fishing boats and the others wanted to join him. Barbara resolved to go too.

So another entire family slipped away, but this time, not quietly. Barbara wanted legitimate compensation for all the improvements she had made to her croft, but despite the change in the law, the laird seemed loath to comply at this time, so that she was forced to appeal to the Crofting Commission. Litigation of any sort is stressful for those unaccustomed to it, but Barbara and her family decided to fight for their rights in this new world where a tenant could question his master.

Sadly, at Quoy, Jane lost another baby early in 1896, a wee soul that looked briefly at the world when it arrived and decided not to stay. Jane once more became a victim of dark despond. Even when she became pregnant soon afterwards, her spirits did not rise. Although Barbara was doing well and the Irvines were certainly pulling together, the constant talk of leaving was disruptive. At the shop, after church and in the evenings a stream of folk spread malignant stories about the future. Everlasting gossip unsettled even the most enthusiastic of people and Jane now had serious doubts about their prospects, doubts she could no longer mention to Tom, since he became irritated and silent when she brought the subject up. Her husband flatly refused to consider leaving, becoming increasingly stressed by the whole situation because he, too, felt pressured. Lowry told Jane to stop making a fuss when she brought the topic up with him. He said that things had been much worse when he was a boy, which was true, but Jane wanted better, not worse.

There was a commotion in the Springfield household when one of her cousins married, just a little later than everyone might have hoped, since the bride was clearly very pregnant on her wedding day. Once they were married, however, everyone rallied round to help. Jane made a special effort to make the girl feel comfortable in her new role and tried to share her excitement about the forthcoming birth, knitting clothes and admiring the new cradle the baby's father had made. Gradually, the effort lifted her out of her own preoccupations, while the Yule celebrations kept everyone busy and lightened the winter gloom.

The Springfield child was safely delivered in January 1897, and named Stewart after his father, which everyone hoped would be a positive signal for his future. Sadly, young Jessie never recovered her strength and died just five weeks later, from one of the myriad of post-partum complications that carried off young women at that time, leaving an orphan baby, just as Jane's mother had done all these years before. To Jane, baby Stewart was another Thomas, with a grieving family struggling to find the food that would enable him to live, while miserably mourning his mother who had been so young, pretty and lively. It was difficult not to question the Good Lord's judgement at times like this. And to wonder why nothing seemed to change.

In February 1897, the Crofter's Commission visited the island. Barbara Irvine had formally claimed her compensation under the Act for improvements she had made while she had been renting her croft, but Bruce continued to resist this payment. The improvements were inspected by the Commission and Bruce was ordered to pay her £24.10 shillings, a sum of money that made all the difference to Barbara's new life in Lerwick and very little to the man who had to pay. For someone who had never supported either the Commission or their work, this was another public humiliation. It seemed to Bruce that the world was turning on its head. For the crofters, it was proof that the laird was no longer supreme.

Jane brooded more and more as she neared her own delivery date. She could not but have her mind linger on young Jessie. The idea clung to her as she went about her daily tasks and she would find herself with silent tears streaming down her face as she thought of Barbara and a new baby, motherless. As the idea took root, she even found herself looking at the unmarried women on the island, wondering who Tom would choose to replace her. Yet all went well when the time came and young Robina was quite perfect. Tom was ecstatic, although Barbara was a little upset to find she had competition for attention after so much undiluted, focused care. Lowry and John congratulated their brother and joked about the need to produce a boy next time, so that they had someone look after them in their old age. Bina was so proud to have a namesake that she spent hours billing and cooing over the child, which hardly helped young Barbara come to terms with her new sibling. Like all Fair Isle children she would have to get used to this, or so she was told.

Gradually Jane felt more confident as the weeks passed. Perhaps this new life was a turning point. Perhaps things would get better now. Certainly, with a new baby taking up her time she was content to stay, for there was little time to think of anything other than survival during the first few weeks. She fell into bed each night, pole-axed with tiredness, sleeping deeply until the baby reminded her that another feed was due. There was neither the time nor energy for long-term planning for anything at Quoy.

At the beginning of March 1897, the island committee announced a communal meeting to discuss the possibility of a mass exodus. However hard the men worked they could not make enough money from saithe fishing, and they had to accept that no one wanted to set up a herring fishing operation at Fair Isle. There were by this time seventy-nine herring stations throughout Shetland and the ongoing popularity of this fish was the death knell for saithe sales. Herring landings would continue to grow, from 72,000 crans in 1890 to 320,000 crans by 1900. It was an incredible harvest. White fish also retained a higher price, but cod, haddock and halibut were the prime catches and they had to be conveyed speedily to market, something the islanders could not guarantee. At the end of a long night, there was no conclusion. Although some were ready to consider leaving, many were still desperate to stay.

Perhaps to encourage people to leave, Bruce then intimated to his tenants that he would no longer run his fish curing enterprise on the island and, furthermore, he would no longer accept the system of truck by which the men exchanged the value of the fish they caught for their rent. So just when the fishing revenue was at its worst, the laird would now demand a cash rent and leave his tenants to manage as they could. To rub salt in the wound, he intended to close the shop, since he could no longer make a profit from it either. All the ties that had held the men back in the good times were to be cut, now that they were no longer in the laird's interest. The community was stunned. It was perhaps Bruce's hope that most of the people would emigrate when they understood the uncertainty of their new position. Perhaps it was irritation at the Crofting Commission, or simply that, at sixty, the man could no longer be bothered with an island that was not commercially viable.

Even with eight acres and a boat, it seemed increasingly unlikely that anyone could be self-sufficient when the price of saithe fell from three shillings a hundredweight in 1894, to two shillings later that year. When in 1897 it fell to nearer one shilling, it became clear that the market for saithe had largely disappeared. Herring continued to develop in popularity. Improvements in transport meant that the fresh fish market was booming. Haddock stood at four shillings and eight pence a hundredweight and halibut was nine shillings and three pence. Although the islanders could catch these fish, they found it difficult to get them to market. Their isolation, they now realised, might be the end of them.

Just to help things along, the weather that spring proved to be amongst the worst in living memory, with a run of gales and extremely heavy seas that challenged fishermen throughout the Northern Isles. On odd days the men had taken the boats out, but the fish still kept their distance so it was hardly rewarding. Thus the Irvines were glad to get out when the wind fell for a bit, taking Andrew Wilson of Gaila to make up the *Lily's* crew. Several boats were out when the wind got up again, so that they all moved back as a body to South Harbour, where conditions made each landing challenging. But these were practised boatmen who understood their harbour in all her humours and knew every rock and its dangers. They did this day in, day out, with scarce a knock or graze to their craft. Tom expertly guided his beloved yoal towards the shore with all the care and attention he had gained over his thirty-odd years.

When both the Irvine and Eunson boats were caught in the rip-tide that propelled them violently against the big black rock opposite the lighthouse pier, there was an awful moment of disbelief. Right on their own doorstep, two four-man crews were smashed against the same rough rock and the first impression was that all were lost in that instant. That's how it is with the sea. One moment you think you are in charge, and the next the sea roughly states its superiority. Then those on the shore saw that the Eunson boat, the *Boys*, was badly damaged but was managing to limp towards the shore. The *Lily*, however, was destroyed.

After the initial frozen moment of horror, a shout went up along the beach. George Stout of Stoneybrake and William Eunson of Stackhool, along with their crews, quickly pushed their craft back into the water. Without a thought for their own safety, they propelled their boats expertly into the maelstrom of bodies and shattered wood that seethed around the rock. It took quite a few minutes of careful manoeuvring to drag the four men from the water. There was nothing to do for the *Lily*, however, so the men quickly took their charges back to shore where a considerable crowd had gathered to help draw both boats and their human cargo out from the sea. Four stupefied bodies were quickly hauled to dry land for closer examination.

Although dazed, Andrew Wilson was largely unharmed, as was Tom, apart from some gashes and scratches, but Lowry and John had been knocked quite senseless. All were variously bloodied, so that it took a while to establish what their injuries actually were. Tom was quite bemused, sitting with his head in his hands and blood running down his arms, hopelessly trying to make his limbs and mind obey him. He stared back and forth at his brothers on either side, each with his own small cluster of rough, male nursemaids, with a terrible, awful certainty that he had killed them both.

Lowry was the first to come round, shaking his head furiously, as if that would help, mumbling who knew what, but John was barely conscious as they carried them both up the road. Since he was known to be fragile, everyone worried about John. Blood was everywhere and the two major head wounds quickly soaked into their makeshift bandages. Andrew Wilson was taken home by friends, ambulant, but a tad fragile. At Quoy the sad party were met by unmitigated panic from Bina and black, organised despair by Jane.

Soon the croft was filled with people helping, giving advice and getting in the way. Young Barbara quickly joined Bina in her wailing, while the baby bawled in sympathy. Jane sat Barbara in a corner and told her to mind the baby in her crib. She ordered Bina to start tearing sheets for bandages. Then she searched for salve and alcohol to clean the wounds. John was her first concern, for he was clearly the most severely injured. Then other women came to the door, bringing bandages, salves and opinions in equal measure, all advising on the best way to treat head injuries and ushering the men out of what was now their domain.

Tom would not be touched by any of them, sitting silently by John's bed, desperately searching for signs of life and normality. Since he seemed relatively unhurt, they left him for the moment. Lowry was forced to lie down and submit to some bandaging, but it was a fair struggle for the women who chose him as a patient, for he was not a man to submit to women's ministrations readily. It was lucky for them that he was still fairly woozy. For an hour or two Quoy was in chaos, until the patients were all washed and bandaged. Even then it was nothing like normal and Jane was grateful for the gift of bannocks and soup brought by Aggie Wilson from Springfield, along with her offer to take young Barbara off their hands for the night. John had fallen into a deep sleep and Bina sat by wretchedly, wringing her hands in despair. When finally they were alone, Jane silently served Tom and Lowry bannocks and soup. She was shocked and exhausted by this household of invalids. And Quoy's yoal was destroyed.

Tom, the healthiest of the three invalids, was totally withdrawn and quite wretched about his mistake. The captain of any vessel, however small, accepts the glory for any triumphs along with responsibility and scorn when his charge founders under his command. Tom had been at the helm when the boat was destroyed. He would forever be remembered as Quoy Tammy, the man who couldn't bring his own boat safely into the harbour. Worse still, his two brothers had suffered much more than he, the consequences of his miscalculation. At the very worst of times the family would now be further handicapped because he had destroyed their livelihood. If Tom was not a good sailor, he was nothing. He could barely look Jane in the eye as she busied herself with the two invalids.

Aggie Wilson came back over from Springfield later to say she would "sit up through the night with the men," for Jane was feeding a baby and would need to get some sleep if she was to keep her milk. Jane was quietly grateful, for by now she was exhausted and Robina should still be a priority in the midst of all the mayhem. Her sister Mary decided to join Aggie, so that they could take turns to nod off for a bit. Then her brothers came over from Taft to see if they could help. Tom must try to get some rest they told him, for he had suffered a shock. A good night's sleep would help them all. It could have been any of them, they told Tom. It was just bad luck.

Tom felt that he would never sleep again. The enormity of his small error, rather than the intransigence of fate, weighed on his mind. He had lost his family's means of survival. Bina was quite sure she would lose one of her brothers in the night and tried to resist being sent to bed, but she was told that she had to be at her best to help Jane in the morning. In truth, apart from John, there was not much sleep in any of Quoy's beds that night, for the baby too seemed to feel the general disquiet and refused to settle under any circumstances. Tom tortured himself by replaying what had happened, remembering that awful moment when they struck the rock. The moment of collision ran and reran, the instant shock of icy water so quickly superseded by the awful clunk of skull (or as it turned out skulls) hitting something hard.

Jane had no energy to comfort him, so taken up was she with her own distress and now the baby seemed more restless than usual. Because of all that had happened in the past, she worried about the slightest change to this child's routine. Thus when they rose to send their helpers home to their own beds in the morning, no one felt any better. The interminable day dragged through, the women in a haze of sleeplessness, trying to focus on the tasks of minding the sick, changing and washing bandages, making tea, talking to visitors, seeing to the baby and keeping Lowry in the house. The next few days were difficult, with the two women fully taken up with their patients, although it has to be said that Lowry was the least amenable to nursing. Never having been seriously ill in his life before, he did not want to stay inside, sit still and be mothered by women. He tried to leave the croft at the slightest opportunity, despite the fact that movement opened his head wounds just as they were settling down, so that blood ran down into his shirt, causing even more washing, as Jane reminded him brusquely.

"Mind your own business woman," he finally told her. "I'm off outside and if anyone tries to stop me, I'll hit them. I want no more of this nursing. Can you not understand that I'm a grown man!"

And with that he made his unsteady path to the door and off into the grey morning.

"Tom, go with him, will you! See he stays on his feet, for goodness sakes!" Jane urged, for numbed as she was, she knew that the last thing she needed was Lowry suffering yet another injury.

Lowry's cuts and bruises were unpleasant but not really serious and once back on his feet he made steady progress. John took much longer to recover, for his asthma and the sudden soaking, coupled with his physical injuries, made him quite ill for some time. Tom kept apologising to everyone, for in truth he couldn't see a way forward. He walked up to Stoneybrake and then to Stackhool to thank his rescuers and finally over to Andrew Wilson to apologise for almost killing him. Andrew tried to explain that it could have happened to anyone, but that didn't help in the least. Tom knew he was guilty, whatever people said. He had become over confident with the passing of the years. He must have taken his mind off what he was doing just at the wrong moment. And now the family's income would diminish during one of the most difficult periods they had known. There were still some of Jane's savings in the post office, but how could he ask her for that, for he knew this small sum was her security.

Two days later, on the 12th March, 1897, baby Robina died.

There was no illness, simply a listless baby in the morning, one who declined to eat and then, a couple of hours later, one who stopped breathing. Jane's grief struck her as heavily as the wave that had destroyed the *Lily*. Bina could only sit in a corner hugging Barbara, battered out of reality. Her family was all she had in life and she had thought it to be a fixed entity. Robina, her namesake and her protégé, had been proof that the Irvines were flourishing, but now she could only shrink into herself, waiting for the next disaster. Barbara, who had been used to a relatively cosseted life until the new baby arrived, was quite bewildered. Suddenly, everyone was either sad, ill, or dead. Barbara simply couldn't understand it at all.

Once she had carefully washed and dressed her for the last time, Jane handed her dead baby to Tom to carry down to the graveyard, with her preacher and all the other men from both churches who turned up to support Tom. Babies didn't always merit a big turnout, but they were doing this for Tom as much as anything else. They understood his pain, guilt and loss. Mary and the Springfield women came over to comfort Jane, along with a procession of other good women, but it was a hopeless task. What can you say to someone who has lost another baby, at such a difficult time?

"It's God's will."

"You'll have another."

"She was too good for this world."

"She's with the angels."

None of it helped in the least. For the next two days Jane said little of note to anyone, so that although they all felt her despair, there was nothing to do that might help her. Tom saw his life eroding in front of him. He had lost his boat and his daughter and for all he knew the croft, while his beloved wife was like another dead thing. It was all his fault. The memory of placing this much loved, tiny baby in the cold, rocky soil of the graveyard would haunt him till his dying day and, worst of all, he felt implicated in her death.

Perhaps, finally, he needed to take Jane away, but to leave his family at the very worst of times seemed like a further betrayal, adding insult to injury. Perhaps if he left to work on one of the Shetland boats for a bit he could save a bit of money, but how could he leave them all with Jane when she was like this? Perhaps they should all move somewhere else. Wretched day followed wretched day so that Quoy was not a pleasant place for anyone that spring.

When a boat landed a copy of the *Shetland News* along with supplies, Lowry was glad to get a read and amused when he found a report on Fair Isle. There it was in black and white, Fair Isle's 'proposed exodus' that they had all been discussing just before the *Lily* went down. Well, it must be a fact if it was in the newspaper.

Then there was a story entitled 'boat accident' along with each of their names. They were famous. Lowry was tickled to see his name in print, but Tom read the small article with deep shame. Now everyone in Shetland knew he was a failure, all of Scotland even. The article pointed out that they would have perished had not the two crews with whom they had been fishing that day risked their lives to save them.

Jane was not the only one wrapped in black introspection.

*Chapter 14*

# *End of an Era*

O n 27th March, 1897, a second mass meeting was called to discuss the island's future, now that people had considered the repercussions of the master's momentous decisions regarding both the end of truck and the shop closure. It began at five o'clock, going on far into the night. Anger and despair mixed irrationally with wild plans for the future, most of which were easily shot down. There were of course all the usual calls for a harbour to be built by someone, anyone, but more realistically the topic of mass evacuation was discussed. Perhaps if they stayed together they could set up a new community in a less difficult location. Perhaps they could travel to Orkney as a group. Perhaps they could follow those who had gone to Canada, or New Zealand, or Australia. But no one was ready to lead the way forward and they had heard it all before.

At the basis of their tragedy lay the fact that most people wanted to stay. If anyone had wanted to leave there had been plenty of opportunity in recent years. But it was now inevitable that more families would give the matter serious consideration, even if they left individually. Perhaps in the end, Fair Isle's clearance would simply occur by small degrees. How very different all this was from the happy, busy time just a few years previously, when there had seemed to be such a positive future. They had thought that all the new houses, roads, the school and churches, along with the lighthouses, were omens of prosperity. How wrong could you be?

The men debated at length the topic of an increased mail service. A weekly mail service, if the vessel then went straight back to Lerwick, could take fresh fish to the market. The current mail service was fortnightly and continued on a further fifty-mile trip to other locations before returning to harbour, which made it impossible for it to carry fresh fish. However, there was little likelihood of the post office altering its schedule to accommodate fish from Fair Isle. That was not what the post office was set up to do.

It was all very frustrating. The discussion went on far into the night, but no conclusion was reached. It was all 'if only'. Families that could guarantee an income from carting coal and other supplies to the lighthouses and provide an occasional keeper's role might hang on, but this was hardly an answer for the majority.

Fair Isle was by no means the only Scottish island facing the problem of continued existence. The survival of many small rural communities had become increasingly hazardous, because subsistence crofting was generally insufficient to support a family and pay a rent at a time when people wanted more rather than less. You needed to have something extra to sell, along with an easily accessed market for your produce. For all the protection acquired from the Crofting Commission, if you could not make enough money to pay your rent you would be evicted.

To satisfy the immediate need for supplies, Strong Eunson of Lerwick stated that he would send a regular order of goods to replace the shop, with Thomas Wilson of Leogh acting as his agent. This would supplement any trips made by the *Gleaner*, so the island would not starve, although there had to be a more sustainable solution in the long term. Meagre savings would quickly run dry and, in truth, not everybody had savings. The meeting voted to petition the government for a weekly mail service and it was agreed that the majority would stick it out for another year if they could. That the people of Foula were granted a weekly mail service at this time was particularly galling.

Quoy, however, paid little heed to decisions made in the village hall, for it continued to be swathed in gloom. Lowry stated at the communal meeting that he intended to die on the island and John, who lived in his shadow, would not dream of diverging from any of Lowry's views. Bina had nothing to say. Bina's life had diminished with all that she had been expected to endure this month, so that she simply got on with her work and chatted to Barbara when everyone else was out of the way. She would not be drawn into any discussion about anything.

Jane also conversed with no one. She looked at no one. In truth, she hardly thought of the future at all. It wasn't that she blamed Tom, or indeed any of them. She simply felt that life at Quoy was pointless. Every single thing they tried to do was destroyed. Young Barbara learned to be quiet and withdrawn in the uncomfortable atmosphere that permeated the house so that, in a surprisingly short period of time, Quoy became more of a mausoleum than a home. It was Lowry who broke the spell. One Sunday afternoon at the beginning of April he asked Tom to come for a walk with him.

"Well, now, this can't go on, you know. That woman of yours is going to make herself ill and the rest of us too. You need to do something, Tom, for yourself as much everyone else. At least we all need to sit down and talk about the future honestly. I can't abide a house with an atmosphere. I don't know what to do or say in my own home any more. It's not good for the bairn either."

"I'm sorry, Lowry. It's just that we both thought this baby would live. She's so upset. On top of everything else... I'm responsible for finishing Quoy off. I'm responsible for destroying the *Lily*!"

Lowry smiled and said, "I don't think Jane is in the least bothered about the boat. I don't think that's why she married you, although it might have helped swing things in your direction. What ails her is not the accident, I believe, though that shook her up. The poor lass doesn't take to losing her bairns and no one can blame her for that. She's just worn down by what's happened over the last few years and, remember, she knew something different for a while. She's not like us. She's been to Edinburgh and seen another life. Have you thought of taking her away for a bit? It doesn't have to be forever. It's a bad time here at the moment, but that might well pass. You can come back. It doesn't need to be forever."

Lowry verbalised the unspoken menace – that Tom must leave Quoy and the rest of the Irvines.

"How could I go now there's no boat? I need to replace it. I'm that sorry, Lowry."

"Aye, well we're all sorry about the yoal, but she's gone and that's that. It could just as well have been me at the tiller, you know, and the mistake, if there was one, could have been mine. Remember that the Eunson boat was caught up in it too, so it was probably just bad luck. We all know what a devil that bit can be when the sea's up. But we were saved and that's the blessing. God man, you might have killed me!"

Lowry put on a silly face to show he was joking. Despite himself, Tom found he was smiling.

"Look, the boat's gone and the bairn's gone and we must all just get on with it. We three will manage fine here on our own, if that's what's holding you back. Bina's learned a lot about the housekeeping from Jane and we never used to have a boat. Folk will give us a place in their yoals, just as they did before. John can work down at the beach when he's not that well and I can go back to working for Anderson. The old bugger is always straight with me at least, and he'll surely be the very last one to go. In fact, I can't see Anderson ever leaving. He'll just sook up all the crofts as they empty, till he's the king of Fair Isle, so he'll need workers since he can't look after it all himself. Anyway, they'll be giving boats away before long. I'll just wait till they all leave Fair Isle and get my choice of what's left behind. I've spoken with John and he agrees. We three can manage on our own. We won't mind. Well, we will a bit. I've no doubt we'll miss Jane's cooking as well as the bairn, but we'll manage."

Tom was surprised that Lowry had so much insight and that the three of them had discussed all this behind his back. He had only half thought on it himself. If the truth be told, he was scared to death at the thought of leaving Quoy and his family. "I'll think about it. I don't know what to do for the best. If we go away and she doesn't know anyone how will she manage as she is? It's like she's all broken up inside."

"Stop it, would you. You're not to blame for it all. Aye, she's down. We're all down at the moment. But you could try somewhere like Kirkwall if you don't want to go too far. She's got family there, after all. And if things get better, you can always come back. Underneath it all, your Jane is strong. I remember how we all had to jump to her tune before you married. She'll come out of it. She's just had a bad time recently. If you go somewhere there are other islanders you'll both get support. As far as I can see, half the world's got some Fair Isle folk by now. Your Jane will manage in Kirkwall, or Aberdeen, or Edinburgh. Don't you worry about that."

"I'll talk to her."

"Sooner rather than later, Tom. She needs to have a reason to get going again. There's been too much sadness of late. We all need to move on."

So Tom, who had never left the island and wanted nothing but to stay on the island, had to find the courage to leave. He left Lowry, to walk by himself up to the North Light where he sat at the edge of the cliff wondering what it would be like to leave the security of this place where he knew every rock, every cliff, every field and every single person. But his children were dying and he had lost the boat and none of this was Jane's fault, so he had to do something to help her. Lowry was right. They could leave and come back again. The steamer that took folk off the island also made a return journey.

He turned from the cliff edge and slowly began the walk home. He had never thought that when he was approaching forty years of age he might have to make such a big change in his life. But other men had done it, and if Lowry thought this was the right thing to do then it must be so. Whatever else people said about him, no one thought Lowry was entirely daft.

That night, when they were together, he told Jane that he was ready to consider leaving, stressing that it might just be for a while. His wife realised how difficult it was for him to say this, but almost immediately she felt a tiny sense of purpose and hope emerging, for she desperately wanted to break away from all this insecurity and hopelessness. They might have a chance somewhere easier, somewhere babies didn't die all the time, somewhere men might not drown, for she had added drowning to her secret store of recurring worries.

Tom had only one condition. "The only thing is, I don't want one of these factory jobs like all the men who have gone to work in that biscuit factory in Edinburgh you talk about. I want to work with the sea. We could go to Kirkwall. You've got family there. Or Aberdeen, or Leith, or England, even. I could try to get a job on one of the herring boats... just not a factory mind. I couldn't stand being inside all day."

Any job that didn't involve the sea sounded more than attractive to Jane just at the moment. Whatever else she had learned at Quoy, she knew that the Irvines were a hard-working bunch. Tom could certainly earn a living elsewhere and Jane knew where she wanted to go. Edinburgh and Leith were her destinations of choice, where she knew people and how things worked. She wanted something quite different, but not as different as Canada, or New Zealand. She knew that life could be better elsewhere, but not Kirkwall. Polly lived in Kirkwall!

"We'll go to Leith. You can work at the docks, or even at the fishing, and if that doesn't work out, Edinburgh is just up the road. There are lots of jobs in the town if Leith doesn't suit you."

"I'll give it a go. I'll surely find a job at the docks. I'm not too old to heave a few sacks around. Who knows, I might get a job blacksmithing if I can't get on a boat."

Jane didn't care. A fresh start offered some relief from the constant pressure of worrying about what the next day would bring. Daily life in Fair Isle was now full of uncertainties that her father had not known. In the eight years since she had come home, earning a livelihood here had just become too difficult.

Once she had a purpose, Jane could not be held back. With money in the savings bank there was enough for the tickets and a few extra pounds to tide them over until Tom found work in Leith. Almost at once she began to make lists: lists of things to take, things to make, lists of people to tell, lists of things to do. She had a reason to get up in the morning.

Lowry was glad for them both, and John too, even though the pair of them could hardly imagine life here without their brother. Bina, however, was distraught. She would lose her beloved Barbara. Quoy had become a more dynamic place when Jane arrived and for the first time Bina had felt part of the mainstream. With Jane, life had improved, as she helped Bina to find a new place in the island's female hierarchy. Lowry told her they must give Tom every support, but her life would change much more than his. She would be alone here again, with no other woman to support her, and she would lose Barbara, the child she thought of almost as her own. She had only just lost Robina. Bina nearly asked if she could go too, but didn't have the courage.

Of course, Jane did not manage to overcome all her demons overnight, but now amidst her mourning and sadness she had a purpose. There was some element of hope. They might have a future. Another Barbara Wilson (Johanna's sister-in-law) had married Willie Eunson in 1892 and the pair had moved to Leith to join some of his family. Willie had a job as a storeman at the docks and they lived in Fort Place, which sounded a very impressive address indeed.

"Come to us," Barbara replied, when she heard from Jane. "Willie will get Tom a job and you can stay with us till you're settled. I will find you a place to live. There are people from all over Shetland here. You will be quite at home."

Now they knew where they were going. Or at least Jane knew. Tom was still a tad bemused, but this was no time for the bemused to ponder. He had to pack his tools and see there was enough space in the kists for all Jane wanted to take. When he became the island's blacksmith Tom had amassed quite a pile of equipment, and now he had to decide what to take and what to leave for Lowry and John. And all the time the entire situation felt unreal. After years of certainty, too much had happened all at once. Even as he made all the sensible preparations he felt the event might not occur.

During the last few days there was a constant stream of visitors, wishing them well, handing over small gifts, or just giving a hug. Each goodbye hurt in a way Tom had not realised, although Jane had known. Occasionally, in the night, she too had doubts but she kept her own counsel. Tom was already spooked. If he imagined for a moment that Jane was having second thoughts he might cancel all the arrangements.

Then there were final farewells, to Jane's remaining family at Taft and the Springfield tribe who had been such a comfort through both good and bad. She would miss them as much as her brothers and sister. Even Willie Stout popped in one evening to wish them well, though of course there was no sight of Maggie. It was particularly hard when it was old people you were leaving. Finally, there was the last visit to the graveyard, to say goodbye to all the people they had loved and, of course, the babies that Tom had buried. Tears were never far from the surface.

Eventually their morning came to catch the steamer. There was a good crowd down at the shore to help Lowry, John, Stewart and Thomas get them into the boat. Aggie Wilson from Springfield had her arms round Mary and other folk helped Bina. Never mind her brother, it was, in the end, Barbara's absence that was quite unthinkable. Tom hugged her and told her to look after John and Lowry, his stomach churning in panic. Only young Barbara had no real idea of what this excitement really meant.

"Goodbye!"

"Look after yourself!"

"Keep in touch!"

"God go with you!"

"Aye to the fore!"

It was, as always, quite awful. Everyone was crying, or almost crying, as quickly the three were hauled on board along with their belongings, for the steamer had only slowed its engines and was anxious to get on its way. All too soon, people, boats and island faded into the horizon, until finally the family turned to look to their new destination. The crew, by now familiar with the sad routine, had left the emigrants to recover before looking at their tickets. Soon they were in Kirkwall, meeting up with family old and new and from there it was all new and challenging. Now they were laughing together at strange experiences. Laughter had not been so common of late in Fair Isle and Tom's spirits rose when he heard it once more. Barbara began to realise that this change might be fun. The trip to Leith was a kind of honeymoon for two adults who had never had time together alone. For once, the sea was kind. Jane was able to explain all the new things to Tom and he began to relax. Gradually he developed positive expectations for the future. By the time they were met off the boat in Leith by the Eunsons, Tom had come to view things as a challenge. Perhaps, after all, he wasn't too old to change.

Back in Quoy things were less cheerful. They all went about their jobs, but it was different. The four children had functioned as a unit since before their father died, taking their lead from Lowry. Then they had learned to accept Jane and Barbara. Now they were just three and all around them were reminders of what had gone – the space where the clock had been, the basket that had held the child's bits and pieces, and Tom's hand-crafted poker and fire-tongs that Lowrie had insisted were his. Quoy now seemed terribly empty and quiet. They would recover, of course, and all the empty spaces would eventually be filled by other things, but it would take time. Bina moved into the small bedroom, but for a long time she felt like an interloper.

Then it was there in the newspaper. Lowry read it out to them both. '*On the 24th April, 1897, Thomas Irvine of Quoy left by the mail steamer for Lerwick, from whence he went to Edinburgh with his wife and child.*' If it was in the paper, it must be true.

It was not just Irvines of Quoy who left that year. A few weeks later, on the 13th May 1897, the *Columbine* took more Fair Isle families to Kirkwall. William Williamson of Mires, his wife and their seven children went on to Leith where it would be the turn of Tom and Jane to welcome them. Andrew and Barbara Wilson of Stackhoull and their six children went to Edinburgh, to be met by the Irvines. Eunsons and Stouts followed. Increasingly, it seemed as if the mass exodus was taking place without any formal decision. Forty-four people left that summer.

⌐~⌐

Nevertheless, on 20th June, 1897, the Fair Isle Diamond Jubilee rejoicings for Queen Victoria were (according to the Shetland newspapers) '*held in magnificent style*'. Both North and South lighthouses were gaily decorated with flags, as were some of the croft houses. Mr McLean, the teacher, was enabled by the generosity of some friends to entertain the scholars and some of their parents to a picnic at Buness. A procession to the picnic was headed by a piper. Finally, a bonfire was lit and the islanders could see the Sumburgh bonfire in the far distance. Thus, despite the exodus, some people still felt they were part of something bigger and the Jubilee celebrations were at least a welcome break from the daily grind.

For the lighthouse men, Fair Isle was a desirable place on which to serve, one where they could live with their families in some sort of comfort. It was their job to maintain an exceptional service to mariners, constantly working to keep all the machinery in perfect order so that the light flashed reliably and properly. They spent their days cleaning the machinery, the light and many panes of glass. They polished brasses, painted, mended and kept a record of all that they did, for a Lighthouse Board superintendent could at any time make an unheralded inspection of the light. They kept watch in the light room at night singly, or working with a partner if there was a fog. They formed a cohesive unit that was happy to mix with the islanders, but in some ways stood apart. For one thing, these men earned a wage that was on a par with a qualified mainland tradesman. They may not have been rich, but they had a level of wealth and security that raised them above their fellows.

By August, some of the remaining islanders were almost destitute as they felt the pressure of this year's hungry gap, before the harvest replenished their stocks. Saithe retained its rock bottom price and, to make things worse, the crops did not look outstanding. However, on the 2nd of September, 1897, a period of good weather created some optimism and there was a lot of banter as different groups made their way out to the fields to begin work. The Northern Lighthouse Board's ship, the *Pole Star*, called that day, landing two passengers – a telegraph linesman and an engineer. Then, as the men and women toiled in the fields, one after the other a succession of ships was silhouetted on the horizon and gradually people stopped to stare. Of course, it didn't take long for some of the island's young men (as well as a few of their more mature colleagues) to feel the tug to barter.

The monotony of life is always lifted by the unexpected, so the women shrugged their shoulders as small groups of bodies rushed whooping and laughing all the way down to the boats, some dashing into crofts on the way to grab eggs, knitting, fresh vegetables and the odd protesting hen. It was well known that the French were particularly partial to a fresh bird for the pot, while the Dutch favoured fresh eggs. In return there might be flour, ship's biscuits, salt beef, tobacco, the odd keg of brandy and who knew what else. With up to fifteen boats to choose from, at the very least the trip would break the monotony of life. So they sorted themselves into crews and threw their produce into the bottom of four yoals before starting to row like demons, for already the ships were drawing well away. A good turn of speed would be necessary to catch up, but this was one challenge they could all deal with readily enough.

The four yoals came close to their individual quarries, each hoping that their chosen victim was amenable to trade. The sea is a lonely place, where any new experience is welcomed, so none dismissed their visitors this day. By the time the men boarded it was mid-afternoon, but the weather was changing. First the wind got up and then the sun darkened, so that before long all four crews decided to make for home. By now they were all far from both their fellows and the island. As time passed and the weather worsened, each individual journey became increasingly difficult. The all too familiar dark, deep waves began to challenge each group and the men began to regret the decision not to stop off for foul weather gear, which would normally have been taken for such a considerable journey. The day's early effort had tired them so that, as evening loomed and bodies began to react to the cold and wet, they felt their powers wane.

However, this was no time to slow down. They must all row. The waves were such that only constant effort would keep them afloat. Gradually, discomfort became suffering and the men imagined what the female side of their families would have to say about this foolish trip. They concentrated on their oars and pulled as if their lives depended on it.

They did.

It was very late in the afternoon before the first yoal made it back, but it was far into the evening before the second came into sight. By now almost everyone was either at the post office or the landing place at South Harbour. What had begun as slightly ill-humoured irritation at the foolish antics of silly men, grew into something more serious for those who waited. Each of the boats that came home caused intense relief to some, Stewart Wilson of Springfield quietly thanking the Lord for the return of his beloved son Jerry, while Bina and John Irvine of Quoy were limp and tearful by the time Lowry came into view. Any joy at those saved, however, was severely tempered by the knowledge that two boats were still missing. As the hours passed, alarm grew and solidified, as anxiety turned into fear. The sound of sobbing could occasionally be heard. No other yoals appeared on the horizon.

The very old and young were finally taken home to try to get some rest, but a night watch was kept by many adults, with increasing despair about what this would bring. Fortunately, it was the time of year when darkness was short-lived and as the early morning broke, each cliff and vantage point still had a little group of bodies loyally keeping watch. The fires they lit to provide light and heat also furnished them with hot water for tea, but by now all were heavy-eyed and exhausted. Yet still they kept to their posts. There was nothing else to do. The lighthouse men had stayed up with their friends, scanning the horizon as soon as it was light. The visiting linesman and engineer were involved too, staring relentlessly from their elevated positions in the light-rooms.

Fear, more desperate than most could remember, was a physical presence amongst the waiting people. Donald McLean was to the fore, along with James Anderson and Stewart Wilson, each hoping that they would not be called upon to fulfil any formal role, all praying that the boats had simply been standing off, waiting for the light to return.

When the ill-named *Star of Hope* finally came into view a flurry of excitement exploded and yoals were immediately dispatched to help her. But this third yoal brought no jubilation. Its crew had spent the previous afternoon, evening and night rowing in dreadful weather, ill-clad and with no nourishment, so that now they were all either exhausted, dying, or already dead.

Alex Eunson of Stackhoull had not long celebrated his fifteenth birthday and had been put at the tiller to allow stronger men to row. Keep to your post, they had told him. He stayed at his post till he died.

James Wilson of Leogh, aged just twenty, had fallen into the bottom of the boat, leaving his father Tom rowing ever more desperately. If only he could get him back to Kirkigeo safely the boy might be saved. Young James Wilson was dead.

Andrew Wilson of Haa was also dead in the well of the yoal, making a double burden for Tom, since Andrew was his brother. Andrew's son John was in the missing boat.

Although 22-year-old John Leslie of Barkland made it into the safety of the harbour, he then collapsed. The schoolmaster and principal lighthouse keeper fought for an hour to save him, but they failed.

Three men and a boy lay dead on the beach. The crowd helplessly watched the efforts to save the dying and all were cowed. Relatives of the dead keened their sorrow. Women were overcome. Men were stunned. Old people collapsed. Exhausted survivors were carried, or helped home by small groups of supporters, but the knowledge of the four corpses allowed no respite. There was little sense of joy in anyone found alive, for all had lost relatives or close friends. Finally, the dead bodies were carried home, each with a small group of mourners.

Williamina Eunson watched as people brought her son Alexander home, in the knowledge that her husband William was still missing.

Tom Wilson went home to Leogh with his dead son James. His brother Andrew was dead and Andrew's son was in the missing yoal.

Helen Wilson of Haa lost her husband, as well as her nephew, James Wilson. She still had to agonise about her son John and her brother James Irvine in the other boat.

William Leslie of Barkland wept as they brought him his beloved son. This family had already lost two children to illness and found life hard even before the disaster.

So the mourning began, as the vigil went on. Lerwick was telegraphed with news of the disaster and passing ships were asked to look out for the remaining boat. From every vantage point a watch was kept, until gradually a terrible truth had to be faced. Unless by some miracle the other boat had been picked up by a passing steamer, the four remaining souls were lost. Given the conditions, their lack of equipment and food, it was most likely that the Stackhool yoal, the *Foam*, was lost at sea with all hands. Of course the watch continued long after all hope had gone, but the four men were never seen again. Acceptance was gradual and for some it took a very long time for hope to die. The *Foam* was a reminder of the 1851 disaster, that without bodies, families are left in limbo.

Finally, they had to accept that William Eunson, George Stout, John Wilson and James Irvine were all dead. On that dreadful 1897 night, the island lost eight men, the island's future. There were four widows.

Helen Wilson of Haa lost her husband, nephew, son and brother, a catastrophe that reduced the woman to a shell of her former self. She still had five children to support, aged seventeen to eight.

Charlotte Irvine of Stoneybrake was left with three young children, the eldest small, brain-damaged Charles Sturrock Irvine, the youngest a babe in arms. That summer, Charlotte had waved her own family off to a new life in Leith.

Williamina Eunson of Stackhoull lost her 15-year-old son Alexander, along with her husband William who had all too recently saved the Irvine boys from disaster. Williamina had eight children, the eldest a girl of eighteen and the youngest a babe in arms.

Margaret Stout was left with six children to care for, aged from eleven to just one year old. Not only did she lose her husband George, but also her brother William Eunson and nephew Alexander.

When people live in such close proximity, all are neighbours, relations and friends to varying degrees. Such a terrible calamity resonates in a way it would not do in another landscape. Twenty-one children lost fathers. Four women lost husbands. Parents lost sons. But others lost neighbours, friends, uncles and cousins, brothers and sisters. No family was unaffected. More importantly, the eight who died were the island's future, men who fished. This truly was a tragedy for a society already struggling to survive. The people seemed physically diminished by the blow.

Donald McLean, who had become close to his neighbours as their missionary and teacher, appealed through the newspapers on behalf of the families. Corn still stood in the fields, with few able bodies to work at it. The autumn farming needs were urgent, but it was as if the community's focus was lost. If people were not to starve this winter, someone had to give them support, for this community was already close to the edge. Even when John Eunson returned from Edinburgh to help with the harvest, this was hardly enough. He lost his brother, nephew and brother-in-law, but no one man could substitute for three. Of course all the remaining island men did their best to undertake extra farming duties. Lowry at Quoy, Stewart and Tom at Taft and Stewart and Jerry from Springfield were not alone in pulling their weight. The remaining men did their best, but there were not enough of them. Even after the funerals, eight fresh graves seemed to dominate the society.

Then the national press took over. In a variety of newspapers around the country the story was told. The telegraph linesmen (who had landed on the morning of the disaster) found themselves quoted at length. The story of heroic Alexander, who had stuck to his post like a man, was central to many of the appeals. Widows struggling in a tiny island that was already under pressure tugged both the heart and purse strings of more people than the islanders might have imagined. Fair Isle, perhaps because of its knitting, or perhaps because of its isolation, already had a place in the hearts of many who had never seen it. Then, of course, there was the Shetland diaspora, who dug deeply, sometimes into shallow pockets.

The *People's Journal* sent a journalist with provisions, including food, boots and clothes. Individuals sent contributions directly to McLean, asking him to use them as he saw fit. Official funds were created in Shetland, Edinburgh and Dundee. Robert McVitie, who employed many Fair Isle men in his Edinburgh factory, put his shoulder behind the fund-raising there. Queen Victoria donated £20. Sums of money were gathered from all around the country and two official funds were finally established, in Edinburgh and Shetland. McLean dispensed any aid he received according to the needs he observed. McLean was indeed the most sensible person to administer help. Finally, there was a sense of relief that the families would be given enough assistance to survive.

To the larger funds, money was donated in threepences, sixpences, shillings and pounds. Donations came not only from Shetland but from fishing communities around the coasts of both Scotland and England. As one of the many journalists said: *'Bereavement without poverty is bad enough, but sore bereavement with absolute poverty, together form a sad combination indeed.'*

It says a great deal that the public was so moved, for fishing communities of the time were littered with tragedies. Indeed, all around the United Kingdom death by disaster at work was not in the least uncommon.

Once the immediate needs had been dealt with, a formal Disaster Relief Fund was set up to amalgamate the major funds, with the provost of Lerwick, the Convenor of the County, a solicitor, a treasurer and, of course, John Bruce in charge. In excess of £1,400 had been raised to ensure that the widows and orphans would be taken care of, a sum of money comparable to a very much larger amount today. Here was a chance for the great British public to see the value of its generosity put to work. With such an august group in charge, no one doubted that a good and thoughtful distribution would come to pass.

However, when the group met, John Bruce assured the committee that there was *'nothing approaching destitution or want in Fair Isle'*. In fact, since he had taken over the island *'matters have so improved that the people compare very favourably with other parts of Shetland and are much in advance of some crofting communities. There are only two paupers on the island, a childless widow and an old man without relatives'*.

Perhaps he thought it was embarrassing to admit that some of his tenants were penurious. Thus they were not penurious. Bruce went on to explain that *'the occasional emigrations are due mainly to the fact that the births exceed the deaths,'* and *'without these occasional emigrations the inhabitants could not live as comfortably as they do'*.

He ignored the haemorrhage of population over recent years, the cessation of his fish processing concern, the rock-bottom price of saithe and the closure of his shop. He stated that although *'adequate and generous relief'* should be made, it was essential that this should be made *'without tending to pauperise'*.

It is a pity that the crofters were not there to hear their laird claim that there was nothing approaching destitution on the island in this terrible year. Had he visited any of the families and seen how they were living? Bruce's definition of destitution clearly differed from that of many other people, although perhaps not that of his peers.

So the decision of the committee was to award the widows, women totally crushed by grief and desperation, what would amount to Parish Relief. Their immediate needs perhaps had been resolved by recent direct donations, so that they all had clothes to wear and, in the short term, some food to eat.

But the problem faced by the women went much further than that of immediate need. They had families to support throughout the coming winter and for years to come. Without husbands, they would need substantial help until their children were old enough to set off on their own and, at this time, there was no longer a sufficiently robust community left to support them. Two of the women were in poor health. They all needed hope for the future and money had been donated for that purpose.

However, Bruce and his cohorts on the committee seemed to lack both understanding and sympathy, both for what the widows had endured and would endure in the future. There was no effort made to provide the families with long-term security through the money that had been donated. It was as if the committee felt that in some way the women did not deserve the money, that it was not their right. Their social superiors in Shetland felt that they could tell these destitute people what they deserved, just as they did to all other paupers.

Essentially, those in charge of the fund decided to keep the bulk of the money for other purposes. The fund was officially turned into a Friendly Society, with six ex-officio members, including the superintendent of Northern Lighthouses and the Home Mission and Endowment Deputy of the Church of Scotland, with five further gentlemen to be elected annually by the county council. If you scanned the names of those regularly elected to committees in Shetland, you would find them on this list, including that of John Bruce.

After some small, initial payments to cover mourning and the like, each widow was allocated £5 per annum, much less, to be sure, than the annual interest on the sum collected for their relief. Each child under fifteen was to be granted £2.13 annually, until they were fifteen years of age. The children's final payment would be a £5 grant for an outfit with which to start work. The elderly mothers of George Stout and James Irvine, who might have received care from their sons, received £2.10 per annum, which would prevent them from becoming a charge on the poor rates. It would seem that the great and the good were intent on ensuring that the families would be kept off the Poor Law roll, rather than obtaining any real benefit or comfort from the nation's generosity.

With some imagination, if not sympathy, this august committee of men might have looked at ways in which the women and children could have received positive, long-term support. There were many ways a widow might have been assisted to support herself. Even a single payment to each widow of perhaps £150, along with advice on how best to spend or save it, would have made a real difference to people burdened by economic despair and grief. A savings book would have removed that dreadful, gnawing worry about tomorrow's needs that haunts those who live close to the edge. Instead, it was felt that these women should not have the money, that they did not really need it and that they would not know how to handle it. There was an official statement made that if anyone wanted their money back (since it was clearly not required by the widows?) this could be achieved. There is no record, however, of anyone asking for this.

It was decided that the money should be used for 'the relief of sufferers of any future disaster, or accident by sea or land'. It was also stated that the fund might be used to provide nursing care on the island, or pay for any islander who desired to emigrate. The topic of a nurse was already on the agenda, but required a cash injection by someone to facilitate its introduction. Essentially, the disaster fund would ensure that any costs for the island that might appear over the next few, difficult years, would not now be borne by Bruce himself. Towards the end of 1902, Bruce offered £60 a year (from the disaster fund) towards the cost of a nurse. He invited the Lighthouse Board to contribute also and, in 1903, when the commissioners offered a further £15 a year, Nurse Payne was employed.

When the fund was set up, there were four widows, two elderly mothers and twenty-one children to consider. Just six years later, one of the elderly mothers had died and only ten of the children still qualified for assistance. By 1911 none of the children qualified, there were no elderly mothers and only three widows were still alive. The fund continued to exist until 1942.

Charlotte Irvine lost her small, brain-damaged son in November 1897 and left the island soon afterwards to join her parents in Leith. She squeezed into their tiny flat with her two girls, aged just four and one, and was helped by her brothers and sisters to survive. Just a year later, her two-year-old caught whooping cough and died. Her remaining daughter never married and cared for her mother for the rest of her life.

Williamina Eunson, who lost both husband and son, was left with eight children and struggled to keep her croft going. Her brother-in-law came back to Fair Isle to help for a while and then married her sister and moved to Nigg, near Aberdeen. Williamina followed them and there she met and married another Fair Isle widower, in 1906, but sadly she succumbed to tuberculosis in 1908.

Margaret Stout also struggled, so that finally she too moved to Nigg, where she can be found living in a room and kitchen in 1911 with her remaining four adult children. She is described as being of 'private means', which is one way of looking at £5 per annum. It appears that later she followed some of her children to Canada.

Helen Wilson stayed in Fair Isle, where she lived a hard and difficult life. Her eldest son had already moved to Edinburgh with his family, where they lived next to Tom and Jane Irvine of Quoy. The feeling is that this family was forever scarred by the tragedy.

In 1896 there were eleven boats and crews available to fish, but by the end of 1897 there were only six boats, with hardly enough fit men and boys to crew them. People wondered if the 1897 disaster might be the death of Fair Isle.

# *Epilogue*

So it was that Fair Isle limped forward into the new century, scarred, battered, but not beaten. In 1891 there were 188 islanders (plus thirty-four lighthouse contractors and their families) on the census. Ten years later the number of islanders was reduced to 135 (with twelve lighthouse men and family members adding to the total). No longer could the birth rate compete with the desire to move and numbers would continue to decline until emigration threatened the community's existence. By this time only a quarter of the local population were Wilsons and, in the 20th century, Stouts and Eunsons would flourish. The lighthouses provided work for a few relief men, who could count on this additional income. Most of the remaining men were retained by the coastguard, having signed up to provide assistance during any emergency.

Thus when the First World War came it took these men, some temporarily and others forever. Brothers Stewart and Robert Eunson died from illness in the Royal Navy hospital in Gosport in 1915, as did William Stout that same year. George Stout died from wounds received in France in 1916. William Eunson died in Lerwick in 1916, also from illness. The island's schoolteacher, Donald McLean, lost two sons in France – Charles and Kenneth. The eighth name on the island memorial is that of Jerome Wilson, whose family left in 1897 only to suffer tragic loss in Edinburgh. Jerome died in France. His one remaining sibling made annual pilgrimages to the island.

Taft stood empty by 1901, until it was taken over by Willie and Maggie Stout in 1903. One wonders what Jane thought of that development. Stewart emigrated to Sault St Marie in Canada, while Thomas travelled to Australia, where he had a successful career in shipping. He was seriously injured during the First World War and his bravery was rewarded by the Military Medal. Mary joined Jane in Edinburgh, before moving to London where she lived close to another contingent of Fair Isle émigrés. She became an accomplished embroiderer and it is said that she worked for royalty. John remained in the Merchant Navy, dying in Archangel during World War I.

Wicked stepmother Polly died in 1904 in Kirkwall and the children of the first and second marriages kept in touch for the rest of their lives. Only Jane and Johanna married and produced children, so that Jane finally inherited her mother's Fair Isle chair from one of her half-brothers in the 1930s. By this time it required its straw back to be replaced, but Tom had not forgotten his skills and it remained a prized possession for the remainder of their lives.

Many of those who moved to Kirkwall remained there happily for the rest of their lives, as did children and grandchildren. Others spread around the world. Jeannie's beloved son James became the skipper of a variety of Orkney's floating shops, until in his fifties he responded to an advertisement and once more became a weaver. A firm in Galashiels sent him a large loom which he accommodated in Maple Cottage in Kirkwall, where he lived until his death in 1935. As he approached his eighties his family had either dispersed or died, so Aggie, one of Polly's spinster children, came to live with him. She cared for James until he died, before moving to Ireland to care for her eldest brother who lived in Belfast. So it continued with many spinster ladies of the time who did not have a trade or profession.

Thomas did finally commemorate his beloved Aunt Barbara. Despite his war injuries, his career blossomed. He died in 1935, leaving a considerable sum to be shared amongst his brothers and sisters, in addition to money for a large memorial to his parents and great aunt in the Fair Isle graveyard. By this time, however, the First World War Memorial was erected and it was felt by the family that a large Wilson memorial would be inappropriate. The suggestion of an organ for the chapel was, even then, considered to be frivolous. So John Irvine (Jane and Tom's son) organised the creation, purchase and installation of a particularly fine set of stained glass windows for the Methodist Chapel, in memory of John Wilson, Barbara his first wife, and Thomas's great aunt Barbara. No mention is made of Polly.

Quoy would remain the home of John, Lowry and finally Bina Irvine, who died there in 1952. The new century did not begin well for this family, as Lowry struggled to earn enough to support his siblings during a very difficult economic time. Whether Tom's leaving made a great difference it is difficult to surmise, but the family fell on bad times. A croft without a boat, with only one man who could work properly, was difficult to maintain. John became increasingly disabled by his asthma and was finally forced to apply to the Poor Law authorities for support, a distressing experience, both for him and his family. There was at that time terrible shame associated with the need to apply for relief.

He died from his illness in 1913, by which time Bina was also in receipt of public support, having had a child out of wedlock, a situation that some of the less charitable islanders found hard to forgive. Others accepted the girl as they would any other child and lived with the fact that Quoy was 'different'. Of course, it would have been unthinkable for an island man not to have married the mother of his child, but this father was a lighthouse keeper who had no such scruples and was able to move on to another posting. Hopefully the Northern Lighthouse authorities posted him to a remote rock station, one where he would not be able to dally carelessly with members of the local population.

Bina did try to take him to court, but was not successful. However, her daughter gave her great joy and later there was a grandson whom she knew and loved. It is unlikely that Tom and Jane heard all the detail of the difficulties experienced by the Irvines during the early years of the century, but the family kept in contact. Jane and Tom never went back, but they never forgot their heritage. Their children and grandchild would visit Quoy throughout the 1920s and '30s, although Maggie Stout would never, ever, let any of them into Taft. The state pension would eventually lift Lowrie and Bina from destitution in their old age and Bina's daughter Bella was a hard worker, who made the land work for herself and her son John.

For Tom, employment at Leith docks did not prove rewarding. Although there was plenty of work to be had in the vast dockland area, the hiring of dockworkers was done on a daily basis. Sometimes you failed to be chosen, or you signed up for what turned out to be only a half-day's work and when bad weather disturbed sailings you might not work at all. Thus you lacked control of your earnings, almost as if you lived in Fair Isle. For a guarantee of regular work, some of the foremen expected you to buy them a drink in the pub the night before, however ill-disposed you were towards them. Tom was willing to work, but the whole point of coming south had been to gain a reliable wage for his labour. After one particularly bad week, when yet again the foremen passed him over to choose one of his 'friends', Tom came home, put on his Sunday clothes, took the bus into town and made his way to McVitie's, where he found the management perfectly happy to employ another man from Fair Isle. Jane was thrilled to be back in Edinburgh and relieved that her husband had reliable, safe employment. They found a flat in the same stair as Andrew Wilson of Haa and his wife Janet Anderson and there were many other old friends living in the area.

McVitie's biscuit factory was a modern, state-of-the-art establishment, where a man was guaranteed a weekly wage and fair treatment in some of the best factory conditions in the city. The fact that so many employees were from Fair Isle enabled the wives to assuage their homesickness with folk they had known all their lives. It did not offer men the freedom and occasional elation of sailing a yoal, but it was safe, regular work for unskilled workers. One of the men's hobbies was working on local allotments, which grew a much wider range of vegetables than they had known before. It was not Fair Isle, but it offered their children more educational opportunities and the possibility of many different occupations. There was security.

There was always the issue that unqualified men from rural areas could find themselves denied better paid jobs because they had not had the opportunity to undertake a formal trade apprenticeship. Tradesmen closely protected a status that had taken them many years to earn. So although Fair Isle men could offer employers a wide range of skills, it was difficult to gain recognition for any special talents, so that the majority found jobs as labourers, earning much less than the 'time-served' men. Their sons, however, could gain qualifications and this some of them did.

The wives knew more than most about managing on a pittance and found that if they were thrifty, they could accumulate a tiny margin above that required for mere subsistence. They were all used to making meals out of both meat and fish offal and well able to eke out a weekly wage to their family's best advantage, quickly learning that local shops sold thing cheaply just before they closed for the day and that cheaper, bruised vegetables made a perfectly fine pot of soup. The women continued to knit, finding outlets for their creations either in small Edinburgh shops, or by sending goods back to Shetland where merchants happily allocated them 'Fair Isle' labels. For those with older children, second, third and fourth wages swelled the coffers. Jane was one of those who took in lodgers when Fair Isle men came south to look for a job, somehow adding three of them to her one-bedroom flat. There were many ways in Edinburgh for the imaginative to make extra money. Tom handed his wage packet to Jane on a Friday night and received in return sufficient to buy one half pint of beer and some tobacco for his pipe. In the early 1900s, thrift and industry enabled the poor to make progress, provided they also had good health and good luck.

For Andrew and Barbara Wilson, who had been living in Stackhool when they left Fair Isle in the summer of 1897, Edinburgh offered freedom from debt and want, even although the couple were saddened that their daughter Robina chose to stay in service in Kirkwall. Andrew and the older children quickly found jobs, so that this family could afford a higher standard of living than those with a single wage earner, even although all were 'labourers'. Only young Andrew was still at school and this was where he caught measles early in 1899. He was sent to die in the fever hospital, since the town's authorities endeavoured to stop the spread of such infection by means of quarantine.

McVitie's employed 20-year-old Thomas as a box maker, but he joined his brother at the City Fever Hospital one week later and followed him to the grave. Jeromina and

Stewart died shortly after. Robina, who had remained in Kirkwall, came to one of the funerals, caught the disease, returned to Kirkwall and died. For Barbara, one of the worst aspects of this nightmare was that her children were taken away to die. By the spring of 1900 she had lost five of her children, most of them adults. It must have been utterly devastating when, that May, her husband (who worked on the railway) was hit by a passenger train and killed. Three years after leaving Fair Isle she was left with just her two boys. The rest of the Fair Isle community closed round to help her survive, but for Andrew and Barbara, Edinburgh had proved disastrous. Tom and Jane remained close to this family until World War I when Barbara died, shortly after hearing that her son Jerome had been killed on the Western Front.

In contrast, Tom's situation improved during the Great War, not least because at the outbreak he was fifty-four and thus too old to fight. Over the years he had used his expertise as a smith to help in McVitie's tin box department and now he found himself promoted to the position of an official tinsmith, many of the time-served men being at war. His wage almost doubled and, since so many men were killed in the war, this position the unions allowed him to keep until his retirement, enabling the family to experience slightly more comfort. He was never rich, but even before the war the Irvines had achieved a relatively comfortable lifestyle.

The couple had further children, two of whom lived. Their beloved Barbara died when she was just twenty-one, due to complications after childbirth. Her husband disappeared and later remarried, never returning to acknowledge his child. Jane now concentrated all her love on Barbara's offspring. Their other daughter (Bella) was academically bright, doing so well at secondary school that she was immediately offered a good position in the Civil Service in London during World War I, aged just seventeen. Having recently lost one daughter, it was a great act of faith to allow the younger one to launch herself into London society at such an age, even if there was an enclave of islanders already there to protect her. Their son John became fascinated with Fair Isle and made many visits to the island during the 1920s and '30s. John had a good job and married well, buying his own home in Edinburgh in the 1930s. Jane and Tom saw their two remaining children aspire to opportunities they would not have encountered on the island.

For those who remained in Fair Isle, the next fifty years would be as challenging and as interesting as the last. This period saw two major wars and worldwide economic meltdown. Soldiers came to Fair Isle, since it was recognised as being vitally important to shipping and with the soldiers came the tensions of the outside world.

The wars not only took the lives of several island men but the lighthouses proved a target for enemy planes during the Second World War. North Light was machine-gunned and bombed twice in 1941, resulting in considerable damage to the accommodation blocks. At South Light in December 1941, the wife of the assistant keeper was killed in a further attack, while in January 1942 both the wife and daughter of the principal keeper (William Smith) were killed, as well as a soldier who was providing machine-gun support to the lighthouse. Having accepted the lighthouse men into their community, these attacks were deeply shocking. William Smith would go on to marry Bina Irvine's daughter Bella, taking her with him when he moved to a new posting. Tragically, Bella's son John died from a fever on the night of the first attack on South Light, so one hopes that William Smith and Bella Irvine managed to provide comfort for one another. Bina was almost eighty by this time and she bravely insisted that Bella leave the island, even though the old lady was now quite alone at Quoy. As had always been the case, one of the island's spinster ladies (Agnes Wilson from Shirva) moved in and looked after Bina until her death in 1952.

The Wilsons of Taft and the Irvines of Quoy were in no way special. They were just two of the many families who struggled to live in Fair Isle during difficult times. There were other groups of Wilsons and Irvines who had equally complex lives and relationships over these years, not to mention all the Stouts, Leslies, Mathers, Eunsons, Andersons and Williamsons. Each croft has its own story to tell.

Both change and progress occurred between 1851 and 1897, but economic pressures and the temptations of a better life elsewhere encouraged the majority to leave. Some prospered in their new environments, while others withered and died away. There are as many tales of heartache as there are stories of prosperity.

While emigration continued to whittle away at the population in the first half of the 20th century, over time the remaining inhabitants adapted to a new world, one where fishing played a less important part in the island's survival. As the century progressed, crofting grants, old age pensions and child benefits were important additions to economies in all rural communities.

Children continued to leave Shetland, however, particularly when secondary education in Lerwick became compulsory, introducing many youngsters to a wide range of different opportunities in the outside world. By 1951, Fair Isle's population was reduced to seventy-three, but this was by no means its death knell. George Waterston purchased the island in 1947, when finally it was placed on the open market. Waterston recognised its potential as the home for an international Bird Observatory, one that would grow and prosper. In 1954 the island was transferred to The National Trust for Scotland, under whose care it is now run.

Today, families inhabit crofts with every modern convenience. Islanders have a boat that takes them to Shetland when the weather is kind and there is a well-established air link, as well as a good shop, a resident nurse and a school. Church and chapel are used on alternate Sundays. There is a strongly innovative local population that is well able to support itself. The need to protect the local marine environment is increasingly recognised as a major issue, one that involves minds in the Scottish parliament, as well as local people. Along with the Bird Observatory's research, this may well provide further employment in the future. Visitors now have a variety of places to stay when they choose to visit and there is still an opportunity to buy knitting.

Thousands of descendants of those who were obliged to leave in the difficult times are spread around the world. Fair Isle is a tiny island with a huge history and a vast diaspora, people who view their ancestors with pride. But Fair Isle was not unique. Two million Scots emigrated between 1800 and 1900. At the beginning of the 19th century, sixty per cent of Scottish people lived on the land, but by 1900 this had reduced to forty per cent, as economic changes and industrial development encouraged people to move from depressed economic areas to new centres of growth. Throughout the 20th century, this trend snowballed.

In 1861, thirty-four per cent of Scottish families were housed in single rooms. A further thirty-seven per cent had two rooms. In growing towns like Glasgow, the numbers living in a 'room' or a 'room and kitchen' would remain at this level until after the Second World War. Crowded homes were the norm in towns, as much as Fair Isle, and in Scotland's cities you lived very close to your neighbours, often in verminous, flea-ridden, damp, old buildings, sharing toilets and poverty. Disease was rampant.

And although fishing was a hard and dangerous occupation, poor workplace conditions also killed and maimed large numbers of men in towns. Today we shudder under the weight of 'health and safety' regulation but, in the past, factories were highly dangerous places to work, while the polluted air that surrounded them killed many of those who lived in their vicinity and, however unpleasant their local environment, men without access to transport had to live close to their workplaces. In Glasgow, often half the deaths were due to pulmonary disease. Mines were even more hazardous for, if you were not killed in an accident underground, there was a high risk of contracting a pulmonary disease that would cripple or kill you before you were forty.

Such poor living conditions attracted men to public houses, where drink could result in alcoholism and brutality at home, as well as the squandering of money. One in four Scottish workers did not have year-round employment at this time, which could result in periods of intense hardship, for there was little or no state support when you were out of work.

So Fair Isle could be said to have been just as good (or as bad?) a place to live as many others in Scotland during the second half of the 19th century. Some people lived long and happy lives there. Most of those who left retained fond memories of the island till the day they died. It was impossible to replicate elsewhere the security and support that came from living in such a place, as part of such an extended family.

When saithe fell out of fashion, there seemed to be no alternative fish product on which to base the island's economy. Bruce, who had indeed done a great deal to modernise the island in the 1870s and '80s, was by now sixty and seems to have stopped making his annual visits. His father bought Fair Isle to make money and this he did, but by 1900 there was little profit to be made from the tenants.

By the late 1800s the average Scottish town worker found that his wages were gradually improving, while this was not generally true in the Highlands and Islands, and certainly not in Fair Isle. As the price of saithe steadily dropped, Fair Isle incomes steadily diminished, until saithe prices and incomes had never been so low. Whether a proper harbour would have saved the island, no one knows. Certainly, without it the fishing was doomed.

Today, people choose to move to the island as well as from it. There is never a shortage of applicants when an empty croft is advertised.

# Photo Credits

**Dave Wheeler**, Fair Isle ........................... Front Cover:-
South Light, Skadan at dusk
Back Cover:-
Fair Isle, aerial oblique looking north

**Science Museum**, London ........................ Pages 131, 132

**Shetland Museum**, Lerwick ..................... Pages 133, 135, 136, 137, 138

**Brian Wilson**, Fair Isle ........................... Page 139

**Noel Hill**, Inverness ............................... Page 141

**Mary Jann**, Kirkcaldy ............................. Page 134, 140

**Andrew Tweedie**, Edinburgh .................... Inside Covers:-
Jane's knitting
Pages 129, 130, 142, 143, 144